D1107412

William C. Blackman, Jr.

BASIC HAZARDOUS WASTE MANAGEMENT

Second Edition

William C. Blackman, Jr.

BASIC HAZARDOUS WASTE MANAGEMENT

Second Edition

Library of Congress Cataloging-in-Publication Data

Blackman, William C.
Basic hazardous waste management / William C. Blackman, Jr. -- 2nd ed.
p. cm.
Includes bibliographical references and index.
ISBN 1-56670-168-6
1. Hazardous wastes--United States--Management. I. Title.
TD1040.853 1995
363.72'87--dc20 95-34462
CIP

International Standard Book Number 1-56670-168-6
Library of Congress Card Number 95-34462
Printed in the United States of America 1 2 3 4 5 6 7 8 9 0
Printed on acid-free paper

Preface

As the demand for a clean, safe environment grows, so also grows the public demand for protection from the horrors of hazardous waste mismanagement. Entrepreneurs of industry and commerce provide daily evidence of the general awakening to the need for reduction or elimination of hazardous waste sources and better management of the wastes that are generated. But the ever-present drive for new product advantage, competition, budget and capital restraints, and the activities of those who have not yet accepted their environmental responsibilities continue to threaten our environmental well-being. Meanwhile the "not in my backyard" (NIMBY) syndrome has reached the point that almost no site is acceptable as a hazardous waste treatment or disposal facility.

This clash of imperatives must be dealt with. We, as a people, cannot permit further episodes of uncontrolled release of hazardous materials/waste to threaten us. We, as a first world society, cannot tolerate the continuing aftermath of our history of uncontrolled hazardous waste disposal. But we, as a viable, self-supporting nation, cannot afford to force industry and commerce to their collective knees in the name of environmental purity.

The national conscience, as expressed in the form of research, technological advances, legislative craft, regulatory issue, fiscal support, and public participation, has brought forth great improvement in our hazardous waste management practice. But most of the easy achievements have been realized. The priorities and demands ahead will require a new generation of environmental managers, greater in number and skills than those who have preceded them.

Our traditional approach to the education of future environmental technologists and managers has guided the undergraduate through some basic skill curriculum, to then be followed by a graduate program in engineering or a science. This text is intended to provide an introductory framework, which can be the foundation for a program of study in hazardous waste management or a component of a related program. It is in an overview format, with many references to more detailed materials, to assist the student or instructor in expansion upon specific topics or to flesh-out complex issues. The instructor is encouraged to expand upon issues or topics to meet the perceived needs of students, regions, or industries. Topics for discussion or review are provided at the end of each chapter.

Organization and Content

The first 11 chapters deal with the topics, impacts, technologies, problems, and issues associated with "conventional" hazardous waste and the management practices and statutory and regulatory controls which have evolved around them. Chapters 12 through 14 introduce the closely related medical/infectious waste, underground storage tank, and radioactive waste management technologies and practices. Chapter 15 introduces the hazardous waste worker health and safety issues and regulatory structures that have become a major focal point and concern for managers and supervisors of hazardous waste facilities and sites.

Objectives are stated as the first element of each chapter. Insofar as is possible or appropriate, the chapters are structured to first outline the issue, subject, or technology, then to describe generic practice, and to then conclude with a summary of the statutory and/or regulatory approach. Historical perspective is provided where appropriate to locale, industry, or other emphasis.

The reader who is unfamiliar with the *Federal Register* (FR) and/or the *Code of Federal Regulations* (CFR) should examine these two entries in the Glossary before proceeding with the regulatory material covered in the book.

Acknowledgments

My reviewers have shared generously of their valuable time and expertise to provide insightful and constructive suggestions. I am particularly indebted to Dr. Nicholas R. Hild of the Department of Manufacturing and Industrial Technology, Arizona State University for his thoughtful and constructive input in reviewing the first and second editions in their entirety. Reviewers of portions of the first edition were Ms. Pamela R. Jenkins, R.N., of the Environmental Resource Center, Fayetteville, NC — the chapter on medical and infectious waste management; Mr. Arthur C. Gehr, Esq., partner in the firm Snell and Wilmer, Phoenix, AZ — the radioactive waste management chapter; and Ms. Lisa Lund, then Manager, Underground Storage Tank Compliance Section, Arizona Department of Environmental Quality and presently Deputy Director, Office of Underground Storage Tank Programs, U.S. Environmental Protection Agency — the underground storage tank management chapter. Many of their respective contributions are retained in the second edition.

Dr. Raymond E. Kary, of Kary Environmental Services, Scottsdale, AZ, provided excellent input to the second edition chapter on toxicology and the standards-setting process. Ms. Susan Y. Pickering, of the Technical and Compliance Integration staff, Waste Isolation Pilot Plant (WIPP) project, Sandia National Laboratories at Carlsbad, NM, contributed excellent advice and insight to portions of the radioactive waste management chapter. Mr. Harold L. Berkowitz, chemical engineer, consultant, and faculty associate at the Center for Environmental Studies, Arizona State University, provided extensive input and improvements to the new chapter on hazardous waste worker health and safety. The valuable assistance of all of the reviewers is deeply appreciated.

Without the editing and word-processing skills, as well as the extraordinary patience of Ms. Cindy Zizner, M.S., and the graphic skills of Mr. Steve Scott, these months of work on the revision would have been much less pleasant. Ms. Zizner and Mr. Scott are private practitioners in Tempe, AZ.

I sincerely appreciate the time and effort of the many contributors of photographic materials. The illustrations for which no acknowledgment is made are either my own or those which have been provided to me on earlier occasions. I can only apologize for lack of adequate memory regarding the sources of the earlier contributions.

The Author

William C. Blackman, Jr. is an environmental engineer and professor for the Center for Environmental Studies, Arizona State University. Professor Blackman was a career engineer and manager assigned to enforcement programs of the U.S. Environmental Protection Agency and predecessor agencies. As Technical Coordinator and Deputy Director of the EPA National Enforcement Investigations Center, he planned and directed early hazardous waste site investigations and participated in the development of the site investigation techniques and site health and safety procedures which have become standard practice.

In 1985, he was appointed Assistant Director, Arizona Department of Environmental Quality where he managed state and federal RCRA and Superfund programs. He joined the ASU faculty in 1989 where he teaches undergraduate and graduate courses in hazardous waste management and control of toxic air pollutants. He has developed and presents a program of seminars on hazardous waste management, underground storage tank management, emergency planning, and hazardous materials transportation regulation. He directs ASU participation in the California–Arizona Consortium, presenting OSHA health and safety training for hazardous waste and underground storage tank workers.

Professor Blackman received his B.S. in Civil Engineering and M.S. in Sanitary Engineering from the University of Missouri at Columbia, his MPA (Environmental Management) from the University of Southern California at Los Angeles, and his DPA (Environmental Management and Public Policy) from the University of Colorado at Denver. He has published a number of papers on water quality and pollution control and on hazardous waste site investigations and safety procedures.

Contents

1 THE HAZARDOUS WASTE PERSPECTIVE

OBJECTIVES

At completion of this chapter, the student should:

- have gained a perspective on the evolution of hazardous waste problems and approaches to management in the United States and other industrialized nations.
- understand the kinds of hazardous waste management/mismanagement practices that create negative health, environmental, economic, and social impacts, and the nature of those impacts.
- have overview familiarity with the federal statutes and legal mechanisms that have been directed toward governmental control of hazardous wastes, why they succeeded or failed, and how they relate to the present-day Resource Conservation and Recovery Act (RCRA) and Comprehensive Environmental Response, Compensation, and Liability Act (CERCLA).
- be similarly familiar with political and administrative approaches to governmental control of hazardous waste, with the successes and failures, and with some cause-and-effect considerations.

INTRODUCTION

This text is intended to provide, to the upper division undergraduate or graduate student or to the practitioner, an overview of the hazardous waste management field of study. It is a wide-ranging overview touching upon literally dozens of related subjects, any one of which is or may be a field of study in its own right. Fortunately or unfortunately, that is the nature of the practice of hazardous waste management. It is a highly complex mix of the life and natural sciences; several fields of engineering and technology; epidemiology, toxicology, and preventative medicine; administration; law; public relations, etc. It goes without saying that a single course cannot deal with any of the associated topics in any detail. But the student should gain sufficient understanding of the field to assist in making decisions regarding field of study and in organizing those studies.

The intent is also to provide an overview of "generic" hazardous waste management and to then relate that understanding to the basic federal waste management law — the RCRA as amended. Such an overview must also include perusal of the CERCLA or "Superfund" as it pertains to site remediation and other environmental, occupational health and safety, and hazardous materials transportation statutes.

In reality, it is difficult to separate generic hazardous waste management practice from RCRA requirements since the structure and format of this very comprehensive and complex law so completely define the practice in the United States and territories. Nevertheless, we will attempt to begin each chapter with a description of the subject or activity, followed by a summary of accepted practice, and conclude with the application of RCRA, CERCLA, and the related statutes and regulations.

The first chapter provides some historical background, some of it anecdotal, to portray the kinds of events, reactions, policies, and outcomes that helped to shape the original RCRA, the amendments that have followed, and the practice of hazardous waste management.

Dawning of the Problem

Among students of environmental management in the United States, it is generally postulated that the beginnings of the nation's effort to gain control of hazardous wastes began with (1) the Love Canal episode and (2) the discovery that the circle of environmental laws (Clean Water Act [CWA], Clean Air Act [CAA], Toxic Substances Control Act [TSCA], Safe Drinking Water Act [SDWA]), enacted since the beginning of the "Environmental Decade" (1970–1980), required closure by the enactment of a hazardous waste control measure.

Love Canal, a water conveyance originally excavated for a hydroelectric project in Niagara Falls, NY, was used by Hooker Chemical Company as a dump site for nearly 22,000 tons of waste chemicals. Hooker closed and capped the site in 1952, and in 1953 the City of Niagara Falls pressured Hooker to sell the canal land to the city for a school site. Hooker filed disclaimers, citing the possible dangers of building over the landfill, but the school board and the city were determined to have the site. After threats of an eminent domain proceeding, Hooker sold the land to the city for $1.* The site was developed and a school and homes were built thereon. In 1978, the site was declared to be a public environmental emergency because hazardous wastes were seeping into the basements of the houses. Nearly 900 families were evacuated. After years of legal wrangling, Occidental Petroleum Corporation, the parent company of Hooker, recently agreed to pay $98 million to the state of New York to cover some of the cleanup costs and will assume responsibility for monitoring and remaining cleanup operations. A federal court rejected the state's claim for $250 million in punitive damages against Occidental, but the company faces additional lawsuits by the federal government, the City of Niagara Falls, and hundreds of former residents who contend that their health problems resulted from toxic materials in the area.

It is correct that the Love Canal horror galvanized public opinion and stimulated much regulatory activity by governments (federal, state, and local). However, hazardous waste horror stories were emerging before Love Canal became a household

* For a more detailed account of the Love Canal episode, *see* Wentz (1989, p. 306ff).

FIGURE 1.1 Abandoned hazardous waste site [Environsafe Services of Ohio, Inc. (ESOI), P.O. Box 167571, Oregon, OH 43616-7571].

word, and the frequency and intensity increased on a near-daily basis. Following the Love Canal disclosures, the U.S. Environmental Protection Agency (EPA) and others mounted studies which determined that more than 750,000 generators had deposited almost 60 million tons of hazardous waste in as many as 50,000 sites. (Even these shocking numbers did not adequately describe the problem.) At that time (1977), the EPA estimated that only 10% of the waste had been disposed of in an environmentally safe manner (Worobec 1986, p. 12) (Figures 1.1 through 1.4).

Early Hazardous Waste Management

Other episodes shocked the nation and brought forth new and intensified efforts to gain control of the problem. In discussing them here, we refer to them as past practices, realizing full well that similar situations and practices can and do continue to this time (Figures 1.5 and 1.6).

The ABM-Wade Site. The ABM-Wade site in Chester, PA was typical of dozens of sites throughout the industrialized areas of the nation. During the mid-1970s, the operator accepted hazardous wastes; filled the former factory building with drums of waste; filled discarded tank trailers with hazardous waste and parked them on the site; and when above-ground space was filled, underground storage tanks and trenches were filled with wastes. In February 1978, the site burned. Nearby residents were endangered by clouds of toxic air pollutants, by the proximate natural gas storage tanks, and by contaminated runoff to the Delaware River (Figures 1.7 through 1.11). The site was remediated by a ten-year, $3 million Superfund project. (*See* Chapter 11)

FIGURE 1.2 Abandoned hazardous waste site (ESOI).

FIGURE 1.3 Abandoned hazardous waste site (ESOI).

FIGURE 1.4 Land disposal of hazardous waste (Mill Service, Inc., 1815 Washington Road, Pittsburgh, PA).

The Hardeman County Landfill. In Hardeman County, TN, 40 families near a rural landfill drank from wells polluted with such pesticides as endrin, dieldrin, aldrin, and heptachlor. The Velsicol Chemical Company had used a neighboring 300-acre site from 1964 to 1972 for shallow burial of 300,000 55-gallon drums of pesticide production residues. Residents complained of a wide variety of ailments including liver and urinary tract problems, dizziness, nausea, and rashes (Council on Environmental Quality 1979, p. 179).

The LaBounty Dump. Salsbury Laboratories, a major manufacturer of veterinary pharmaceuticals, is located in the small northern Iowa community of Charles City. From 1953 until December 1977, Salsbury disposed of chemical wastes in the LaBounty Dump along the Cedar River (Figure 1.12). The Cedar River flows southeasterly through much of the state (Figure 1.13). Wells in the river alluvium supply domestic water to many thousands of users along its course. The Iowa Department of Environmental Quality (DEQ) discovered that pollutants (arsenic and a variety of organic chemicals) had leached from the dump to the underlying groundwater and to the Cedar River. The Iowa DEQ issued an executive order requiring Salsbury to remove all hazardous wastes and contaminated materials from the LaBounty site, but Salsbury convinced the courts that the cleanup costs would exceed the company's net worth, and the removal order was stayed (Dahl 1980).

Union Carbide — Uravan. In the early 1950s, the Union Carbide Corporation began uranium mining and milling operations on the banks of the San Miguel River

FIGURE 1.5 Hazardous waste dump site (Arizona Department of Environmental Quality).

at Uravan, CO. During the years of operation the mill produced more than 10 million tons of uranium-vanadium ore, in excess of 10 million tons of tailings, millions of gallons of waste liquid raffinate, raffinate crystal residue, and other milling wastes containing radioactive materials (uranium, radium, thorium), metals (selenium, aluminum, arsenic, cadmium, zinc, and others), and other inorganic contaminants. Mining, milling, and waste disposal practices have resulted in:

- wind and surface water dispersal of the tailings materials and the uncontrolled release of radon from the tailings piles.
- seepage of contaminated liquids into soils and groundwater from several areas in the mill complex and waste disposal areas.
- concentrations of large quantities of wastes in locations that pose a risk to public health and the environment.

Prior to remediation, soils in the vicinity of the mill contained elevated levels of heavy metals and radionuclides. The San Miguel River, a tributary to the Dolores

FIGURE 1.6 Hazardous waste site investigation (ESOI).

FIGURE 1.7 ABM-Wade site (EPA).

FIGURE 1.8 ABM-Wade site (EPA).

FIGURE 1.9 ABM-Wade site (EPA).

FIGURE 1.10 ABM-Wade site (EPA).

FIGURE 1.11 ABM-Wade site (EPA).

FIGURE 1.12 LaBounty Dump site (EPA).

River, the Colorado River, and Lake Mead, is contaminated with radium 226. For nearly two decades, process wastewaters were discharged to seepage ponds scooped in the alluvium of the San Miguel (Figure 1.14). Contaminated groundwater from the tailings area emerged from the walls of the San Miguel Canyon (Figure 1.15) and continued subsurface movement toward the river.

The site was listed on the National Priorities List (NPL) in 1986, but the massive cleanup was conducted under a consent decree in the U.S. District Court for the District of Colorado (*State of Colorado* v. *Union Carbide Corporation and Umetco Minerals Corporation*, 1983).

The Kepone Disaster. In 1973, Allied Chemical Company subcontracted the production of the pesticide Kepone to Life Sciences Products, a small company operating out of a converted service station in Hopewell, VA, near the James River. Within two months following startup, discharges from the plant had killed the aerobes in the Hopewell sewage treatment system. Life Sciences employees were poisoned by Kepone; the site was hopelessly contaminated; fish, shellfish, waterfowl, and a variety of aquatic organisms from the James River and Chesapeake Bay demonstrated classic bioaccumulation of Kepone; Kepone contaminated sediments accumulated in the James River and Chesapeake Bay; and particulates from air samplers near the plant were found to contain as high as 40% Kepone. Life Sciences was unable to pay for the cleanup, and Allied settled with the court by donating $8 million to establish the Virginia Environmental Endowment. Allied then recouped much of the settlement by taking a tax deduction on the endowment (Wentz 1989, pp. 59–68).

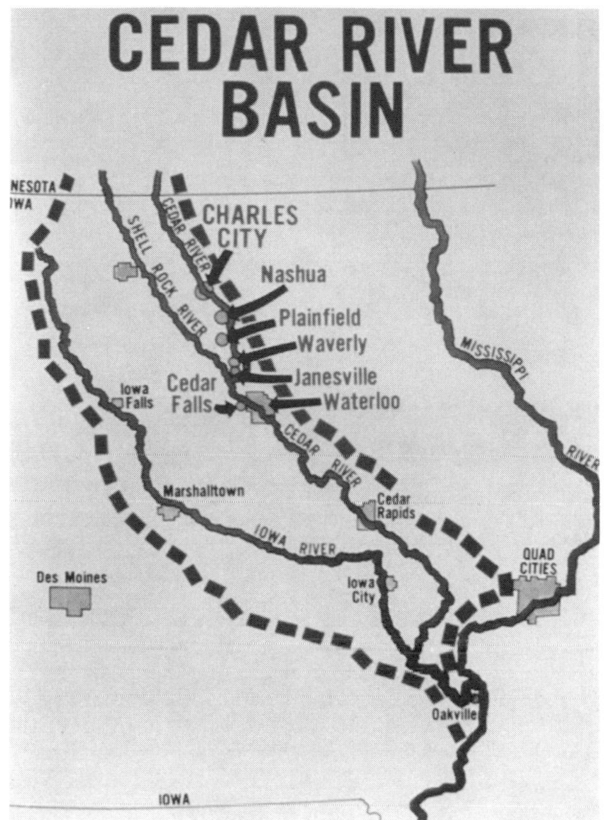

FIGURE 1.13 Cedar River basin downstream of LaBounty dump site (EPA).

Reiley Tar & Chemical Corporation. The site in St. Louis Park, MN was the location of the Republic Creosote Company from 1917 until 1972. Reiley Tar & Chemical Corporation operated the facility after 1972. Extensive soil and groundwater contamination has resulted from discharge of contaminated wastewater over land to wetlands adjacent to Minnehaha Creek. Polynuclear aromatic hydrocarbon (PAH) contamination of the Prairie du Chien-Jordan Aquifer has forced closing of seven municipal water supply wells. Investigative and cleanup activity has continued for more than a decade. Further response actions will be required to complete remediation of deep wells and major aquifers providing water supply to the Minneapolis suburbs (Beckwith 1990, personal communication).

Minamata Bay. As Americans began learning hard lessons from hazardous waste disposal practices and began looking to ocean disposal as an easy solution, the Japanese began learning hard lessons from that very practice. During the period 1932 to 1968, an acetaldehyde production facility discharged mercury-laden wastes to a river which flowed to nearby Minamata Bay. The mercury was converted to the methyl form, in the bottom sediments, and became concentrated in marine organisms, including fish and shellfish. Among nearby villagers, for whom the fish and shellfish were a diet staple, at least 46 died and an estimated 3000 were poisoned.

FIGURE 1.14 "Treatment" pond, Union Carbide-Uravan (EPA).

FIGURE 1.15 San Miguel River Canyon — emergent seepage from tailings ponds, Union Carbide-Uravan (EPA).

Japanese courts were continuing to struggle with liability rulings in 1993. (Dawson and Mercer 1986, p. 422; *Los Angeles Times*, November 27, 1993; Nebel and Wright 1993, p. 316).

Dioxin Discovered. In Italy, near Seveso, Industrie Chemiche Meda Societa Aromia (ICMSA) operated a plant producing 2,4,5-trichlorophenol. A production unit was allowed to overheat and released 2,3,7,8-tetrachlorodibenzo-*p*-dioxin (2,3,7,8-TCDD) or "dioxin." A small quantity of this highly toxic material was released to the atmosphere and drifted southward toward Milan. This necessitated the evacuation of residents, slaughter of livestock, and condemnation of fruit and vegetable crops. Exposed children developed chloracne and adults were sickened (Wentz 1989, p. 7ff). After seven years of cleanup activity, the dioxin waste was concentrated into 41 drums. This deadly concentrate passed through the hands of several handlers and was hauled from one end of France to the other, through Paris and, ultimately, to a barn in Anquilcourt-le-Sart. Throughout this odyssey the drums were identified only as containing tar (Lesser 1984).

"Take It Out Back and Dump It"

In 1950, before North Korea interrupted my academic endeavors, I took a part-time job at a local dry cleaning establishment. As the owner finished demonstrating how I was to clean the filters, I asked what to do with the filter sludge. His response was "take it out back and dump it." The dump site was easily recognized and frequently used. Later, after some enlightenment regarding such practices, the memory of that scenario returned to haunt me repeatedly. Thirty-five years later, the discovery that a dry cleaner in Phoenix, AZ took his used Perc out back and dumped it down a dry well was sad irony indeed. What we did in 1950 was assignable to ignorance. The 1985 episode tells us something about our progress in hazardous waste management and in educating the public regarding hazardous waste management (Author).

Disposal of hazardous waste has been accomplished in every mode of behavior — careful and careless, casual and furtive, clever and mindless, etc. The simple "take it out back and dump it" routine was commonplace. As case histories of contaminated sites are developed, the practice of dumping solvents and other liquid wastes onto the ground, into ditches and (incredibly) drainage wells, into seepage pits, and in trash dumps is too often found to be the mechanism or practice involved.

"Midnight dumping" became a familiar term, as disposers sought to find ways to "get rid of the stuff." The 55-gallon drum rolled into the roadside ditch or onto unwatched property became a familiar sight. Disposers contrived dump trucks with tanks arranged to discharge the contents when elevated. Such "tippers," as they were known in Britain, drove along country roads and dumped contents of the tank by tipping it to a high angle while in motion. The intent was, of course, to distribute the wastes over a great area and to do so without being detected.

Workers in manufacturing facilities where environmental rules were being enforced discovered drums or other containers of unknown wastes which suddenly

FIGURE 1.16 Surface impoundment (ESOI).

appeared on loading docks or elsewhere in the plants. These sudden appearances were referred to as "immaculate conception" events, but created serious hazards and disposal problems. "In-house" incidents of this nature demonstrated the fact that ignorance as well as unsavory and irresponsible attitudes toward hazardous waste management were present among rank-and-file workers, as well as corporate cost-center managers.

Even more reckless schemes were not uncommon. A favorite among criminal elements was the theft of a semitrailer (or tractor and trailer), acceptance of a load of hazardous wastes in drums (for a fee, of course), and abandonment of the stolen truck with load intact. Others carelessly or unknowingly discharged loads of waste into dumps or pits containing incompatible wastes and were overcome or killed on the spot or subjected others to similar fates.

"Treatment" and Other Assorted Techniques

Very large volumes of liquid hazardous wastes were provided treatment and/or disposal in depressions, impoundments, and excavations which the EPA referred to as "pits, ponds and lagoons" or PPLs (Figure 1.16). The expression referred to unlined holding and flow-through facilities that provided no protection against seepage and contamination of groundwater (Figure 1.17). Most provided no treatment other than settling of solids, radiation from the sun, and some modicum of aeration (Figure 1.18). Very large numbers of today's remedial sites are former PPLs.

FIGURE 1.17 Surfacc impoundment (Mill Service).

FIGURE 1.18 Surface impoundment (EPA).

Solid hazardous wastes, wastes that should have been recognized as "hazardous," and wastes of unknown composition were allowed to accumulate in piles and later were:

- awarded legitimacy as treatment units (*see* Subparts L of 40 CFR 264 and 265).
- excluded from definition as hazardous wastes because of their "high volume-low toxicity" character (*see* 40 CFR 261.4).
- declared to be materials that were "awaiting recycling."

Many of these waste piles also became today's remediation sites, and some were recycled in a process known as "dump leaching." Great strides were realized in extraction processes, during recent years, and previously worked ores became lucrative targets for further working. In practice, waste piles containing metals or other values were sprayed with weak acid or other solute-producing liquid, and the leachate was collected for extraction. Without underlining or removal to an impervious surface for leaching, much of the leachate was lost to the groundwater or resurfaced with base flow of nearby streams. The emerging metals-laden acidic leachate mixed with the natural alkalinity of receiving streams, with the resultant precipitation of metallic salts and/or hydroxides. The precipitate, known by practitioners as "Yellow Boy," can destroy a stream by blanketing the streambed as illustrated in Figures 1.19 and 1.20. A related practice, known as "heap leaching," is used to extract precious metals from low-grade ores. Heap leaching practitioners claim that liners or impervious layers used to capture the valuable leachate also prevent surface or groundwater contamination. Even today, the dump leaching process is common in copper mining areas of the southwestern United States The strong metals extraction industry lobby has been highly successful in obtaining exclusions from various hazardous waste regulatory requirements.*

Early and mid-1900s industrial waste generators also enjoyed the option of discharge of hazardous wastes to publicly owned sewerage. Prior to imposition of the National Pollutant Discharge Elimination System (NPDES) permitting, it made little difference whether industrial wastes were discharged directly into surface waters or reached the discharge point via municipal sewerage. As publicly owned, secondary sewage treatment plants came online, it soon became evident that untreated industrial wastes "can have serious impacts on the ability of systems to operate properly, on options for sludge disposal, and on water quality" (Council on Environmental Quality 1977, p. 37).

Not only were industrial wastes passing through publicly owned treatment works (POTWs) with ineffective or inadequate treatment, the toxic constituents in the industrial wastes were deleterious to the biota in the secondary treatment systems. Moreover, "municipal" sludge from the POTWs receiving industrial waste contained high concentrations of heavy metals, making digested sludge unsuitable for land disposal. In February 1977, the EPA reissued proposed national pretreatment guidelines (42 FR 5986) and, in 1978, began adopting pretreatment standards (43 FR 27736).

* *See* Bevill Amendment in Glossary.

FIGURE 1.19 Surface stream ruined by inflow from a dump leaching operation (EPA).

Major delays in the implementation of the pretreatment requirements, as well as "loopholes" in the RCRA regulations, have allowed the continued discharge of some hazardous industrial waste components to POTWs; however, the EPA and some state agencies have recently strengthened enforcement of pretreatment rules. Industries discharging to municipal systems, as well as the entities responsible for implementing pretreatment programs, are the subject of enforcement actions. Recent cases brought in federal district courts include *U.S.* v. *Crown Cork de Puerto Rico*; *U.S.* v. *Easton, PA and Harcros Pigments, Inc.*; *U.S. and Indiana* v. *New Albany* (U.S. EPA 1994a).

Numbers and Impacts

Uncontrolled releases continued through the 1970s. The EPA estimated hazardous waste generation at 20 to 50 million tons annually in 1977, adding the estimate that no more than 10% was disposed of in a manner that was safe to the environment (Council on Environmental Quality 1977, p. 50). Dams and dikes forming hazardous waste impoundments routinely failed, contaminating streams, rendering water supplies useless, and killing fish. Regulatory gaps and inadequacies continued to provide options for release of hazardous wastes to the air, water, or land. Early remediation of sites having groundwater contaminated with volatile organics frequently involved pumping the contaminated groundwater to the surface and air-stripping the contaminant, without further treatment or capture, to the atmosphere. (*See also* Dawson and Mercer 1986, pp. 3–4)

As was the case with the Love Canal exposures, the Hardeman County contamination of domestic water supplies, and the Minimata Bay fish and shellfish contami-

FIGURE 1.20 "Yellow-Boy" blanket on streambed resulting from a dump leaching operation (EPA).

nation, mismanagement of hazardous waste was clearly exacting a price in human health. The mechanisms were not well understood (and continue to be so), but there could be no doubt of the connection between exposure and disease incidence. Increased incidence of carcinogenic, mutagenic, and teratogenic effects; damage to reproductive systems; respiratory effects; brain and nervous system effects; and many lesser effects were increasingly associated with direct and indirect exposure to hazardous wastes. (*See also* Enger et al. 1989, Chapter 15)

Environmental effects were even more pronounced and frequently better understood. Olin Chemical Corporation's release of more than 4000 metric tons of DDT* manufacturing residue to a marsh near Triana, AL resulted in DDT contamination of Indian Creek and the catfish from the creek. Mallard ducks from a nearby wildlife refuge were found to contain 480 parts per million (ppm) DDT. Entire populations of waterfowl have disappeared from the area. Similar environmental tragedies were related to hazardous waste mismanagement throughout the nation and world.

* DDT (dichlorodiphenyltrichloroethane) is a highly persistent insecticide which was banned for use in the U.S. in 1972.

Table 1.1 Estimated Quantities of Hazardous Waste Generated in the U.S.

Source	Million Tons	Comment
1981 EPA National Survey	247 (135–402)[a]	Sample survey
1981 Office of Technology Assessment (OTA)	255–275[a]	State data
1983 Congressional Budget Office (CBO)	266 (223–308)[a]	Industry data
1984 Chemical Manufacturers Association (CMA)	247	Chemical industry survey
1985 EPA National Survey	272	Census of treatment, storage, and disposal facilities
1986 CMA	220.5	Chemical industry survey
1989 EPA	198	1994 Biennial RCRA Report
1991 EPA	306[b]	EPA530-S-94-039 (U.S. EPA 1994b)

[a] Range.

[b] The EPA attributes this increase to newly regulated wastes.

The esthetic effects of hazardous waste mismanagement through the mid-1900s are well understood by most citizens. The rise of the NIMBY (Not-In-My-Backyard) syndrome exemplifies the fear and revulsion of the public toward hazardous materials* in general, and hazardous wastes* in particular. The esthetic concerns quickly transition to economic issues as property values are affected, jobs are created or eliminated, and public administrators come under increasing pressures to craft solutions that solve all problems and resolve all issues. Facility siting became a major preoccupation among governments, the regulated industries and facilities, and the public. By the 1980s, public opposition to hazardous waste facilities had become so pervasive and intense that even sites with excellent operating records faced closure, simply because they were "there." Environmental equity issues, usually focused on location of hazardous materials/waste facilities in poor or minority neighborhoods, came to the forefront of the urban agenda in the 1990s.

The economics of hazardous waste management and mismanagement have intruded upon nearly every facet of life in America. From the relatively minor costs of the local dry cleaner's shift from dumping to recycling to the projected $230 billion for cleanup of the nation's nuclear weapons facilities, management of currently generated and earlier mismanaged hazardous waste has become a major element of the economy.

By 1979, the EPA estimate of hazardous *waste* generation was 51 million tons per year (Council on Environmental Quality 1979, p. 181). Estimates by the chemical industry and various federal agencies, in subsequent years (Table 1.1), indicate that generation of hazardous wastes continues in the 200 to 300 million ton range, even

* As in developed in later chapters, the distinction between hazardous *materials* and hazardous *waste* is derived largely from (1) lists of each that are published by various agencies and (2) whether a material is used or unused (virgin). However, the public generally perceives no distinction between the two.

as regulatory constraints intensify, as treatment and disposal costs escalate, and as waste minimization efforts are being enforced by regulatory agencies.

Table 1.1 statistics leave much unsaid. For example, by the mid-1980s the amounts of hazardous waste "created" by site cleanup activity had become significant, and these quantities continue to grow. Moreover, much of the remedial waste material is not "captured" by the reporting system. Since 1980 the numbers of generators which have been brought under regulation have increased greatly. Similarly, the definition of "hazardous waste" has changed, thereby bringing more wastes under the definition. An interesting aside is that when/if petroleum products or mining wastes are brought under the hazardous waste regulations, the quantities of hazardous waste generated will triple or quadruple.*

Early Efforts — What Worked/Didn't Work

Any summary of "What Worked/Didn't Work" is incomplete without mention of the key role played by Murray Stein and his Enforcement Conference procedure, conducted under the authorities of the Federal Water Pollution Control Act (FWPCA) (33 U.S.C. 466 et seq.), the precursor to the CWA. Stein, a lawyer, was Chief Enforcement Officer of the EPA's predecessors the Federal Water Quality Administration, and earlier, the Division of Water Supply and Pollution Control, U.S. Public Health Service.

The FWPCA contained provisions for collective action to abate interstate pollution or contamination of fish or shellfish. The extreme limitations (compared to present legislative and regulatory powers) of those authorities notwithstanding, Stein convened Enforcement Conferences on all manner of environmental issues from industrial wastes in Raritan Bay to radioactivity in the Colorado River Basin and from mining waste in the Great Lakes to petrochemical wastes in Galveston Bay.

Stein gathered federal, state, and local officials; media; scientists; and industrialists together. He orchestrated the conferences as if they were judicial proceedings; extrapolated from the most minimal of technical "evidence"; and extracted wide-ranging concessions, compromises, and commitments from polluters. The early cleanup achievements of Stein and his conferences and the impacts of these pioneering enforcement procedures deserve a prominent place in whatever form is eventually given the environmental history of America.

Legislation/Litigation

As the hazardous waste mismanagement outrages were thrust upon an unknowing public, governments — local, state, and federal — began attempts to coerce and force perpetrators, variously, to clean up contaminated sites, stop dumping, stop generating, treat properly, recycle, reclaim, or destroy the waste. Individuals and governments sought relief in the courts by tort actions. Nuisance is the most common of tort claims in the field of environmental law.

* *See* Bevill Amendment and Bentson Amendment in Glossary.

Nuisance is defined as "the class of wrongs that arise from the unreasonable, unwarrantable or unlawful use by a person of his own property either real or personal, or from his own lawful personal conduct working an obstruction of or injury to the right of another or of the public and producing material annoyance, inconvenience, discomfort or hurt" (Sullivan 1985, p. 10).

It should be noted that prior to 1972 with the promulgation of the Clean Water Act Amendments, most environmental remedies were conducted under nuisance legislation. And, nuisance law was only minimally helpful in addressing the broad range of environmental insults. Two pre-RCRA cases are illustrative.

- In a 1973 case, *Harrison* v. *Indiana Auto Shredders*, the Seventh Circuit Court of Appeals refused to permanently enjoin operation of an automobile shredding and recycling plant based on a nuisance action. The court held that under the evidence presented and in the absence of an imminent hazard to health and welfare — none of which was established — the defendant could not be prevented from continuing to engage in its operation (Sullivan 1985, p. 15).
- The Earthline Corporation attempted to operate an industrial waste recovery, treatment, storage, and disposal site on a 130-acre site in Illinois. Ninety acres are located within the village of Wilsonville and the remaining acres are adjacent to the village. The operation accepted hazardous wastes and toxic substances. In 1979, the village sued Earthline to stop the operation and also to require the removal of those hazardous wastes and toxic substances that had been deposited on the site. The court ruled that the site was a public/private nuisance, issued an injunction against Earthline's further operation of the site, and required them to remove all wastes and contaminated soil (Sullivan 1985, p. 16).

In 1970, the federal government resurrected the long-dormant 1899 Rivers and Harbors Act* and established a permit system for control of water pollution. The efficacy of the act and the permit system, for control of hazardous wastes, was limited in that it applied only to "navigable waters." (Debate over the navigable waters designation became the focus of many of the actions.) The act was successful in beginning the long-overdue elimination of indiscriminate dumping of all wastes into the streams and rivers of the nation, but the enforcement process was cumbersome, and the FWPCA and the successor CWA processes soon obscured the earlier mechanism.

The Atomic Energy Act of 1954 vested authority, for management of most *radioactive* wastes, in the Atomic Energy Commission (AEC) and the Nuclear Regulatory Commission (NRC). The AEC was responsible for managing nuclear wastes generated by the 17 nuclear weapons production facilities which it operated. Nuclear weapons development and production activities were assumed by the U.S.

* Also known as the "Refuse Act" — 33 U.S.C. § 407.

Department of Energy (DOE) in 1977. The NRC has responsibility for nuclear waste management oversight at the nation's nuclear-generating plants. For many years, the AEC gave weapons production the highest priority, generating huge quantities of radioactive process wastes. These wastes were stored or disposed of without treatment, or with inadequate treatment, at the production sites, some of which are now so badly contaminated that they may require 50 to 60 years to clean up, and "...there are some sites we are not going to be able to clean up" (Satchell 1989, p. 20).

The Solid Waste Disposal Act (SWDA) of 1965 was the first federal government attempt to improve solid waste disposal practice. It provided funding for development of state solid waste management programs and began the regulation of municipal waste management. The increasing concerns for human health and environmental protection led to amendment of the act with the 1970 Resource Recovery Act (RRA), but neither the 1965 SDWA nor the 1970 RRA had significant impact on the emerging problems of hazardous waste management. These two statutes were the predecessors to the RCRA of 1976, discussed later in this overview.

The CAA of 1970 was, as implied by the name, directed at controlling sources of air pollution and improving ambient air quality. The 1970 act did little to enhance hazardous waste management. In fact, emission control equipment installed by industry to meet CAA-required National Ambient Air Quality Standards (NAAQS), as well as CAA-required state implementation plans, has generated large volumes of hazardous and toxic material which must be managed as hazardous waste. By 1990, National Emission Standards for Hazardous Air Pollutants (NESHAPS), required by Section 112 of the act, had been established for only seven chemicals. The 1990 CAA Amendments require the EPA to issue standards for 189 additional NESHAPS by the year 2000.

The National Environmental Policy Act of 1970 (NEPA) required agencies and activities of the federal government to prepare an environmental impact statement (EIS) for any project that might affect the environment. Unquestionably, NEPA stimulated some hazardous waste management activity and improvement by many agencies. Numerous lawsuits have been filed against the agencies; however, the suits did not directly compel cleanup or compliance with environmental law. The nature of the suits has been largely to the effect that (1) no EIS was prepared, (2) the EIS was inadequate, or (3) the environmental assessment performed was inadequate (Wentz 1989, pp. 39–40). The Departments of Defense and Energy have, until recently, largely ignored NEPA requirements. (*See also* Vanderver 1985, pp. 374–375; Satchell 1989, pp. 20–22)

The Federal Insecticide, Fungicide, and Rodenticide Act of 1972 (FIFRA) as amended regulates storage and disposal of pesticides and requires informative and accurate labeling of pesticide products. In May 1974, the EPA promulgated regulations for the storage and disposal of pesticides (39 FR 15236, 1 May 1974) (40 CFR 165) and proposed others which were never implemented (39 FR 36874, 15 October 1974). These regulations detailed the appropriate conditions for incineration, soil injection, and other means of disposal of pesticide wastes. They devote considerable attention to the disposal of pesticide containers, which have caused a significant proportion of accidental poisonings (M. Miller 1985, p. 430).

The Marine Protection Research and Sanctuaries Act of 1972 (MPRSA) or "Ocean Dumping Act" regulates the dumping of materials at sea and was intended to prevent or limit the dumping of materials which would have adverse effects. However, ambiguities in the original language of the act left unclear the intent of Congress as to ending all ocean dumping or allowing it only where it is the best disposal alternative and will not unduly affect the marine ecosystem. This ambiguity was heightened by Congress and the EPA permitting ocean dumping of sludge from POTWs along the East Coast [33 USC Section 1412(a)]. Municipal sludge, particularly that generated by older cities in the East, may be laced with heavy metals from industrial sources on the collection systems. The 1988 amendment to MPRSA, the "Ocean Dumping Ban Act" (33 USC Chapter 27), effectively ended ocean dumping of municipal sludges and industrial wastes after December 31, 1991 (U.S. EPA 1991, pp.1, 40).

The FWPCA of 1972* was significantly modified in 1977 to deal with toxic water pollutants and was renamed the CWA. The act has five main elements:

- The NPDES permit program which requires all municipal and industrial waste sources that discharge wastes into "waters of the United States" to have a permit
- A system of minimum national effluent standards for each industry
- Receiving water quality standards
- Specific provisions for oil spills, discharges of toxic chemicals, and nonprocess discharges such as contaminated plant site runoff
- A construction grant program to assist in funding POTW and related construction; the grant program was replaced by the State Revolving Loan Fund (SRLF) Program, established per Title VI of the CWA

In similarity to the CAA, implementation of the CWA achieved the intended removal of waste materials from municipal and industrial wastewater streams, but created new waste management challenges. Sludges and residues from pretreatment and treatment systems were not regulated initially and were frequently mismanaged.

Industrial facilities that discharge into collection systems serving POTWs are required to meet pretreatment standards. Thus, the CWA controls and limits discharges of hazardous wastes directly to surface waters and indirectly through POTWs. The CAA controls (at least some) emissions of hazardous wastes to the atmosphere. MPRSA limits dumping of hazardous wastes at sea. Through these various statutes, Congress had, by the mid-1970s, theoretically and statutorily shifted the entire burden of ultimate disposal to the land.

---

* The 1972 FWPCA was also the first federal environmental statute to use "technology-forcing" standards. Where existing treatment technology did not meet industrial treatment needs, Congress reasoned that it could "force" the desired technological development and achieve the "zero discharge" goal by 1983. This was highly significant lawmaking and a harbinger of laws of the future.

The SDWA of 1974 (embodied the potential to provide significant protection to underground sources of drinking water through two major provisions:

- The EPA was authorized to designate individual areas as having an aquifer which is the sole source of water supply to the area and which would create a significant hazard to public health if contaminated. Once an area is so designated, no federal assistance may be provided for any project in the area which the EPA determines may contaminate the aquifer. Any "person"* may petition the EPA for a Sole Source Aquifer designation (U.S. EPA 1987, p. 1). To date, the EPA has applied this provision to about 50 sites.
- The act regulates underground injection to protect usable aquifers from contamination. Underground injection is usually thought of as the deep, high-pressure pumped injection well. The 40 CFR 144 standard defines undergound injection as the subsurface emplacement of fluid through a well or dug-hole, whose depth is greater than its width. This definition encompasses five classes of injection wells used for a variety of purposes including the disposal of hazardous wastes. The EPA designated all states as requiring underground injection control (UIC) programs, and the agency must promulgate the program where a state fails to do so. The EPA missed the 1979 deadline for these promulgations, and the program moved forward slowly in the early 1980s. (J. Miller 1985, pp. 199, 204–205). A new 40 CFR 148 brought injection of hazardous wastes in Class I (deep) wells under the land disposal restrictions, with implementation dates ranging from August 1988 through June 1995. The EPA is expected to introduce new standards for Class V (shallow) injection wells in 1995 (*see* Chapter 7).

The TSCA of 1976 provides the EPA with authority to require testing of chemical substances, both new and old, entering the environment and to regulate them where necessary. It may also be used to regulate the development of biotechnology and genetic engineering (M. Miller 1985, pp. 141–142). The TSCA empowers the EPA administrator to place restrictions on the production, distribution, use, and disposal of toxic substances. The TSCA was the first legislation in which Congress singled out a specific substance, by name, for regulation. Section 2605(e) directed the EPA to phase out the manufacture and use of polychlorinated biphenyls (PCBs) according to a statutorily regulated timetable. Subchapter II provides the authority and structure for regulation and control of asbestos.

The RCRA of 1976, as indicated earlier, was the outgrowth of the SWDA of 1965 and the RRA of 1970. RCRA Subtitle D continued and expanded the solid waste management programs of the 1965 act, but remained relatively weak on hazardous waste management. Subtitle C, the framework for the federal hazardous waste management program, was strengthened somewhat by amendments in 1980, but more significantly by the Hazardous and Solid Waste Amendments of 1984 (HSWA). The HSWA required the EPA to develop and implement the land disposal

* Individual, corporation, company, association, partnership, state, municipality, or federal agency.

restrictions, created the new "conditionally exempt small quantity generator" category, and in Subtitle I authorized the underground (petroleum) storage tank regulations. Subtitle J, the Medical Waste Tracking Act (MWTA), was enacted in 1988, but was allowed to expire at the end of the five-year statutory life.

In RCRA, Congress attempted to provide "cradle-to-grave" management of hazardous waste by imposing regulatory requirements upon generators; transporters of hazardous wastes; and owners and operators of treatment, storage, and disposal facilities. Although this text deals with hazardous waste management, in general, the focus will be upon RCRA Subtitle C, which is the federal regulatory apparatus for control and management of hazardous waste in the United States and its territories. (*See also* Hall and Bryson 1985, Chapter 2; U.S. EPA 1990, Section I)

The RCRA does not address the equally serious problem of abandoned and inactive hazardous waste sites. Legislation establishing remedies and allocating responsibilities for correcting problems at these sites is contained in CERCLA of 1980, commonly known as Superfund. CERCLA provides federal funding for response and site remediation where responsible parties cannot be identified or are unwilling or unable to accomplish the necessary cleanup. The EPA then may sue identified responsible parties for recovery of funds expended in the remediation. CERCLA was extensively modified by the Superfund Amendments and Reauthorization Act of 1986 (SARA). In addition to renewal of Superfund authorities and funding, SARA significantly broadened the reach of CERCLA. Title I of SARA required the Secretary of Labor to issue workplace health and safety standards for hazardous waste workers. Title III of SARA, known as the Emergency Planning and Community Right-to-Know Act (EPCRA), imposed an emergency planning regime upon states and communities and required community right-to-know and toxic release reporting. The intent was to make information regarding chemical use and storage information available to communities and to require states and communities to prepare and implement planning for chemical disasters such as that which devastated Bhopal, India.

The Hazardous Materials Transportation Act of 1975 (HMTA) authorizes the regulation of marking, labeling, and packaging of hazardous materials for transportation, thereby including the transportation aspects of hazardous waste management. In RCRA, Congress recognized the potential for overlap of regulatory issue by the EPA and the U.S. Department of Transportation (DOT) and specifically instructed the EPA to coordinate all transportation-related regulations with the DOT. The HMTA was substantially amended by the Hazardous Materials Transportation Uniform Safety Act of 1990 (HMTUSA). The 1990 amendments were implemented in the form of a general overhaul of the packaging standards to bring American practice into accord with international standards.

Political

Early efforts at hazardous waste management by state and local governments ranged from effective to nonexistent. The early federal legislation was intended to provide funding, technical assistance, and moral support to state and local governments to prod them into more effective actions and postures. The federal grant-in-aid was the most common mechanism. Typically, the grant provided startup funds to staff, train, and equip state and local agencies, enabling them to launch specific programs. As time passed, the federal statutes, regulations, and policies increasingly tied funding to levels of performance. Federal programs were "delegated" to states, and funding depended upon the favorable outcomes of periodic reviews of program accomplishments. RCRA delegation and state program oversight by the EPA continues to this day. Most states have opted for delegation, and many have adopted RCRA regulations "by rule." The state agency director thereby takes on the role of the EPA administrator in implementation of most elements of RCRA within the state.

States' rights and police powers issues helped to shape the form of early legislation and policy toward environmental management and cleanup of hazardous waste sites. It was widely held that environmental problems were best managed at the state and local level, and that view was reflected by Congress in the federal legislation and by the federal agencies in the implementation thereof.

Although there were obvious exceptions, the state and local agencies were frequently inadequately funded and hampered by limited staff and equipment. The EPA and its predecessor agencies, although similarly limited, were able to focus staff and laboratory capability on specific problems. Congress sought to assist state and local governments in the development of decentralized programs by funding technical assistance capability in the federal agencies. Technical assistance programs were frequently helpful in source identification, problem definition, and impact assessment, but somewhat less helpful in securing prevention and remediation of hazardous waste problems.

The early legislation, programs, and policies were too frequently ineffective in securing the intended protection of public health and the environment. Activists and the public demanded direct and rigorous action to bring hazardous wastes under control.

A careful review of the progression of federal legislation, from the 1965 SWDA through the 1984 HSWA, shows increasingly direct and detailed involvement by Congress in hazardous waste management in the United States As will be shown later in this text, this same impatience with progress was not ameliorated by the direct involvement of federal agencies. In HSWA, Congress took the then unprecedented step of writing regulatory language, standards, and calendar deadlines into the statute.

By 1994, the extent, range, and detail of congressional and federal agency involvement in hazardous waste management, and environmental management in general, had burgeoned to the point that public and political sentiment had turned against these regulatory programs. Federally imposed "unfunded mandates" were a major issue of the 1994 elections, and the new Congress promised to "review" many of these programs.

Administrative

As the Environmental Decade (1970s) progressed, federal, state, and local agencies and officials learned that large numbers of constituents have lively interests in environmental matters. Public hearings, and similar forums, became procedurally ingrained in most legislation, regulation, and policy. It is now taken as routine that no significant environmental decision is made at any level of government without full public participation, usually through a hearing process. In countless instances, these hearings have sharply affected the course of resolution of major issues.

In recent years, several federal agencies have been shown to be among the worst offenders of hazardous waste management statutes, regulations, and policies. In 1978, President Carter ordered federal agencies to comply with the nation's environmental laws, but his executive decree had little effect. In 1980, Congress passed CERCLA, but exempted federal government facilities. Not until 1986 were federal agencies brought under Superfund rules. During this same period the Departments of Energy and Defense hid their hazardous waste practices behind the national security curtain, and the true picture of these practices is only now beginning to emerge. These practices have so severely contaminated some sites that officials of the Departments of Energy and Defense have been quoted to the effect that there may be no way to clean them up (Satchell 1989). In these matters, public meetings, hearings, and forums were ineffective, and administrative approaches to hazardous waste management actually served to conceal the extent of the problems.

"Administrative" actions and policies brought about serious delays in the implementation of the newly enacted RCRA and CERCLA, under the direction of EPA Administrator Anne Gorsuch (Burford), during the early 1980s. Gorsuch and her hazardous waste program manager Rita Lavelle held strongly negative views toward environmental regulation in general and toward hazardous waste regulation in particular. These ideologies were further strengthened by political activism which put party advantage far above environmental urgency. In sworn testimony before a congressional committee, Lavelle offered a "frankly political motive for shutting off Superfund help to western mining waste sites. She was afraid that the mining states would resent the federal intrusion and that the 1984 election campaigns of western Republican senators might suffer." Gorsuch testified that "she had held up a $6 million grant to clean up the huge Stringfellow acid pits in Riverside, California, because Jerry Brown, then governor of California and Democratic candidate for the Senate, might get the credit" (Lash et al. 1984, pp. 82–83). The serious student of the politics of the environment should read the referenced book in its entirety.

Technical

Approaches to definition of hazardous wastes, their identification, impacts, and remedies have progressed along similar lines to the developments cited previously. The initial environmental and public health concerns with hazardous waste sites had a "fires and explosions" focus. The early history is replete with cases and episodes wherein sites burned and/or exploded, releasing huge amounts of heat energy, toxic vapors, and particulates. Many were established arson cases and many more were suspect. Other sites emitted toxic vapors without fire or explosion.

Such events were often spectacular, frequently hazardous to human health, and always frightening to the public. But the exposures they created tended to be short-lived (i.e., a few hours or days), with a relatively small number of acute health effects, fewer fatalities, and even fewer cases of chronic health effects.

In 1975, a senior engineer, assigned to an EPA field office, was detailed to the Office of the Assistant Administrator for Water and Hazardous Materials and given the task of evaluating the agency's groundwater management efforts. When he had completed his report, he made the rounds briefing the program managers on his findings. As he attempted to explain to a Deputy Assistant Administrator (DAA) the threat to groundwater quality posed by toxic metals and organics leaching from land disposal of hazardous wastes, the DAA interrupted him and sneered, "Ah b—— s——, the rocks and the sand strain that stuff out." A drinking water program official declared: "We don't have a groundwater problem."

Not until the January 1977 rendition of *The Report to Congress: Waste Disposal Practices and Their Effects on Groundwater*, prepared by a major consulting firm under contract to the EPA Offices of Water Supply and Solid Waste Management Programs, did the magnitude of the groundwater impacts begin to be understood by policy makers. The report confirmed what a few professionals in the agency had been saying — the real human health and environmental impacts of hazardous waste mismanagement were (are) to the groundwater resources of the nation.

The groundwater resource was then known to supply drinking water to over half the populace and to be the source of water for 30% of the domestic water systems (U.S. EPA 1977, p. 1). Aquifers were being contaminated with a wide range of soluble and leachable inorganic and organic pollutants, many of which are toxic.

Whereas the release of toxic air pollutants and heat energy from fires and explosions could be measured in days, hours, minutes, or even seconds, the impacts of groundwater contamination may persist for decades or centuries. As experience was gained, it was seen that similar differences of scale prevailed in cleanup costs. Congress and the regulatory agencies began to shift their focus to prevention of groundwater pollution and remediation of contaminated aquifers. This shift of focus became most evident in the 1984 HSWA provisions, which will be a frequent topic throughout this text.

Large East Coast cities, for many years, barged their industrial waste-laden sewage sludge to ocean dumping areas. During the 1970s, the ever-tightening restrictions of the CAA and the NPDES permits, together with the disappearing land disposal sites, caused ocean disposal of hazardous wastes to become a popular alternative. Opposition mounted to these practices, and in 1977 Congress amended MPRSA to require the EPA to "end the dumping of sewage sludge and industrial wastes into ocean waters." The EPA had never developed criteria for safe ocean disposal, and the new amendment contained language defining sewage sludge and industrial wastes as materials which unreasonably degrade or endanger human health or the environment (J. Miller 1985, pp. 465–467). The lack of a more precise definition of "industrial waste" hampered the effectiveness of the amended MPRSA, and several court decisions allowed some dumping to continue. Public pressure and the Ocean Dumping Ban Act of 1988 effectively ended the practice (U.S. EPA 1991, p. 40).

Thus, the legislation and implementation of the 1970s had the effect of diverting most hazardous wastes onto the land or beneath the land surface. Surface impoundments and land "farming" were offered up as treatment, and landfills and deep well injection systems were regarded as acceptable disposal techniques. The realities were that the impoundments and land treatment facilities provided little treatment and made their hazardous constituents available to the groundwater resource. The landfills similarly made leachable and liquid hazardous constituents available to the groundwater, and the environmental safety of deep well disposal was in doubt among many professionals. These considerations were paramount when Congress enacted HSWA in 1984. (*See also* Piasecki and Davis 1987, Chapter 3)

By the early 1990s, a wide range of treatment and destruction technologies had evolved, and prospects for significant reductions in quantities of hazardous waste managed in land treatment and disposal were good. But increasingly vigorous activism and public opposition to siting of new treatment and destruction facilities caused widespread withdrawl of RCRA permit applications, cancellation of construction plans and contracts, and a marked reluctance toward corporate involvements in major new facilities. Old line waste management companies adopted strategies of buying out smaller companies, expanding and upgrading existing facilities, and generally lowering profiles.

International Aspects

The opening of the Iron Curtain and the emerging horror stories of environmental mismanagement in eastern Europe aside, Europeans have been perceived to be several steps ahead of America in the evolution of hazardous waste management. The long-standing perception is that land has not been available in Europe for land disposal to have its day as the alternative of choice. Incineration became the early choice, and remains so to this day, but land disposal is practiced in varying degrees. Britain is a case in point, with 85% of hazardous waste disposed of in landfills (Skinner 1987, p. 7). Denmark, (Muller 1987, p. 118), France (Leroy 1987, p. 144), and the former West Germany (Sierig 1987, pp. 128–130) utilize land disposal, but clearly emphasize treatment and destruction processes.

The West German chemical industry began ocean incineration of waste chlorinated hydrocarbons to avoid costly scrubbers for land-based incinerators. High-temperature incineration effectively destroys the chemical waste, but emits hydrochloric acid (HCl) in the exhaust gases. The buffering capacity of the limitless seawater was counted upon to neutralize the HCl emitted by ocean-going incinerators. Europeans have become disenchanted with this technology and, in two international agreements, have forced the phase out of ocean incineration (Piasecki and Davis 1987, p. 68). As discussed in a later chapter, an American company made major investments of money and resources in an ocean incineration venture. The project was eventually abandoned. (*See also* Piasecki and Davis 1987, Chapters 3 and 4; U.S. EPA 1991, Chapter 5)

The frequently proclaimed European sophistication in matters of hazardous waste management is somewhat overstated. In Britain, an early cornerstone of the toxic waste plan was codisposal — the deliberate mixing of hazardous wastes with conventional municipal wastes in permeable landfills. The practice was based upon the belief that the leaching of toxic chemicals will change the wastes into nontoxic substances over time by dilution and biological degradation (Piasecki and Davis

1987, p. 193). Skinner (1987, p. 7) states: "There is little evidence of problem landfill sites in the UK … This is attributed to comprehensive land use controls, favorable geology and control of ground water usage." (*See also* Wilson 1987, pp. 256–257)

In Holland, much of which is below sea level, fill is often required before construction can take place on land. For more than 40 years, solid wastes containing hazardous chemicals were utilized as fill material. Authorities estimate that up to 8 million metric tons of hazardous chemical waste may be buried in that small country (Enger et al. 1989, p. 379). The government estimates that there are now nearly 5000 leaking waste sites. The small village of Lekkerkerk is the Dutch version of Love Canal, where local government allowed dumping of chemical wastes as fill material (Piasecki and Davis 1987, pp. 190–191).

Canadian provincial hazardous waste efforts parallel, to some extent, those in the United States Primacy for regulatory programs resides with the provinces; however, the federal government has some interprovincial authority (Dawson and Mercer 1986, p. 37). But Canada has limited capacity for offsite treatment or volume reduction of hazardous wastes. Therefore, extensive and prescriptive regulations governing treatment and disposal of hazardous wastes are not in effect. The Canadian Environmental Protection Act lists nine hazardous classes of materials which are either prohibited or release is controlled. Recent amendments add a Leachate Extraction Procedure similar to that of RCRA (Krieger and Austin 1995, p. 90).

In the outlying areas of Mexico, discharge of toxic materials goes on virtually uncontested (Dawson and Mercer 1986, p. 37). This absence of controls invited the import of hazardous wastes from the United States, but the RCRA required exporters to provide detailed notification to the EPA and to obtain the consent of the receiving country (40 CFR 262–263). Burgeoning industrial development along the U.S.–Mexican border has brought hazardous waste management sharply into focus. The maquiladora* industries supposedly bring their hazardous wastes from their Mexican facilities into the United States to ensure safe treatment and/or disposal and to meet "duty-free" requirements of United States and Mexican customs regulations. The RCRA (40 CFR 262) also regulates import of hazardous waste into the United States As discussed later in this text, accountability of maquila-generated hazardous wastes has not proven satisfactory, and the environmental impacts of these activities in industrialized border areas are severe.

Hazardous waste management in Central and South America is primitive at best. Management is hampered by less than vigorous enforcement. The Japanese environmental focus is on protection of worker health, and although new, more comprehensive legislation has been enacted, bureaucratic battles have limited the implementation of the new laws. Other Pacific Rim countries hazardous waste management programs have generally lagged industrial development (Krieger and Austin 1995, pp. 92–99).

* Maquila (twin) industrial facilities are established on both sides of the U.S.–Mexican border, usually by American companies, to take advantage of significantly less stringent regulatory burdens and labor costs on the Mexican side. Work that is labor intensive or that may involve use of toxic chemicals is performed in the Mexican facility. Subassemblies, etc. are shipped to the American side for final assembly, inspections, distribution, etc. (*see* "maquiladora" entry in the Glossary).

The United Nations Environment Programme (UNEP) has limited global environmental oversight functions. Acting through various suborganizations and in concert with international organizations, such as the World Health Organization (WHO), UNEP organizes various conventions and manages environmental databases, some of which are specific to hazardous waste management. Pertinent conventions include the London Convention on Ocean Dumping, the Oslo Convention on Incineration-At-Sea, and the Basel Convention on the Control of Transboundary Movements of Hazardous Wastes and Their Disposal. A database specific to international hazardous waste management is the International Register of Potentially Toxic Chemicals (IRPTC). (*See* U.S. EPA 1991, p. 9ff; UNEP 1992, pp. 28–29, 42)

TOPICS FOR REVIEW OR DISCUSSION

1. The hazardous waste mismanagement episodes summarized in the "Early Hazardous Waste Management" section of this chapter suggest several regulatory measures that might be needed to protect human health and the environment. Discuss a few such possibilities.
2. Discuss two undesirable effects of the discharge of toxic industrial wastes to municipal sewerage.
3. Review the progression of environmental laws and regulations that culminated in the need to regulate hazardous waste management in the United States
4. Identify at least two provisions of the 1984 HSWA which had major significance or impact.
5. What event(s) of the mid-1980s has (have) caused, and will continue for some time to cause, annual increases in the quantities of hazardous wastes generated.
6. SARA Title I was an unusual legislative step — discuss.
7. Public hearings on environmental issues are now taken for granted. Discuss any that may have been held in local jurisdictions and any impacts they may have had.
8. If major and minor world powers suddenly began development of new weapons systems that threatened world peace or even human survival, would the United States be justified in again postponing environmental controls on weapons production in order to quickly build an offsetting defensive arsenal of these weapons?

REFERENCES

Beckwith, Douglas C. 1990. Minnesota Pollution Control Agency. Personal communication.

Council on Environmental Quality. 1977. *Environmental Quality: The Eighth Annual Report of the Council on Environmental Quality*. U.S. Government Printing Office, Washington, D.C. Stock No. 041-011-00035-1.

Council on Environmental Quality. 1979. *Environmental Quality: The Tenth Annual Report of the Council on Environmental Quality*. U.S. Government Printing Office, Washington, D.C. Stock No. 041-011-00047-5.

Dahl, Thomas O. 1980. "Salsbury Laboratories — LaBounty Site, Phased Approach to a Hazardous Waste Disposal Problem." U.S. Environmental Protection Agency, National Enforcement Investigations Center, Denver, CO.

Dawson, Gaynor W., and Basil W. Mercer. 1986. *Hazardous Waste Management*. John Wiley & Sons, New York.

Enger, Eldon D., J. Richard Kormelink, Bradley F. Smith, and Rodney J. Smith. 1989. *Environmental Science: The Study of Interrelationships*. Wm. C. Brown Publishers, Dubuque, IA.

Hall, Ridgeway M., and Nancy S. Bryson. 1985. "Resource Conservation and Recovery Act." *Environmental Law Handbook*, Eighth Edition. Government Institutes, Inc., Rockville, MD.

Krieger, Gary R. and Ian Austin. 1995. "International Legal and Legislative Framework." *Accident Prevention Manual for Business and Industry — Environmental Management*, Gary R. Krieger, Ed. National Safety Council, Itasca, IL.

Lash, Jonathan, Katherine Gillman, and David Sheridan. 1984. *A Season of Spoils*. Pantheon Books, New York.

Leroy, Jean-Bernard. 1987. "Hazardous Waste Management in France." *International Perspectives on Hazardous Waste Management,* William S. Forester and John H. Skinner, Eds. Academic Press, New York.

Lesser, George H. 1984. "Trends and Problems in International Legislation on Transportation of Hazardous Materials." In *Atmospheric Dispersion of Hazardous/Toxic Materials from Transport Accidents*. Elsevier Science Publishing Company, New York. p. 2.

The Los Angeles Times, November 27, 1993.

Miller, Jeffrey G. 1985. "Marine Protection, Research and Sanctuaries Act." *Environmental Law Handbook*, Eighth Edition. Government Institutes, Inc., Rockville, MD.

Miller, Marshall Lee. 1985. "Federal Regulation of Pesticides." *Environmental Law Handbook*, Eighth Edition. Government Institutes, Inc., Rockville, MD.

Muller, Klaus. 1987. "Hazardous Waste Management in Denmark." *International Perspectives on Hazardous Waste Management,* William S. Forester and John H. Skinner, Eds. Academic Press, New York.

Nebel, Bernard J., and Richard T. Wright. 1993. *Environmental Science*. Prentice-Hall, Englewood Cliffs, NJ.

Piasecki, Bruce W., and Gary A. Davis. 1987. *America's Future in Toxic Waste Management — Lessons from Europe*. Quorum Books, New York.

Satchell, Michael. 1989. "Uncle Sam's Toxic Folly." *U.S. News and World Report*, March 27, pp. 20–22.

Sierig, Gerhard. 1987. "Hazardous Waste Management in The Federal Republic of Germany." *International Perspectives on Hazardous Waste Management,* William S. Forester and John H. Skinner, Eds. Academic Press, New York.

Skinner, John H. 1987. *International Perspectives on Hazardous Waste Management,* William S. Forester and John H. Skinner, Eds. Academic Press, New York.

Sullivan, Thomas F. P. 1985. "Environmental Law Fundamentals and the Common Law." *Environmental Law Handbook*, Eighth Edition. Government Institutes, Inc., Rockville, MD.

United Nations Environmental Programme. 1992. *Two Decades of Achievement and Challenge*. Information and Public Affairs Branch, Nairobi, Kenya.

U.S. Environmental Protection Agency. 1977. *The Report to Congress: Waste Disposal Practices and Their Effects on Groundwater*. Office of Water Supply and Office of Solid Waste Management Programs, Washington, D.C.

U.S. Environmental Protection Agency. 1987. *Sole Source Aquifer Background Study: Cross-Program Analysis*. Office of Ground-Water Protection, Washington, D.C. EPA 440.6-87-015.

U.S. Environmental Protection Agency. 1990. *RCRA Orientation Manual*, 1990 Edition. Office of Solid Waste, Washington, D.C.

U.S. Environmental Protection Agency. 1991. *Report to Congress on Ocean Dumping 1987–1990*. Office of Water Supply, Washington, D.C. EPA 503/9-91/009.

U.S. Environmental Protection Agency. 1994a. *Enforcement Accomplishments Report FY 1993*. Office of Enforcement, Washington, D.C. EPA 300-R-94-003.

U.S. Environmental Protection Agency. 1994b. *The Biennial RCRA Hazardous Waste Report (Based on 1991 Data)*. Office of Solid Waste and Emergency Response, Washington, D.C. EPA 530-S-94-039.

Vanderver, Timothy A., Jr. 1985. "National Environmental Policy Act." *Environmental Law Handbook*, Eighth Edition. Government Institutes, Inc., Rockville, MD.

Wentz, Charles A. 1989. *Hazardous Waste Management*. McGraw-Hill, New York.

Wilson, David C. 1987. "Hazardous Waste Management in The United Kingdom." *International Perspectives on Hazardous Waste Management,* William S. Forester and John H. Skinner, Eds. Academic Press, New York.

Worobec, Mary Devine. 1986. *Toxic Substances Control Primer*. The Bureau of National Affairs, Washington, D.C.

2 DEFINITION OF HAZARDOUS WASTE

OBJECTIVES

At completion of this chapter, the student should:

- understand the generally accepted definitions of "hazardous waste," and why the *definition* is of singular importance.
- understand the Resource Conservation and Recovery Act (RCRA) definition of hazardous waste and the importance, application, and limitations thereof.
- understand the relationship of RCRA "solid waste" and RCRA hazardous waste.
- have an overview familiarity with the perspective of various professionals in the management and control of hazardous wastes.
- understand the differences in perception of hazardous *waste* and hazardous *materials* management by regulators, environmentalists, the public, and the media.
- be familiar with other definitive approaches — state and foreign — and their strengths and weaknesses.

INTRODUCTION

If every person who creates, handles, or manages hazardous waste was sufficiently knowledgeable, motivated, capable, and unfailingly trustworthy regarding roles and responsibilities, regulation of hazardous waste management would not be necessary. Unfortunately, we live in an imperfect world, and it has become obvious that hazardous waste management must be regulated. Clearly, if a regulatory agency is to regulate something, there should be an unambiguous means of identifying and describing that something which is to be regulated.

One source tells us that:

> The definition of hazardous waste varies from one country to another. One of the most widely used definitions, however, is contained in the U.S. Resource Conservation and Recovery Act of 1976 (RCRA). RCRA considers wastes toxic and/or

> hazardous if they 'cause or significantly contribute to an increase in mortality or an increase in serious irreversible, or incapacitating reversible illness; or pose a substantial present or potential hazard to human health or the environment when improperly treated, stored, transported, disposed of, or otherwise managed.' Having read this definition you can begin to appreciate the complexity in regulating the problem. (Enger et al. 1989, p. 372)

Imagine having to determine whether or not the contents of a truckload of drums meet this criteria, while the driver waits, and other trucks are lined up behind it.

Countless such scenarios hang upon the legal *definition* of hazardous waste, and the importance of a workable definition cannot be overemphasized. In this chapter, we will explore this matter of definition of hazardous waste. In the study and management of hazardous waste, the terms "hazardous" and "toxic" are frequently used interchangeably. There is a technical difference, and it is important, as well, to recognize that distinction.

"Toxic" commonly refers to poisonous substances which cause death or serious injury to humans and animals by interfering with normal body physiology. The term is properly used to describe a pure substance, whether or not it has become a waste (i.e., "toxic substance" or "toxic chemical"). A toxic effect is imposed intrinsically.

"Hazardous," a broader term, refers to all wastes that are dangerous for any reason, including those that are toxic (i.e., flammable, explosive, or reactive). A hazardous waste may impose the effect intrinsically or extrinsically.

The Chemist

The analytical chemist, perhaps to a greater extent than others, must deal with the definition of hazardous waste from a number of standpoints. He/she may be called upon to define hazardous waste in terms that will enable analytical determinations and/or screening procedures to be carried out expeditiously, at reasonable cost, and to be sufficiently comprehensive so that definitional loopholes are not created. He/she may be called upon to develop analytical or screening procedures or to select the most appropriate option from several procedures. The chemist may find it necessary to configure a laboratory to most efficiently handle the analytical requirements of a particular source. He/she may be involved in manufacturing or treatment process control where wastes may vary from hazardous to nonhazardous as a result of control factors.

The chemist is particularly concerned with the safety of analytical procedures. Where screening techniques are employed, for decisionmaking in the field or onsite, the chemist must devise procedures which enable the decision to be made without exposing the analyst and/or others to hazards. He/she is expected to define hazardous waste in chemical terms that are sufficiently simple so that needed tests can be performed safely, in the field, by semiskilled workers, yet be sufficiently precise to withstand the rigors of the courtroom. This dichotomy is made more pronounced by the fact that many of the analytical methods prescribed by SW 846 (U.S. EPA 1986) are highly complex, requiring sophisticated instrumentation and procedures that are incomprehensible to courts, the media, and the lay public.*

Analytical chemists are frequently called as expert witnesses or to testify regarding chemical determinations. The regulatory definition, grounded in the statute, is the criteria against which the hazardous or nonhazardous status of a sample is judged. Ambiguity or an unnessessarily complex definition can cause the testimony to be beyond the capability of the nonlawyer and can make credible enforcement actions difficult or impossible. Needless to say, the findings in such cases can have enormous significance.

The Life Scientist/Health Professional

The roles of the life scientist and the health professional in hazardous waste management are closely related and deal with the biological impacts of exposure of living cells to hazardous wastes. The life scientist is primarily concerned with the exposure impacts upon nonhuman cells, as indicator organisms. The health professional is concerned with the incidence of disease or genetic effect, the hazardous waste constituents that cause the disease or genetic effect, and the pathway(s) or means by which the waste constituent impacts the human target.

The life scientist may be called upon to develop or improve bioassay procedures that will be used to establish or modify exposure criteria, or to evaluate a consignment or category of waste against established criteria. He/she may be called upon to evaluate rates and/or impacts of bioaccumulation of toxic constituents of hazardous wastes, to evaluate a given waste treatment process in terms of biopopulations, or to prescribe a bioremediation process that may be expected to meet a cleanup criterion.

The health professional may be assigned the task of translating the life scientists' data, regarding nonhuman exposure, to human exposure criteria. Other responsibilities may include establishing a threshold level based upon morbidity statistics and measured exposure level or providing expert testimony regarding cause and effect in exposure cases.

The life scientist and the health professional are expected to define hazardous waste or evaluate a waste material in terms of an established life science or health standard. As before, circumstances rarely permit real-time, detailed, or complex scientific evaluations of a waste shipment or a collected batch of waste. The challenge, also as before, is to define hazardous waste in terms that will meet environmental and human health protection goals, without significant failure, yet keep the procedure simple and timely.

The Environmentalist

The broad context of the environmentalists' concern with hazardous waste releases is any alteration of the environment caused or induced by such releases.

* SW 846 — a massive document, published by the EPA and available from the Government Printing Office, detailing the analytical procedures that are "approved" for use in identifying hazardous wastes. *See* Glossary.

Specifics of his/her concern lie in acute and chronic toxicity to organisms, bioconcentration, biomagnification, genetic change potential, etiology, pathways, change in climate and/or habitat, extinction, persistence, and esthetics such as visual impact. More broadly still, the environmentalist seeks to protect the environment from hazardous waste impacts by education, activism, statutory and/or regulatory development, and advocacy.

For the environmentalist, derivation of a workable *definition* of hazardous waste is critical and frustrating. The DDT issue was resolved by the clear association of the material with bioaccumulation, thinning of egg shells, and threatened extinction of important species. DDT was a specific chemical for which substitutes were available and which could be banned and eventually purged from the environment. Few such possibilities exist among the innumerable wastes, constituents, combinations, and concentrations which may be released or may occur subsequent to release.

Criteria which may be suggested or proposed by the environmentalist are certain to be the subject of challenge by special interests demanding proof of direct cause-and-effect. The actual process of determining the environmental impact of a substance may be obscured in a variety of subprocesses and may require years to run its course. Sadly, the committees, hearing boards, bureaucracies, legislatures, and courts which must find words to construct the definition continue to fall back on the nebulous "harmful-to-the-environment" generalities. Those who must make the definition work, if the environment is to be protected, are frequently hard pressed to do so. (*See also* Nebel and Wright 1993, Chapter 14)

The Legislator/Lawyer/Administrator/Diplomat

Perhaps without significant distinction from what was previously stated, legislators, lawyers, administrators, and diplomats are concerned with the "workability" of the definition. Statutes must provide the basis for regulations. Regulations must be understandable and enforceable. Administrators of regulatory agencies must have the statutory and regulatory authority and the financial resources provided to protect the public from exposure to harmful concentrations or quantities of hazardous waste. Workable approaches to the definition clearly do not include development of proof, in every situation that may arise, that the substance in question has "cause(d) or significantly contribute(d) to an increase in mortality or an increase in serious irreversible, or incapacitating reversible illness; or pose(d) a substantial present or potential hazard to human health or the environment" [RCRA Section 1004(5)].

Diplomatic efforts to achieve international and/or regional hazardous waste management agreements and treaties are continuously preoccupied with sorting out each participating government's notion of what wastes are being discussed. The United Nations Environmental Programme (UNEP) makes exactly the point: "...Off-site recycling is widely uitilized to achieve waste minimization, but ill-defined and ill-specified exports of wastes destined for recovery open the door to illegal traffic" (UNEP 1994, p. 2). As noted later, various nations may work with highly sophisticated definitions, while others may simply resort to the rationale that any chemical that is discarded is a hazardous waste.

Responsible officials, generators of hazardous waste, and/or owners of hazardous waste facilities expect their regulatory requirements to be understandable and

The RCRA regulations (40 CFR 261 and 262) specify that a solid waste is a hazardous waste if it is not *excluded* from regulation and meets any of the following conditions:

- Exhibits any of the *characteristics* of a hazardous waste
- Has been named as a hazardous waste and *listed* as such in the regulations
- Is a *mixture* containing a listed hazardous waste and a nonhazardous solid waste
- Is a waste *derived from* the treatment, storage, or disposal of a listed hazardous waste

FIGURE 2.1 Identification of RCRA hazardous wastes.

workable and their efforts at compliance to be measurable without ambiguity. Lay citizens expect regulatory agencies to protect them from exposure to harmful substances by *preventing* the release thereof. We expect contaminated sites to be cleaned up without prolonged exposure of test organisms to prove the contaminant to be hazardous. It is not difficult to envision the absurd scenarios that could arise from the RCRA definition, if left standing without workable implementing language in the regulations.

Implementing the RCRA Definition of Hazardous Waste

Congress defined hazardous waste, but left it to the U.S. Environmental Protection Agency (EPA) to develop the regulatory framework that would *identify* those solid wastes that must be managed under Subtitle C of RCRA (U.S. EPA 1990, p. III-4). Some European countries began identifying hazardous wastes by drawing up lists of known wastes that present no significant short-term handling or long-term environmental hazards and defined hazardous waste by exclusion, i.e., as any wastes not listed. In the U.K., the exclusive list was employed until 1972 (World Health Organization 1983, p. 12). The *exclusive* list has obvious shortcomings in application in regulatory programs.

The inclusive list is more commonly used, either with or without accompanying criteria. This approach is currently employed in Belgium, Denmark, France, the former West Germany, the Netherlands, Sweden, and the U.K. (World Health Organization 1983, p. 12). Other nations and UNEP apparently consider any toxic chemical a hazardous waste when "thrown away" (UNEP 1992, pp. 28–29). The EPA adopted the listing approach, but also defined "characteristics" and conditions under which wastes become or remain hazardous. The four methods prescribed by the RCRA for identification of hazardous wastes are highlighted in Figure 2.1.

The first step in identifying a RCRA hazardous waste is the determination that a waste meets the RCRA definition of a *solid waste*. Section 1004(27) of the statute defines solid waste as any garbage, refuse, sludge from a waste treatment plant or air pollution control facility and other discarded material, including solid, liquid, semi-

Any solid waste that exhibits one or more of these characteristics is classified as hazardous under RCRA:

- Ignitability
- Corrosivity
- Reactivity
- Toxicity*

* As determined by the Toxicity Characteristics Leaching Procedure (TCLP) which is described in EPA Publication SW 846, "Test Methods for Evaluating Solid Waste, Physical/Chemical Methods."

FIGURE 2.2 RCRA hazardous waste characteristics.

solid, or contained gaseous material resulting from industrial, commercial, mining, and agricultural operations and from community activities, but does not include solid or dissolved material in domestic sewage or solid or dissolved materials in irrigation return flows or industrial discharges which are (regulated by the Clean Water Act or Nuclear Regulatory Commission). The EPA translation of this language to the regulatory language of 40 CFR 261.2 speaks of discarded material which is *abandoned*, *recycled*, or considered *inherently waste like*. Each of these terms have specific meanings, which are detailed in 40 CFR 261 and which should be studied by the newcomer to the practice.

Hazardous Waste Characteristics

At this writing, the EPA has established four characteristics for hazardous waste identification (Figure 2.2). The EPA applied two criteria in selecting these characteristics:

- The characteristic must be defined in terms of physical, chemical, or other properties that cause the waste to meet the definition of hazardous waste in the act.
- The properties defining the characteristics must be measurable by standardized and available testing protocols.

The second criterion was adopted because the primary responsibility rests with generators for determining whether a solid waste exhibits any of the characteristics. EPA regulation writers believed that unless generators were provided with widely available and uncomplicated methods for determining whether their wastes exhibited the characteristics the identification system would prove unworkable (U.S. EPA 1990, pp. III-4, III-5). [*See also* discussion of carcinogenicity, mutagenicity, bioaccumulation potential and phytotoxicity (U.S. EPA 1990, p. III-5)]

The EPA has studied several other characteristics, including an "organic toxicity" characteristic, but the four described in 40 CFR 261 continue to be used. These four characteristics and their respective rationales are summarized as follows.

Ignitability. The EPA's reason for including ignitability as a characteristic (Figure 2.3) was to identify wastes that could cause fires during transport, storage, or disposal. Many used solvents are ignitable wastes.

Corrosivity. The EPA chose pH as an indicator of corrosivity (Figure 2.4) because wastes with high or low pH can react dangerously with other wastes or cause toxic contaminants to migrate from certain wastes. It chose steel corrosion because wastes capable of corroding steel can escape from their containers and liberate other wastes. Examples of corrosive wastes include acidic wastes and used pickle liquor (employed to clean steel during its manufacture) (U.S. EPA 1990, pp. III-5, 6).

Ignitability. A solid waste that exhibits any of the following properties is considered a hazardous waste due to its ignitability:

- A liquid, except aqueous solutions containing less than 24% alcohol, that has a flashpoint less than 60°C (140°F)
- A nonliquid capable, under normal conditions, of spontaneous and sustained combustion
- An ignitable compressed gas per U.S. Department of Transportation (DOT) regulations
- An oxidizer per DOT regulation

(40 CFR 261.21) (D001)

FIGURE 2.3 Ignitability characteristic.

Corrosivity. A solid waste that exhibits any of the following properties is considered a hazardous waste due to its corrosivity:

- An aqueous material with pH less than or equal to 2 or greater than or equal to 12.5
- A liquid that corrodes steel at a rate greater than 0.25 in./year at a temperature of 55°C (130°F)

(40 CFR 261.22) (D002)

FIGURE 2.4 Corrosivity characteristic.

Reactivity. A solid waste that exhibits any of the following properties is considered a hazardous waste due to its reactivity:

- Normally unstable and reacts violently without detonating
- Reacts violently with water
- Forms an explosive mixture with water
- Generates toxic gases, vapors, or fumes when mixed with water
- Contains cyanide or sulfide and generates toxic gases, vapors, or fumes at a pH between 2 and 12.5
- Capable of detonation if heated under confinement or subjected to a strong initiating source
- Capable of detonation at standard temperature and pressure
- Listed by DOT as Class A or B explosive

(40 CFR 261.23) (D003)

FIGURE 2.5 Reactivity characteristic.

Reactivity. Reactivity was chosen as a characteristic (Figure 2.5) to identify unstable wastes that can pose a problem at any stage of the waste management cycle, e.g., an explosion. Examples of reactive wastes include water from TNT manufacturing operations, contaminated industrial gases, and deteriorated explosives.

Toxicity. The term toxicity refers to both a characteristic of a waste and a test. The Toxicity Characteristics Leaching Procedure (TCLP) is designed to produce an extract simulating the leachate that may be produced in a land disposal situation. The extract is then analyzed to determine if it includes any of the toxic contaminants listed in Table 2.1. If the concentrations of any of the Table 2.1 constituents exceed the levels listed in the table, the waste is classified as hazardous.

Listed Hazardous Wastes

The inclusive listing adopted by the EPA includes separate lists of nonspecific source wastes, specific source wastes, and commercial chemical products. These lists are described briefly, as follows:

- *Nonspecific source wastes*, also called "F" wastes because their EPA waste identification codes begin with the letter F, are generic wastes, commonly produced by manufacturing and industrial processes. Examples from this list include spent halogenated solvents used in degreasing, wastewater treatment sludge from electroplating processes, as well as dioxin wastes, most of which are "acutely hazardous" wastes due to the danger they present to human health and the environment (40 CFR 261.31).
- *Specific source wastes* ("K" code) are from specially identified industries such as wood preserving, petroleum refining, and organic chemical manufacturing. These wastes typically include sludges, still bottoms,

Table 2.1 Maximum Concentration of Contaminants for the Toxicity Characteristics

Contaminant	Regulatory Level (mg/l)
Arsenic	5.0
Barium	100.0
Benzene	0.5
Cadmium	1.0
Carbon tetrachloride	0.5
Chlordane	0.03
Chlorobenzene	100.0
Chloroform	6.0
Chromium	5.0
o-Cresol	200.0[a]
m-Cresol	200.0[a]
p-Cresol	200.0[a]
Cresol	200.0[a]
2,4-D	10.0
1,4-Dichlorobenzene	7.5
1,2-Dichloroethane	0.5
1,1-Dichloroethylene	0.7
2,4-Dinitrotoluene	0.13[b]
Endrin	0.02
Heptachlor (and its epoxide)	0.008
Hexachlorobenzene	0.13[b]
Hexachlorobutadiene	0.5
Hexachloroethane	3.0
Lead	5.0
Lindane	0.4
Mercury	0.2
Methoxychlor	10.0
Methyl ethyl ketone	200.0
Nitrobenzene	2.0
Pentachlorophenol	100.0
Pyridine	5.0[b]
Selenium	1.0
Silver	5.0
Tetrachloroethylene	0.7
Toxaphene	0.5
Trichloroethylene	0.5
2,4,5-Trichlorophenol	400.0
2,4,6-Trichlorophenol	2.0
2,4,5-TP (Silvex)	1.0
Vinyl chloride	0.2

[a] If *o*-, *m*-, and *p*-cresol concentrations cannot be differentiated, the total cresol (D026) concentration is used. The regulatory level of total cresol is 200 mg/l.

[b] The quantification limit is greater than the calculated regulatory level. The quantification level therefore becomes the regulatory level.

Source: 40 CFR 261.24.

wastewaters, spent catalysts, and residues, e.g., wastewater treatment sludge from pigment production (40 CFR 261.32).

- *Commercial chemical products* ("P" and "U" codes) include specific commercial chemical products or manufacturing chemical intermediates. This list includes chemicals such as chloroform and creosote, acids such as sulfuric and hydrochloric, and pesticides such as DDT and kepone (40 CFR 261.33).

The EPA makes an important additional distinction among the listed wastes — one which may easily be overlooked by the newcomer to the hazardous waste management practice. Certain wastes have been identified by the EPA as being so dangerous that small amounts are regulated in a manner similar to larger amounts of other hazardous wastes and are designated as *acutely* hazardous. They are the F020-F023 and F026-F028 wastes listed in 40 CFR 261.31 and the "P" wastes listed in 40 CFR 261.33. The *acute* designation has major significance in the determination of the categories of hazardous waste generators, the definition of "empty" containers, and limits placed upon accumulation and storage.

The EPA developed the lists by examining different types of wastes and chemical products to determine whether they met any of the following criteria:

- Exhibit one or more of the four characteristics of a hazardous waste
- Meet the statutory definition of hazardous waste
- Are acutely toxic or acutely hazardous
- Are otherwise toxic

The "Mixture" and "Derived-From" Rules

The EPA has also ruled that most mixtures of solid wastes and listed hazardous wastes are considered hazardous wastes and must be managed accordingly. This applies regardless of what percentage of the waste mixture is composed of listed hazardous wastes. Without such a regulation, generators could evade RCRA requirements simply by mixing or diluting the listed wastes with nonhazardous solid waste. Wastes derived from hazardous wastes, such as residues from the treatment, storage, and disposal of a listed hazardous waste, are considered a hazardous waste as well. ***Caution:*** *The mixture and derived-from rules contain a variety of conditions, exceptions, and exclusions. The student or reader should carefully examine the text of 40 CFR 261.3 before reaching conclusions regarding the applicability of these rules.*

Hazardous Waste Identification Rule Development

A series of related and somewhat parallel events and actions have the original listing/characteristics/mixture rule/derived-from rule approach to hazardous waste identification under serious scrutiny. A December 6, 1991 decision of the U.S. Court of Appeals for the District of Columbia vacated the mixture and derived-from rules due to procedural deficiencies in the 1980 promulgation of these rules (*Shell Oil Company* v. *EPA*, 950 F .2d 741 CA DC; 1991). The EPA subsequently reinstated the rules on an interim basis and solicited comment thereon (57 FR 49278). An enormous volume of comment and technical material was received by the agency, and the review and analysis of these materials caused the agency to exceed the "sunset" provisions applicable to the interim rulemaking.

Further litigation ensued, with the EPA again being challenged on procedural grounds (*Mobil Oil Corp.* v. *EPA*, CA DC, 1994). After Mobil's challenge was filed, Congress intervened with legislation stating that the interim mixture and derived-from rules were not to be terminated or withdrawn until revisions are promulgated and become effective. Congress imposed a deadline of October 4, 1994. That deadline was also missed, and the EPA was again sued in separate actions by the Chemical Manufacturers Association and other industry groups and by the Environmental Technology Council. Both actions sought court-ordered immediate action by the EPA to reinstate the rules (57 FR 49278). (*See also* McCoy and Associates 1992, p. 2.1ff)

During the same time period, the EPA began an extensive review of the rules for identification of hazardous wastes. A Hazardous Waste Identification Rule (HWIR) was proposed on May 20, 1992 (57 FR 21450). The rule embodied two general concepts:

- A concentration-based exclusion criteria (CBEC) would exempt wastes from RCRA identification as a hazardous waste if concentrations were less than technology-based exemption levels. The criteria were to be based upon concentrations achievable by proven technologies.
- An expanded characteristics option (ECHO) would have provided "entry" to the regulatory system as before, but would now provide "exit" from the system as well. The four existing characteristics would have remained in place, but the number of constituents listed in Table 2.1 would be greatly expanded or a similar table would be added.

Based upon criticism of the rule, and upon the realization that a new rule must deal with the remanded mixture and derived-from rules, the EPA withdrew the proposed hazardous waste identification rule on October 30, 1992 (57 FR 49280) and began a series of outreach conferences and "round-table" meetings in an attempt to reach consensus on a workable approach.

As these events unfolded, a new regulatory imperative required attention. The EPA had regulated "contaminated media" removed from remediation sites by imposing the "contained-in" policy. The policy held that media containing a listed hazardous waste are also a hazardous waste once excavated or otherwise brought under management. The agency had recognized that the policy brought significant quantities of slightly contaminated material under regulation. With increasing numbers of site remediation projects producing growing quantities of waste, the need to correct the problem took on new urgency. Accordingly, the HWIR development effort has, at this writing, moved toward even broader objectives. The effort appears to be focused upon entry and exit criteria which would meet some or all of the identification objectives.

The HWIR project embodies the potential to greatly impact the identification criteria and, thereby, the whole of hazardous waste management practice in the United States Needless to say, the practitioner should endeavor to stay abreast of these developments.

TOPICS FOR REVIEW OR DISCUSSION

1. As noted in this chapter, some nations have rationalized identification of hazardous wastes by simply declaring any discarded chemical as "hazardous." Is this workable in the United States? If so, how? If not, why not?
2. In describing wastes, the scientific and technical communities assign a clear difference to the meanings and applications of the terms "toxic" and "hazardous." Provide a short definition of each, making this distinction clear.
3. What is the rationale for the distinction, made by RCRA, between hazardous waste and acutely hazardous waste?
4. Why is the mixture rule of such great importance to practitioners and regulators?
5. Similarly, why is the derived-from rule important?
6. Why is a scheme such as the characteristics necessary? Why not rely entirely on lists?

REFERENCES

Enger, Eldon D., J. Richard Kormelink, Bradley F. Smith, and Rodney J. Smith. 1989. *Environmental Science: The Study of Interrelationships*. Wm. C. Brown Publishers, Dubuque, IA.

McCoy and Associates. 1992. *The Hazardous Waste Consultant*. May/June, Lakewood, CO.

Nebel, Bernard J., and Richard T. Wright. 1993. *Environmental Science,* Fourth Edition. Prentice-Hall, Englewood Cliffs, NJ.

UNEP. 1992. *UNEP Two Decades of Achievement and Challenge*. Information and Public Affairs Branch, United Nations Environment Programme, Nairobi, Kenya.

UNEP. 1994. *Environmentally Sound Management of Hazardous Wastes Including the Prevention of Illegal International Traffic in Hazardous Wastes*. United Nations Environment Programme, Nairobi, Kenya.

U.S. Environmental Protection Agency. 1986. *Test Methods for Evaluating Solid Waste: Physical/Chemical Methods; Third Edition*. Superintendent of Documents, Government Printing Office, Washington, D.C. EPA SW-846

U.S. Environmental Protection Agency. 1990. *RCRA Orientation Manual, 1990 Edition*. Office of Solid Waste, Washington, D.C.

World Health Organization. 1983. *Management of Hazardous Waste*. WHO, Copenhagen.

3 PATHWAYS, FATES, AND DISPOSITION OF HAZARDOUS WASTE RELEASES

OBJECTIVES

At completion of this chapter, the student should:

- understand basic theories of movement, mobility, dispersion, and natural breakdown mechanisms.
- have gained overview familiarity with the generally accepted and established pathways and measurements of releases to the environment.
- be able to relate some important pathways and movement mechanisms to impacts on human health, the environment, land and marine life, and global changes.

INTRODUCTION

Although nearly two decades of cradle-to-grave management of hazardous wastes are behind us, it remains difficult to quantify the contributions of particular source categories. The U.S. Environmental Protection Agency (EPA) estimates of total quantities generated have continued in the 200 to 300 million tons per year range, but there are significant possibilities for error (U.S. EPA 1994a, pp. ES-2ff). For example, wastes exhumed from a remediation site and transported to an approved treatment, storage, and disposal facility may or may not be counted as newly generated. Hazardous wastes disposed of onsite or otherwise without the Resource Conservation and Recovery Act (RCRA) system generally are not tallied. The National Solid Waste Management Association reports that 16% of hazardous waste generators manage all wastes onsite, and another 22% manage "some" of their wastes onsite (Institute of Chemical Waste Management 1989, p. 2).

The Emergency Planning and Community Right-to-Know Act (EPCRA) of 1986 requires *manufacturing* facilities to report the disposition of more than 300 "toxic" chemicals, including the quantities released to the environment or sent offsite to waste treatment or disposal facilities. In 1989, the EPA began publishing summaries of data from these reports in the publication *Toxic Release Inventory: A National Perspective* (TRI) (U.S. EPA 1989). While much hazardous waste is generated by facilities other than manufacturing, the TRI provides useful insight to the kinds and relative magnitude of sources of hazardous waste releases to the environment. Our reference throughout this chapter to the TRI is not in the context of overall quantification of hazardous waste generation, but is to provide insight regarding entry into the pathways of human exposure and environmental impact.

Releases of Chemicals to the Environment

Releases to the Atmosphere

Atmospheric releases may be thought of as being either controlled or uncontrolled. Open burning of wastes is no longer condoned in most jurisdictions, but legal and illegal burning occurs. The RCRA regulates both the generation, marketing, and burning of "hazardous waste fuel" and the destruction of hazardous wastes by permitted combustion facilities. The overall thrust and objective of these regulations is to ensure that combustion of hazardous waste is accomplished under conditions which ensure their destruction and that hazardous waste residues are captured and managed effectively. The practice of mixing hazardous waste with other fuels, followed by burning in boilers and industrial furnaces (BIFs), became a highly contentious issue during the early 1990s. The practice, technologies, regulations, issues, and policies pertaining to hazardous waste combustion are discussed in Chapters 7, 9, and 10.

As discussed in Chapter 1, until 1990 only seven National Emission Standards for Hazardous Air Pollutants (NESHAPS) had been finalized by the EPA, leaving hundreds of hazardous chemical constituents uncontrolled by the Clean Air Act. State and local agencies had regulated some of those, but the limits of their jurisdictions left many hazardous emissions uncontrolled. Title III of the Clean Air Act Amendments of 1990 (PL 101-549, November 15, 1990) listed 189 additional hazardous air pollutants (HAPs) and established a schedule according to which the EPA must promulgate emission standards for the listed HAPs.

Automobile wrecking yards routinely spill fluids from fuel tanks, transmissions, engine blocks, radiators, and brake systems. They similarly release chlorofluorocarbons (CFCs) from automotive refrigeration systems. Land "farming" operations involving bulk disposal make volatiles available for evaporation, and the heavier fractions are left to percolate into the soil. Hazardous waste impoundments, by design or default, release their volatiles to the atmosphere. As late as 1980, technical papers describing optimized evaporation facilities for pesticide wastes were being reprinted in EPA publications (Egg and Reddell 1980; Hall 1980).

Remediation projects continue to air strip contaminated groundwater without capture or destruction of the stripped volatiles. Land "treatment" facilities continue the practice of thinly spreading hazardous wastes containing volatiles on the land surface where the intent is to enhance vaporization. Sewage treatment plants regularly release or flare digester gases containing volatiles from sludge. Hazardous waste tank storage facilities similarly release the lighter volatiles as vapor pressure in the tank varies. The 1990 amendments to the Clean Air Act placed new emphasis on such releases, and the EPA is preparing standards which should eventually control them.

The TRI reports the 1992 release of more than 1.8 billion pounds of toxic chemicals to the atmosphere. Atmospheric releases thus amount to approximately 24% of the total 7.5 billion pounds of TRI-reported chemical releases and transfers into the environment in 1992. The chemical products industry was the source of more than 500 million pounds of those industry categories, and each reported atmospheric releases exceeding 100 million pounds (U.S. EPA 1994b, pp. 42–43). The chemical releases reported in the greatest quantities were methanol and toluene, each totaling nearly 200 million pounds, followed by ammonia, acetone, 1,1,1-trichloroethane, and xylene, each totaling more than 100 million pounds (U.S. EPA 1994b, p. 58).

Even these carefully compiled statistics do not provide the real totals. The 1992 TRI does not include waste chemical releases from hazardous waste facilities; companies that used less than 10,000 pounds of chemicals during the year; or the thousands of small businesses such as dry cleaners, paint shops, and service stations. Moreover, releases of materials during or following transfer are not included.

The TRI reports that of the 1.8 billion pounds of toxic chemical emissions to the atmosphere, 1.3 billion pounds (70%) were point source emissions, while 549 million pounds (30%) were fugitive emissions (U.S. EPA 1994b, p. 42). The latter statistic is highly suspect. The student should consider how many fugitive sources are actually measured or even reported. The point to be understood is that very large quantities of hazardous wastes continue to be emitted to the atmosphere via controlled and uncontrolled sources.

TRI-reported atmospheric releases, in 1992, were reduced by 0.8 billion pounds (31%) from the 1987 TRI report totals. This improvement probably reflects some combination of improved control technology, regulatory activity, waste minimization efforts, and more complete reporting. Waste minimization/pollution prevention programs (covered in a later chapter) continue to be the best hope for reducing the transfer of hazardous waste constituents to the atmosphere.

Releases to Surface Waters

The TRI-reporting facilities released 273 million pounds of toxic chemicals to surface waters such as rivers, lakes, ponds, and streams and transfered 381 million pounds of toxic chemicals to publicly owned (sewage) treatment works (POTWs). The two release categories were approximately 3.6 and 5% of the total releases and transfers of toxic chemicals to the environment in 1992. Comparisons with 1988 through 1990 TRI data are difficult because of the 1991 delisting of a single chemical — sodium sulfate. Total releases of TRI chemicals to surface waters increased by 12.2%, while total transfers to POTWs decreased by 3.7% from 1991 to 1992 (U.S. EPA 1994b, p. 24). By chemical category, the highest volume releases to surface waters, in 1992, were of phosphoric acid, ammonia, sulfuric acid, and methanol. The greatest volumes transferred to POTWs were of methanol, ammonia, ammonium sulfate solution, sulfuric acid, and hydrochloric acid (U.S. EPA 1994b, pp. 58, 61). Again, it is important to remember that these releases were from *manufacturing* facilities only.

Pretreatment regulations, standards, and codes are intended to compel the removal or destruction of the hazardous constituents in industrial waste streams prior to discharge to publicly owned sewerage. Significant amounts of the liquid component in sewage are discharged to surface waters. Chemicals in the sewage may pass through or interfere with treatment processes, thereby escaping removal in the sewage treatment plant. Chemicals that are removed by sewage treatment processes may be transferred to the environment in the form of air emissions or as sewage sludge. Activated sludge and aeration basins in sewage treatment plants very effectively strip volatiles from the sewage and, unless captured, release them to the atmosphere. State and local regulatory agencies have come under increasing pressure by the EPA to improve compliance with pretreatment requirements and to strengthen pretreatment ordinances and regulations. Industrial waste discharges to wastewater treatment facilities must receive appropriate pretreatment if surface water and urban air quality objectives are to be achieved.

Ocean dumping has been curtailed by the Marine Protection Research and Sanctuaries Act (MPRSA), but significant quantities of hazardous wastes have continued to find their way into the marine environment. The implementation of the act was made uncertain by a U.S. district court ruling growing from a city of New York lawsuit, alleging that the EPA had incorrectly implemented the law (Dawson and Mercer 1986, p. 417). Ocean disposal of sludge and permitted dumping of hazardous waste continued in the face of strong opposition by environmentalists and the public. The Ocean Dumping Ban Act of 1988 made ocean dumping of industrial waste and municipal sludge unlawful after December 31, 1991 (U.S. EPA 1991, p. 1, Chapters 1, 4, 5). Both practices were halted somewhat earlier, but some permits for "emergency" dumping of industrial wastes have been issued since that date.

The toxic chemicals that pass through primary sewage treatment plants along coastlines are also ultimately deposited in the oceans. Past abuses, such as the dumping of 38,000 drums of chlorinated hydrocarbon wastes in the North Sea during 1963–1969 (Piasecki and Davis 1987, p. 68), the uncontrolled dumping in U.S. coastal waters prior to MPRSA, and continued dumping by other nations, together with ongoing discharges to coastal waters (foreign and domestic), require us to consider the oceans as waste sinks and exposure pathways.

Releases to the Land

Earlier, the point was made that the evolution of environmental legislation in the United States has had the effect of driving hazardous waste treatment and disposal to the land. The continuing evolution, including RCRA, Hazardous and Solid Waste Amendments (HSWA), and the site remediation rules and policies of the Comprehensive Environmental Response, Compensation, and Liability Act (CERCLA), have focused upon reducing the human health hazards and environmental impacts of the land treatment and disposal practices. Nevertheless, large quantities of hazardous waste continue to be treated and/or deposited upon and beneath the land surface.

The EPA 1977 survey, mentioned earlier, concluded that 48.3% of hazardous wastes went into unlined surface impoundments and 30.3% was deposited in nonsecure landfills. A 1981 survey indicated radical changes in the predominant *methods* of land disposal, but more than 90% of hazardous waste went to land disposal (Dawson and Mercer 1986, pp. 125–126). By 1991, the EPA reported that 76% of the national total was managed in aqueous treatment units and that land disposal accounted for only 9% (U.S. EPA 1994a, p. ES-4). Clearly, a major shift away from land disposal has occurred. That, of course, was the intent of Congress in the HSWA land disposal restrictions. The 1993 suspension of permitting of combustion facilities, embodied in the EPA's proposed "Combustion and Waste Minimization Strategy," has only minimal potential to affect the trend, since only 1.1% of the 1991 national total was managed in thermal units (U.S. EPA 1994a, p. ES-4).

Regardless of trends, significant quantities of hazardous wastes continue to be released to the air, surface water (directly and indirectly), land, and subsurface. It is now important to gain an understanding of the fates of the waste constituents following these dispositions.

Movement, Fates, and Disposition

It is an oversimplification, but conceptually useful to say that waste constituents achieve their impacts according to the concentrations present at the point and time of exposure, the extent to which the concentrations increase or decrease during the exposure, and the time over which the exposure continues (more on this in Chapter 4). With this concept in mind, rates of dispersion, accumulation and decay rates, and residence times take on great importance. The concept can be extended to say that human health and environmental impacts of a hazardous waste release may be greatly dependent upon the medium to which it is released and to the forces which act upon the waste following release.

Behavior of Waste Constituents Released to the Atmosphere

The earth's atmosphere extends several hundred miles above the earth's surface, but about 95% of the total air mass is concentrated in a layer some 12 miles deep. The lower part of that 12-mile layer containing most of the air mass is called the troposphere. The troposphere is about 5 miles thick at the poles and about 10 miles thick at the equator. It is the behavior of the troposphere and the forces acting upon it that govern the behavior of the pollutants released to the atmosphere. The sun's energy warms the tropospheric air by radiation, conduction, and convection. All play a role in the behavior of air pollutants, but convection heating and the rotation of the earth are basically responsible for the pollution dispersing winds that blow across continents (Hare 1989, Chapter 7). (*See also* Nebel and Wright 1993, p. 359ff)

Air is a mixture of gases of which nitrogen (78%) and oxygen (21%) are the major components. Air, in the natural state, also contains particulates and water vapor. These constituents, together with heat energy and photochemical activity, can and do bring about an endless variety of chemical reactions involving hazardous wastes released to the atmosphere. Although the roles of sulfur releases in the formation of sulfur oxides and acid rain, the conversion of emitted nitric oxide (NO) to nitrogen dioxide (NO_2) and nitric acid (HNO_3) in the atmosphere, and the formation of carbon monoxide (CO) and carbon dioxide (CO_2) in combustion processes are widely publicized, other chemical reactions in the atmosphere concern the hazardous waste manager. In later chapters, the releases of heavy metals and aromatic hydrocarbons will occupy our attention. These releases are subject to further physical and chemical changes in the atmosphere.

Releases to the unconstrained atmosphere are more likely to be dispersed quickly than are releases to the land or water. Atmospheric releases usually result in concentrations at the point and time of exposure, which are greatly less than at the point of release. Concentrations of atmospheric pollutants usually diminish with time following their release. These characteristics tend to impose chronic rather than acute effects. Horne states the problem clearly:

> ...in dispersing a pollutant, two things happen: (a) control is lost over the pollutant and the capability of surveillance over the pollutant diminishes, and (b) the pollutant is really 'thrown away,' and any possibility of future utilization of the pollutant is lost. (Horne 1978, p. 121)

The latter might also be couched in terms of treatment or destruction, but the point is well made.

Releases trapped under an inversion may accumulate to dangerous levels in relatively short times, may persist through the period of inversion, and may produce acute human health impacts. Indoor and workplace releases can produce both acute and chronic health impacts. Some of the important health effects of atmospheric releases will be reviewed in Chapter 4.

The nearly uninhibited movement, activity, and reactivity of hazardous chemicals in the atmosphere has been clearly shown and is well established, and movement from one media to another is evident. Polychlorinated biphenyls (PCBs) and the banned pesticide DDT have migrated from contaminated soils into the air and, eventually, have accumulated in the fish and wildlife of the Great Lakes (Poje et al. 1989, p. 5). Among the most-reported TRI chemicals released, acetone, toluene, and xylene react with other compounds to form ozone, a lower atmospheric pollutant. Methanol, which has a vapor density of 1.11, tends to remain at or near the surface as it either disperses or collects in surface depressions. In either case, it remains a fire hazard until dispersed. Released 1,1,1-trichloroethane is highly persistent and can migrate to the upper atmosphere where it becomes a contributor to the depletion of the protective ozone layer in the stratosphere. Ammonia is an extremely dangerous irritant and asphyxiant when encountered in high concentrations, but disperses rapidly into the atmosphere. Interstate, transborder, and even intercontinental movement of acid rain components, with fallout upon the land and water surfaces, has been well documented (Enger et al. 1989, pp. 405–406; Nebel and Wright 1993, pp. 360–368). Movement of ozone-depleting waste CFCs from the earth's surface to the outer fringes of the atmosphere has been established (Poje et al. 1989, p. 5; Nebel and Wright 1993, pp. 377–381).

Movement of Hazardous Waste Constituents in Surface Waters

Movement of released chemical constituents in surface streams is somewhat more constrained than in the atmosphere due to the confining effect of the stream channels. Volatile organic compounds (VOCs) are released at the water–air boundary. Higher molecular weight organics and soluble inorganics are available for transfer to the groundwater from losing streams. Downstream diversions may transfer pollutants to the land surface (there, subject to further transfer to the atmosphere or the groundwater) or to domestic or industrial water supplies. Water treatment plants may precipitate inorganics and deposit them upon the land or return them to the source stream in concentrated form or may strip the organics in aeration processes and vent them to the atmosphere.

Two major classes of chemical waste constituents in surface waters are major environmental detriments. They are the heavy metals and their compounds and nonbiodegradable synthetic organics. Even in minute concentrations these chemicals may be concentrated to pathological or lethal levels as they ascend the food chain. The Minimata Bay (methyl mercury) and Life Sciences Products/Allied Chemical Company (Kepone) cases are classic examples of these processes. Movement of hazardous waste constituents in surface streams is significant because of the ultimate flow to the fragile environments of the coastal waters (*see* Figure 3.1).

Releases to impounded surface waters may have even greater concentrating effects and may similarly transfer hazardous constituents to the atmosphere or to groundwater. Surface impoundments which are artificially aerated also transfer VOCs to the atmosphere. A survey by the EPA in the late 1970s counted 132,709 sites having waste impoundments, of which 75% contained industrial wastes (U.S. EPA 1978, p. 32). This number is undoubtedly reduced greatly, by now, but the newly found focus upon aqueous treatment may involve similar losses to the atmosphere. Many of these ponds were designed to dispose of wastewater by evaporation or seepage or both (U.S. EPA 1978, pp. 10–11). The EPA, elsewhere, using standard leakage coefficients, estimated that more than 100 billion gallons of industrial wastewaters had entered the groundwater system from these impoundments (U.S. EPA 1977, p. 108).

Pathways of Hazardous Waste Constituents Reaching Groundwater

Groundwater constitutes a very large percentage of the freshwater supply of the United States More than 50% of the populace is dependent upon groundwater for domestic purposes. Water-bearing formations of the earth's crust act as conduits for transmission and storage of water. Water enters these formations from the ground surface or from bodies of surface water, after which it travels slowly for varying distances until it returns to the surface by action of natural flow, plants, or man or until it percolates to deeper formations. Groundwater emerging into surface stream channels as "base flow" aids in sustaining stream flow when surface runoff is low or nonexistent (Todd 1960, pp. 5–7). These phenomena are illustrated graphically in Figure 3.2.

Practically all groundwater originates as surface water. Principal sources of natural recharge include precipitation, stream flow, lakes, and reservoirs. Other contributions, known as artificial recharge, occur from man's activities, such as excess irrigation, but more to the point, from liquid waste disposal in pits, impoundments, landfills, and other land applications and from leaching of solid or semisolid hazardous wastes (Figure 3.3).

Implementation of HSWA land disposal restrictions (with help from other state and federal regulations) has brought about significant reductions in the quantities of

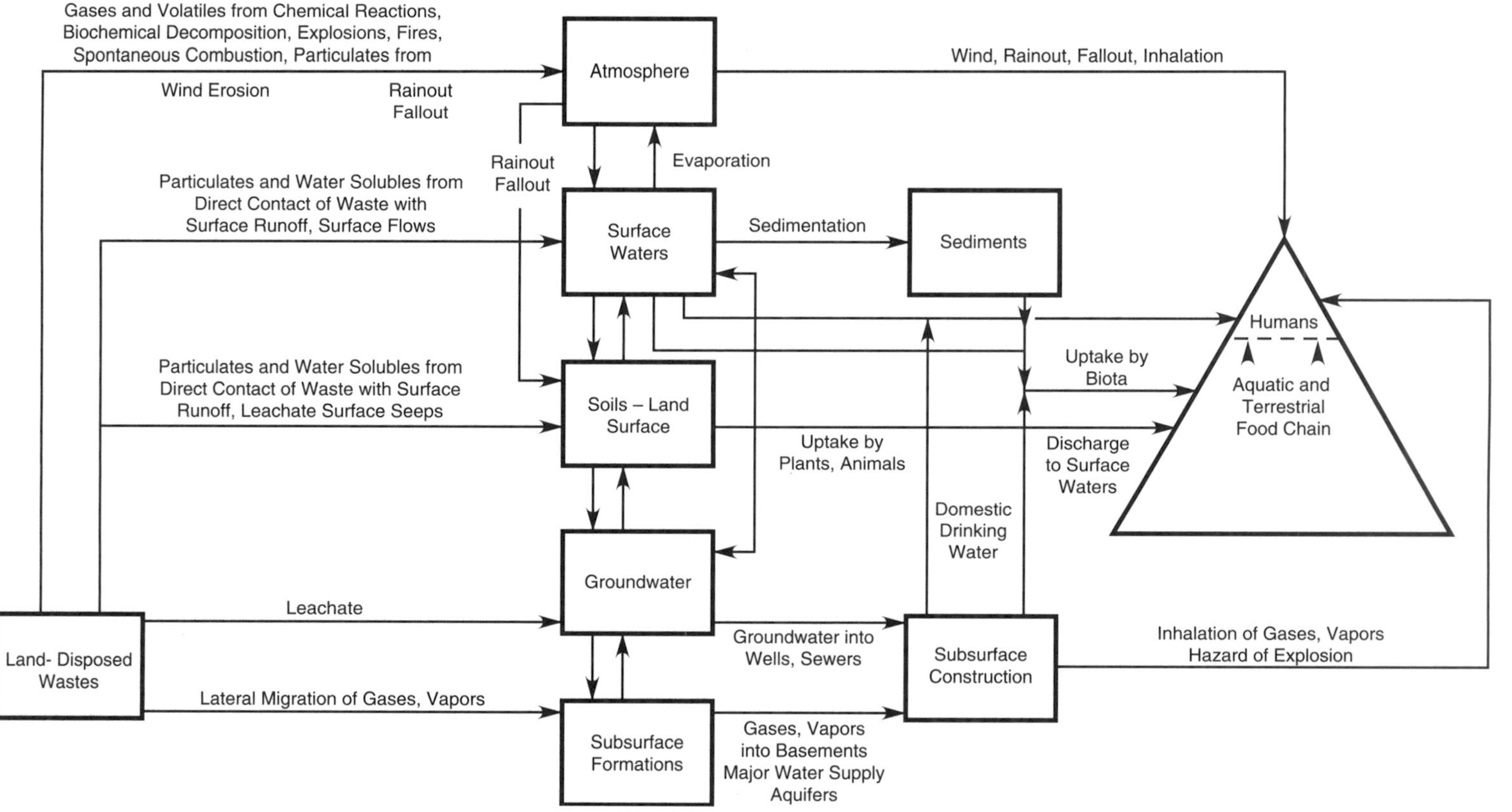

FIGURE 3.1 Flow of land-disposed waste contaminants through the environment (EPA).

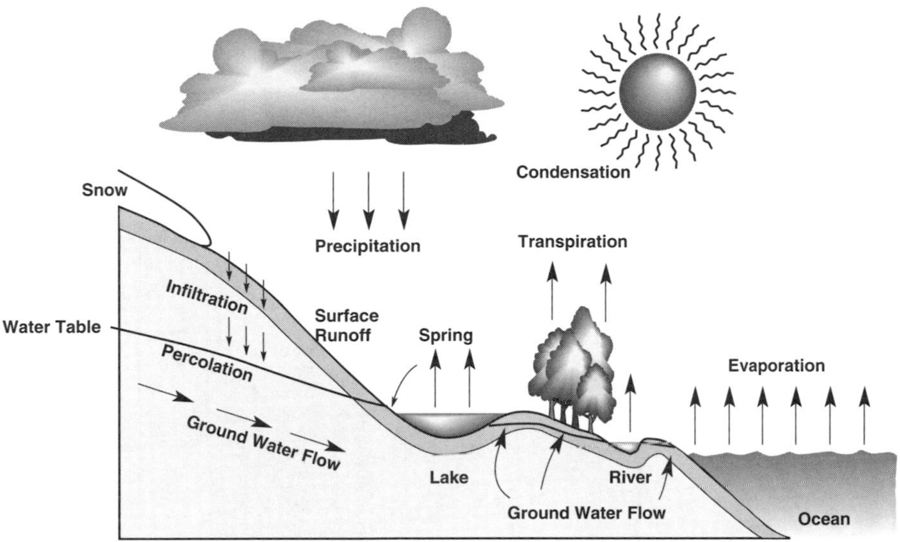

FIGURE 3.2 The hydrologic cycle. (Adapted from Todd, David K., 1960. *Ground Water Hydrology*. John Wiley & Sons, New York. With permission.)

wastewaters being treated, stored, or disposed of in unsealed surface impoundments. In 1989, the EPA estimated that approximately 31 million gallons of liquid hazardous wastes were being committed to surface impoundments. These impoundments were required to meet the no-migration standards of RCRA Section 3005(j) or be taken out of service (FR November 22, 1989, p. 48472). As implementation of the land disposal restrictions progressed, the EPA estimated that alternative capacities had to be found for:

- *treatment* of 29 million gallons per year of liquid waste then "treated" in waste piles.
- *storage* of 76 million gallons per year of liquid waste then stored in waste piles.
- *disposal* of 240 million gallons per year then disposed of in landfills, 6 million gallons per year then disposed of in land treatment units, and 5,164 million gallons per year then disposed of by underground injection (FR November 22, 1989, p. 48472).

The preponderance of generated hazardous wastes, reported in 1991 and discussed earlier, is reflected in these estimates. Theoretically, the disposal in nonsecure land treatment facilities and impoundments has been ended. Disposal by underground injection (23 million tons) remained nearly unchanged from the 1989 figure (U.S. EPA 1994b, p. ES-4).

The ultimate fate of deep well-injected wastes continues to be the subject of controversy. Of the hazardous constituents of those wastes now released to the land

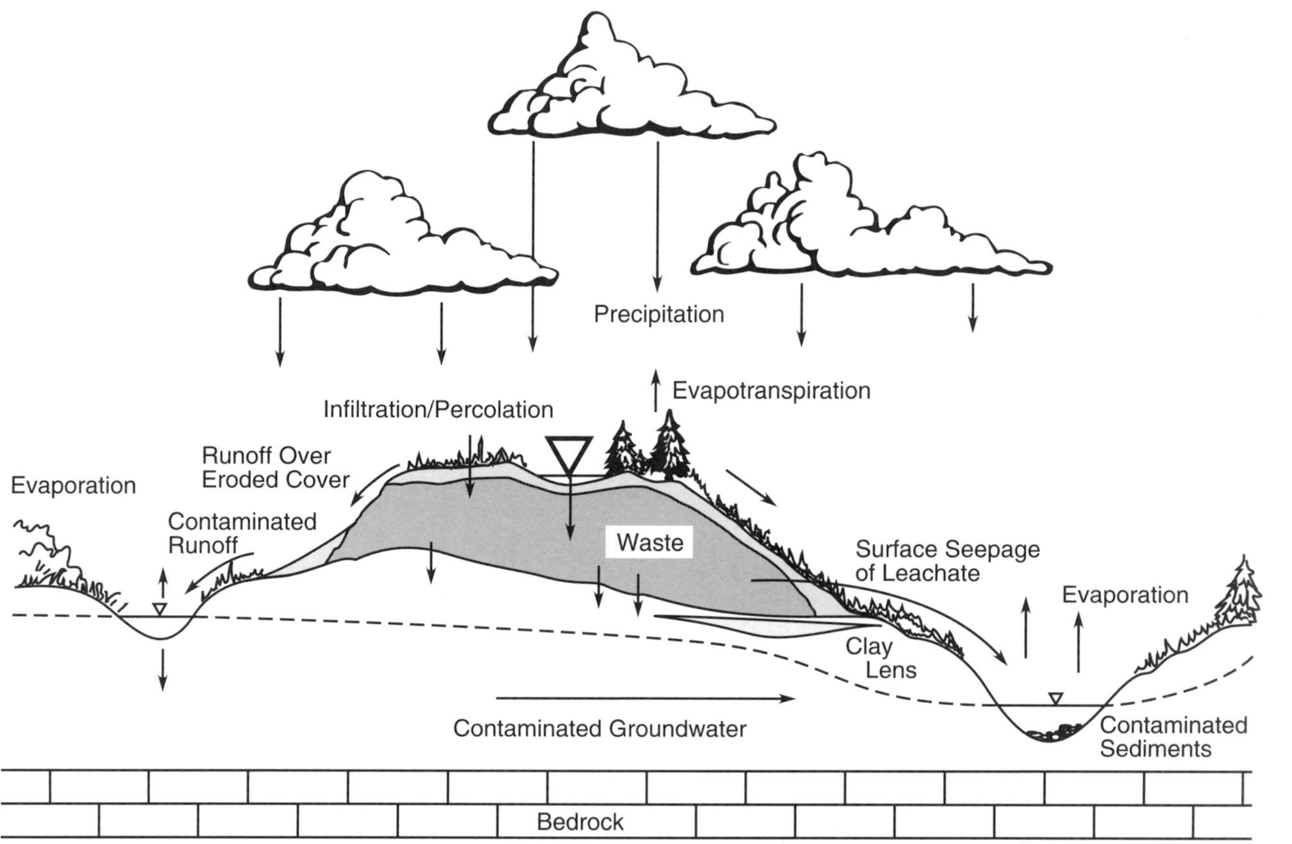

FIGURE 3.3 Hydrologic pathways for contamination by waste disposal sites (EPA).

surface, the higher molecular weight organics and inorganics are subject to erosion and surface runoff and to percolation to the subsurface. Hazardous waste constituents released by spills, by contaminated sites awaiting cleanup, and by sites not subject to RCRA continue to make their way to the atmosphere, surface waters, and groundwater.

The point to be made is that great quantities of land-deposited (stored/treated/disposed) hazardous wastes have evaporated to the atmosphere, runoff to surface waters, and percolated to groundwaters (Figure 3.4). The atmospheric and surface water releases become comingled with other releases or are lost to natural processes, but the groundwater contamination may remain highly concentrated, relatively localized, and persistent for decades or centuries. These quantities are being reduced, but the continuing releases together with the previously released materials have contaminated and are contaminating aquifers in many areas, and many groundwater supplies have been impaired or ruined.

Chemical Transformations

Recent findings of chemical transformations of groundwater pollutants are disturbing if not alarming. Two of the most ubiquitous hazardous waste releases have been of trichloroethylene (TCE) and tetrachloroethylene (PCE, commonly known as Perc) to the land surface, to landfills, and to surface impoundments. Both have been widely used as cleaning solvents and degreasers and, until serious controls were applied, disposed of by the most readily available method. Both are considered hazardous wastes (40 CFR 261.33); both attack the liver, kidneys, eyes, respiratory system, and central nervous system (U.S. Department of Health and Human Services 1994); PCE is a confirmed carcinogen; and TCE is a suspect carcinogen (Lewis 1993, p. 998, 1264). Evidence is accumulating that TCE, PCE, and other chlorinated compounds, in the presence of bacteria from sewage or septic tank leachate, are transformed to vinyl chloride (Vincent 1984; Science Applications International Corporation 1985). Vinyl chloride is a potent carcinogen, having a drinking water risk level approximately two orders of magnitude greater than that of trichloroethylene (Science Applications International Corporation 1985, p. 1). Some observed transformations and products are diagrammed in Figure 3.5.

The behavior of mercury is an excellent example of environmental chemodynamics of a hazardous waste. Mercury has been released by a wide variety of industrial processes and, despite rigorous controls, continues to escape into the atmosphere and to surface and groundwater. Manufacturing facilities included in the 1987 TRI data released nearly 86,000 pounds of mercury (U.S. EPA 1989, p. 59). By 1992, TRI reported transfers and releases totaling more than 310,000 pounds. Of that amount, approximately 125,000 pounds were transferred to treatment or recycling, but more than 184,000 pounds were released or transferred to disposal (U.S. EPA 1994b, pp. 66–67). To the extent that the TRI data represents overall management of the waste, the amount of waste mercury entering the environment apparently increased by 114% during the five-year period. Moreover, releases of mercury in small business manufacturing and repair, nonmanufacturing sectors, and breakage and discard of instruments, if documented, could increase the totals by substantial increments.

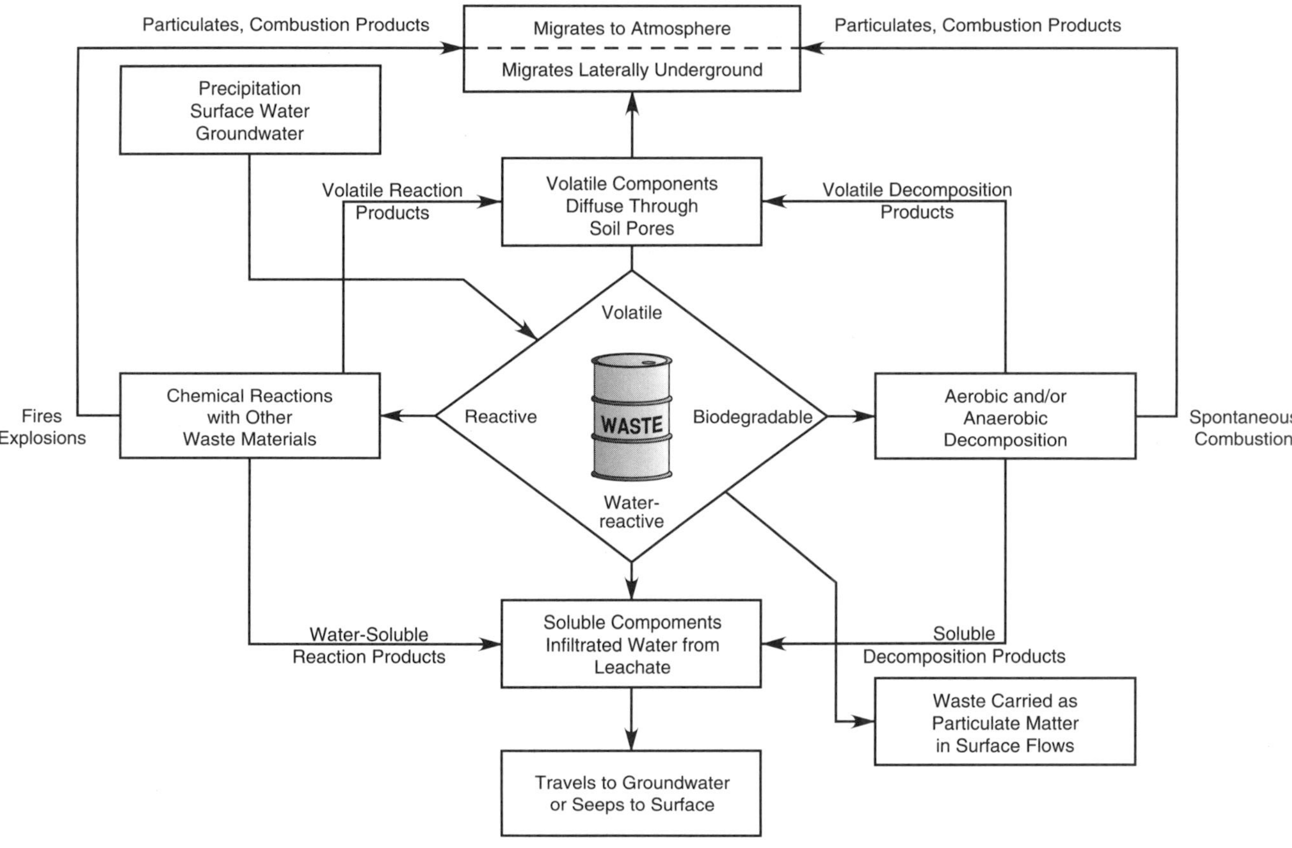

FIGURE 3.4 Initial transport processes at waste disposal sites (EPA).

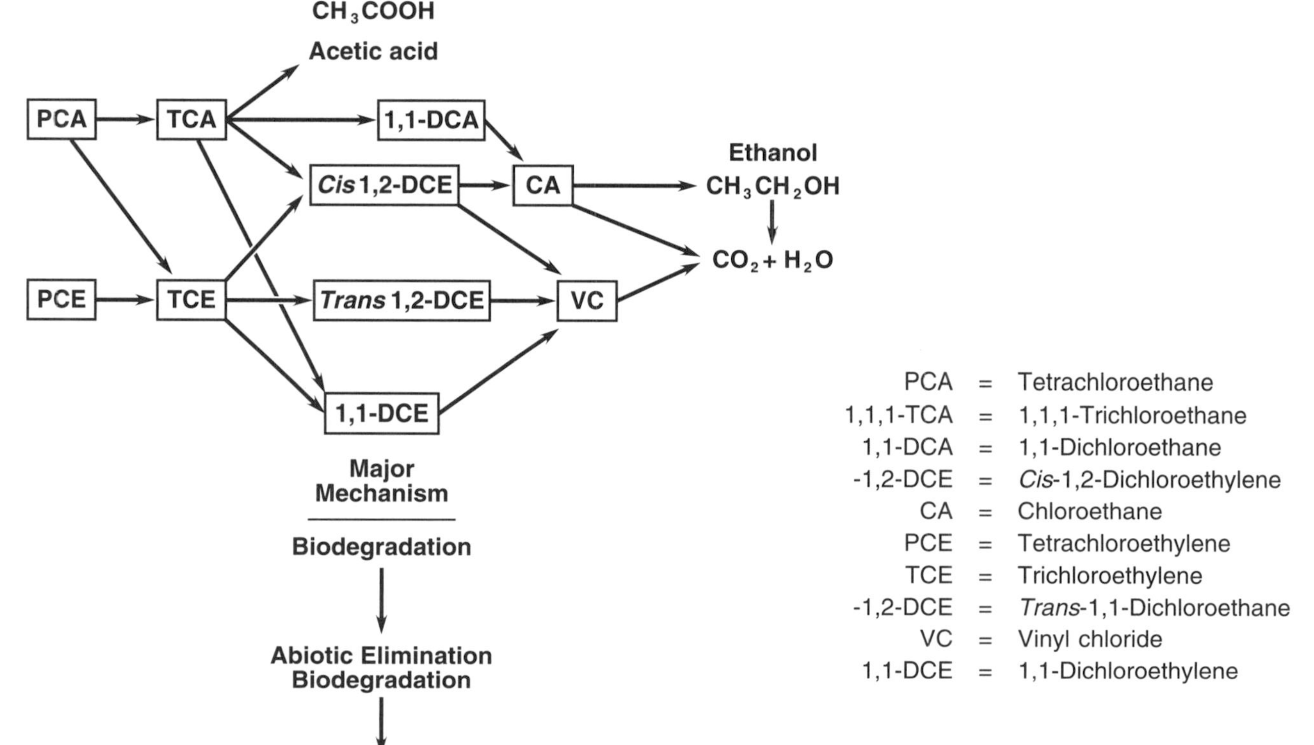

FIGURE 3.5 Transformation of aliphatic hydrocarbons. (Adapted from Davis, Andy, and Roger L. Olsen. 1990. "Predicting the Fate and Transport of Organic Compounds in Groundwater." *Hazardous Materials Control* 3(4), July-August. With permission.)

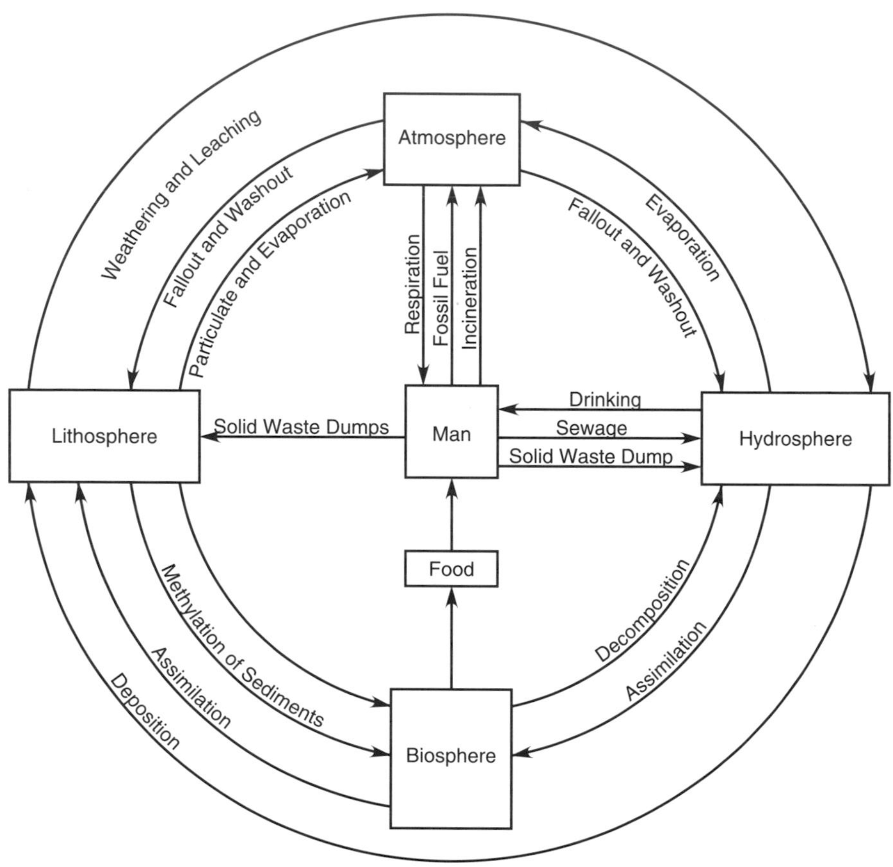

FIGURE 3.6 Mercury mobility and cycling in the environment. (From Horne, R. A. 1978. *The Chemistry of Our Environment.* John Wiley & Sons, New York. With permission.)

Mercury may exist in elemental form as any of dozens of organic and inorganic compounds and as a solid, liquid, or vapor. It is handily biotransformed, taken up by plant life, and concentrated by food chains. It moves with apparent ease through the atmosphere, hydrosphere, biosphere, and lithosphere. This mobility is illustrated graphically in Figure 3.6. Although other hazardous wastes may be more or less easily transformed, mobile, and/or threatening to the environment and human health, their mobility and activity are major considerations in their management. These factors add greatly to the complexity of the control systems that have been (and will be) imposed. (*See also* Cothern et al. 1986; Vincent 1984; Thibodeaux 1979; U.S. EPA 1982, pp. 4–5; Meyer 1989; Krieger et al. 1995)

TOPICS FOR REVIEW OR DISCUSSION

1. Explain how it is possible for mercury to move so easily through the environment.

2. Chemicals may be intentionally or accidentally released to the atmosphere, surface waters, or the land. Which release is more likely to lead to chronic exposure of humans to the released chemical? Why?
3. Why is there so much concern regarding releases of CFCs such as Freon®* (including a ban on the manufacture of the compound).
4. Explain the term pretreatment as applied by the Clean Water Act implementation program. Why is pretreatment necessary? Why are some large coastal cities major sources of toxic chemical discharges to the oceans?
5. How is it possible for a chemical pollutant to move from a land disposal site to the groundwater, to a stream, and possibly back to an aquifer?
6. How does it happen that municipal sewage treatment plants can be a source of atmospheric releases of volatile organics?

REFERENCES

Cothern et al. 1986. "Estimating Risk to Human Health." *Environmental Science & Technology* 20(2).

Dawson, Gaynor W., and Basil W. Mercer. 1986. *Hazardous Waste Management.* John Wiley & Sons, New York.

Davis, Andy, and Roger L. Olsen. 1990. "Predicting the Fate and Transport of Organic Compounds in Groundwater." *Hazardous Materials Control,* 3(4) July-August.

Egg, Richard P., and Donald L. Reddell. 1980. "Design of Evaporative Pits for Waste Pesticide Solution Disposal." *Treatment of Hazardous Waste*, Proceedings of the Sixth Annual Research Symposium. U.S. Environmental Protection Agency, Washington, D.C. EPA 600-9-80-011.

Enger, Eldon D., J. Richard Kormelink, Bradley F. Smith, and Rodney J. Smith. 1989. *Environmental Science: The Study of Interrelationships.* Wm. C. Brown Publishers, Dubuque, IA.

Hall, Charles V. 1980. "Holding and Evaporation of Pesticide Wastes." *Treatment of Hazardous Waste*, Proceedings of the Sixth Annual Research Symposium. U.S. Environmental Protection Agency, Washington, D.C. EPA-600-9-80-011.

Hare, F. Kenneth. 1989. "Climatology and Meteorology." *Environmental Science and Engineering*, J. Glynn Henry and Gary W. Heinke, Eds. Prentice-Hall, Englewood Cliffs, NJ. Chapter 7.

Horne, R. A. 1978. *The Chemistry of Our Environment.* John Wiley & Sons, New York.

Institute of Chemical Waste Management. 1989. *Managing Hazardous Waste: Fulfilling the Public Trust.* National Solid Wastes Management Association, Washington, D.C.

Krieger, Gary R., Mark J. Logsdon, Christopher P. Weis, and Joanna Moreno. 1995. "Basic Principles of Environmental Science." *Accident Prevention Manual for Business & Industry — Environmental Management,* Gary R. Krieger, Ed. National Safety Council, Itasca, IL. Chapter 5.

Lewis, Richard J., Sr. 1993. *Hazardous Chemicals Desk Reference. Third Edition.* Van Nostrand Reinhold, New York.

Meyer, Eugene. 1989. *Chemistry of Hazardous Materials.* Prentice-Hall, Englewood Cliffs, NJ.

Nebel, Bernard J., and Richard T. Wright. 1993. *Environmental Science,* Fourth Edition. Prentice-Hall, Englewood Cliffs, NJ.

Piasecki, Bruce W., and Gary A. Davis. 1987. *America's Future in Toxic Waste Management — Lessons from Europe.* Quorum Books, New York.

* Freon® is a registered trademark of E.I. Dupont de Nemours and Company, Wilmington, DE.

Poje, Jerry, Norman L. Dean, and Randall J. Burke. 1989. *Danger Downwind.* National Wildlife Federation, Washington, D.C.

Science Applications International Corporation. 1985. *Summary of Available Information Related to the Occurrence of Vinyl Chloride and Ground Water as a Transformation Product of Other Volatile Organic Chemicals.* Science Applications International Corporation, McLean, VA. NTIS PB86-117868.

Thibodeaux, Louis J. 1979. *Chemodynamics.* John Wiley & Sons, New York. pp. 1–5.

Todd, David K. 1960. *Ground Water Hydrology.* John Wiley & Sons, New York.

U.S. Department of Health and Human Services. 1994. *NIOSH Pocket Guide to Chemical Hazards.* Superintendent of Documents, Government Printing Office, Washington, D.C.

U.S. Environmental Protection Agency. 1977. *The Report to Congress: Waste Disposal Practices and Their Effects on Groundwater*, January. Office of Water Supply and Office of Solid Waste Management Programs, Washington, D.C.

U.S. Environmental Protection Agency. 1978. *Surface Impoundments and Their Effects on Ground-Water Quality in the United States — A Preliminary Survey.* Office of Drinking Water, Washington, D.C. EPA 570/9-78-004.

U.S. Environmental Protection Agency. 1982. *Handbook for Remedial Action at Waste Disposal Sites.* U.S. EPA, Washington, D.C. EPA 625/6-82-006.

U.S. Environmental Protection Agency. 1989. *The Toxics-Release Inventory: A National Perspective.* Office of Pesticides and Toxic Substances, Washington, D.C. EPA 560/4-89-005.

U.S. Environmental Protection Agency. 1991. *Report to Congress on Ocean Dumping 1987–1990.* Office of Water, Washington, D.C. EPA 503/9-91/009.

U.S. Environmental Protection Agency. 1994a. *The Biennial RCRA Hazardous Waste Report (Based on 1991 Data).* Solid Waste and Emergency Response, Washington, D.C. EPA 530-S-94-039.

U.S. Environmental Protection Agency. 1994b. *1992 Toxics Release Inventory Public Data Release.* Office of Pollution Prevention and Toxics, Washington, D.C. EPA 745-R-94-001.

Vincent, J. R. 1984. *South Florida Drinking Water Investigation.* U.S. Environmental Protection Agency, National Enforcement Investigations Center, Denver, CO. EPA 330/1-84-001.

4 TOXICOLOGY AND THE STANDARD-SETTING PROCESSES

OBJECTIVES

At completion of this chapter, the student should:

- understand the basic mechanisms of human exposure.
- be able to relate the exposure mechanisms to the pathways overviewed in Chapter 3 and to the common release mechanisms.
- be able to locate appropriate data on the toxicology of the chemical constituents of hazardous wastes.
- know the components of the general risk assessment process and understand their relationship to each other.
- understand how toxicological and human health considerations have been addressed in RCRA, and how RCRA measures, regulates, and attempts to minimize toxic and health impacts of hazardous wastes.

INTRODUCTION

Living organisms are composed of cells, and all cells must accommodate and facilitate a variety of chemical reactions to maintain themselves and perform their functions. Introduction of a foreign chemical into a cell may interfere with one or more of these cellular reactions, leading to impaired cell function or viability. All chemicals are toxic, but the concentration, route of entry, and time of exposure are factors that determine the degree of toxic *effect*.

Toxicology is the study of how specific chemicals cause injury to living cells and whole organisms. Such studies are performed to determine how easily the chemical enters the organism, how it behaves inside the organism, how rapidly it is removed from the organism, what cells are affected by the chemical, and what cell functions are impaired. A risk assessment process is used to derive a reliable estimate of the amount of chemical exposure which is considered acceptable for humans or other organisms. It is important to recognize that, for many chemicals, current toxicological knowledge is insufficient to answer this question with assurance (ICAIR 1985, p. ES-1). It is this very basic insufficiency which so frequently causes the standards-setting process to be exceedingly lengthy and/or seemingly endless. (*See also* Kamrin 1989, Chapter 1)

Public Health Impacts

Toxicity Hazard

Acute Toxicity — Adverse effects on, or mortality of, organisms following within hours, days, or no more than two weeks after a single exposure or multiple brief acute exposures, within a short time, to a chemical agent.

Chronic Toxicity — Adverse effects manifested after a lengthy period of uptake of small quantities of the toxicant. The dose is so small that no acute effects are manifested, and the time period is frequently a significant part of the normal lifetime of the organism. (Adapted from Hodgson and Levi 1987, pp. 357, 360)

In the hazardous waste context, toxicity is the ability of a chemical constituent or combination of constituents in a waste to produce injury upon contact with a susceptible site in or on the body of a living organism. *Toxicity hazard* is the risk that injury will be caused by the manner in which a waste is handled.

Chemical constituents of wastes may be acutely or chronically hazardous to plants or animals via a number of routes of administration. Phytotoxic wastes can damage plants when present in the soil, atmosphere, or irrigation water. Phytotoxicity is the result of a reduction of chlorophyll production capability, overall growth retardation, or some specific chemical interference mechanism.

Chemical components that are acutely toxic to mammals may be injurious when inhaled, ingested, and/or contacted with the skin. Symptoms resulting from acute exposures usually occur during or shortly after exposure to a sufficiently high concentration of a contaminant. The concentration required to produce such effects varies widely from chemical to chemical. Data pertinent to a single route of administration may not be applicable to alternative routes. For example, asbestos dust is toxic at very low levels when present in air, but asbestos particles in water are believed to pose no ingestive threat at low concentrations.

"Acute exposure" traditionally refers to exposure to "high" concentrations of a contaminant and/or short periods of time. "Chronic exposure" generally refers to exposure to "low" concentrations of a contaminant over a longer period. Chemical contaminants may be chronically toxic to mammals if they contain materials that (1) are bioaccumulated or concentrated in the food chain or (2) cause irreversible damage that builds gradually to a final, unacceptable level. Heavy metals and halogenated aromatic compounds are classic examples of chronic toxicants (HHS 1985, p. 2-1; Dawson and Mercer 1986, p. 62; Kamrin 1989, p. 134).

The U.S. Environmental Protection Agency (EPA) has classified some 35,000 chemicals as either definitely or potentially harmful to human health. A number of them, including some heavy metals (cadmium, arsenic) and certain organic compounds (carbon tetrachloride, toluene), are carcinogenic. Others, like mercury, are mutagenic and may tend to induce brain and bone damage (mercury, copper, lead), kidney disease (cadmium), neurological damage, and many other problems. Multiple exposures can be additive or synergistic, but in most cases, the risk resulting from exposure to more than one of these substances at the same time is not known (Enger et al. 1989, p. 377).

A wide variety of reference materials are available which provide basic toxicity data on specific chemicals. The *Registry of Toxic Effects of Chemical Substances* (RTECS) has been widely used and quoted (HHS 1975). In recent years, the *Health Assessment Guidance Manual*, published by the Agency for Toxic Substances and Disease Registry (ATSDR), has become widely accepted among toxicologists and related practitioners (HHS 1990). Moreover, ATSDR is preparing individual toxicological profiles for 275 hazardous substances found at Superfund sites. These profiles may be obtained from NTIS* as they become available. *A Textbook of Modern Toxicology*, by Hodgson and Levi (1987), is an excellent introductory text and provides a wealth of references on individual topics. The *Handbook of Toxic and Hazardous Chemicals and Carcinogens* (Second Edition, 1985) by Sittig is an authoritative source. The *NIOSH Pocket Guide to Chemical Hazards* is a handy, quick-reference guide to chemical hazards (HHS 1994). The American Conference of Governmental Industrial Hygienists (ACGIH, 1994–1995) publishes a handbook of threshold limit values (TLVs) and biological exposure indices (BEIs) for a variety of chemical substances and physical agents. The EPA operates a database — *Integrated Risk Information System* (IRIS)** — containing up-to-date health risk and EPA regulatory information pertaining to numerous chemicals. Other new databases with current toxicology data and search capabilities are becoming available.

For a chemical to exert a toxic effect on an organism, it must first gain access to the cells and tissues of that organism. In humans, the major routes by which toxic chemicals enter the body are through ingestion, inhalation, and dermal absorption. The absorptive surfaces of the tissues involved in these three routes of exposure (gastrointestinal tract, lungs, skin) differ from each other with respect to rates at which chemicals move across them.

Ingestion. Ingestion brings chemicals into contact with the tissues of the gastrointestinal tract. The normal function of the tract is the absorption of foods and fluids that are ingested, but the gastrointestinal tract is also effective in absorbing toxic chemicals that are contained in the food or water. The degree of absorption generally depends upon the hydrophilic (easily soluble in water) or lipophilic (easily soluble in organic solvents or fats) nature of the ingested chemical. Lipophilic compounds (e.g., organic solvents) are usually well absorbed, since the chemical can easily diffuse across the membranes of the cells lining the gastrointestinal tract. Hydrophilic compounds (e.g., metal ions) cannot cross the cell lining in this way and must be "carried" across by transport systems in the cells. The extent to which the transport occurs depends upon the efficiency of the transport system and upon the resemblance of the chemical to normally transported compounds.

If the ingested chemical is a weak organic acid or base, it will tend to be absorbed by diffusion in the part of the gastrointestinal (GI) tract in which it exists in its most lipid-soluble (least ionized or polar) form. Since gastric juice in the stomach is acidic

* The National Technical Information Services, 5285 Port Royal Road, Springfield, VA.

** *See* the IRIS entry in the Glossary.

and the intestinal contents are nearly neutral, the polarity of a chemical can differ markedly in these two areas of the GI tract. A weak organic acid is in its least polar form while in the stomach and, therefore, tends to be absorbed through the stomach. A weak organic base is in its least polar form while in the intestine and, therefore, tends to be absorbed through the intestine. Some caustics can cause acute reactions within the GI tract.

Another important determinant of absorption from the gastrointestinal tract is the interaction of the chemical with gastric or intestinal contents. Many chemicals tend to bind to food, and so a chemical ingested in food is often not absorbed as efficiently as when it is ingested in water. Additionally, some chemicals may not be stable in the strongly acidic environment of the stomach, and others may be altered by digestive enzymes or intestinal bacteria to yield different chemicals with altered toxicological properties. For example, intestinal bacteria can reduce aromatic nitro groups to aromatic amines, which may be carcinogenic (ICAIR 1985, pp. 4-1, 4-3). Irrespective of the route of absorption, once the chemical enters the bloodstream, it is then delivered to the target organ.

The ingestion route of exposure is seldom a factor in industrial situations, with the exception of the inadvertent incident. For example, workers eating lunch in a battery factory might ingest lead with their sandwiches (Beaulieu and Beaulieu 1985, p. 12). Ingestion gains importance with long-term intake of contaminants in water supplies.

Inhalation. Inhalation brings chemicals into contact with the lungs. Most inhaled chemicals are gases (e.g., carbon monoxide) or vapors of volatile liquids (e.g., trichloroethylene). Absorption in the lung is usually great because the surface area is large and blood vessels are in close proximity to the exposed surface area. Gases cross the cell membranes of the lung via simple diffusion, with the rate of absorption dependent upon the solubility of the toxic agent in blood. If the gas has a low solubility (e.g., ethylene), the rate of absorption is limited by the rate of blood flow through the lung, whereas the absorption of readily soluble gases (e.g., chloroform) is limited only by the rate and depth of respiration.

Chemicals may also be inhaled in solid or liquid form as dusts or aerosols. Liquid aerosols, if lipid soluble, will readily cross the cell membranes by passive diffusion. The absorption of solid particulate matter is highly dependent upon the size and chemical nature of the particles. The rate of absorption of particulates from the alveoli* is determined by the compound's solubility in lung fluids, with poorly soluble compounds being absorbed at a slower rate than readily soluble compounds. Small insoluble particles may remain in the alveoli indefinitely. Larger particles (2 to 5 μm) are deposited in the trachea or bronchial (upper) regions of the lungs where they may be cleared by coughing or sneezing, or they may be swallowed and deposited in the gastrointestinal tract. Particles of 5 μm or larger are usually deposited in the nasal passages or the pharynx where they are subsequently expelled or swallowed (ICAIR 1985, p. 4-3). A chronic effect on the lung can be caused if the defense mechanisms are overwhelmed with particles from smoke, coal dust, etc.

* Tiny cavities at the terminal end of the bronchiole, in the lungs, where the exchange of oxygen and carbon dioxide occurs.

Inhalation of air contaminants is probably the most important route of entry of chemicals to the body in industrial situations. A worker exposed to 1000 ppm of toluene over an eight-hour work shift could be expected to show dramatic symptoms of eye and respiratory irritation and depression of the central nervous system (CNS). This response to toluene demonstrates local effects (at the point of entry — eye, lung) and systemic effects where the chemical was absorbed into the bloodstream and affected the CNS.

Some chemicals do not provide "warning properties" in the gaseous or vapor state. For example, carbon monoxide (CO) is odorless and colorless and can inflict serious toxic effects to the unsuspecting victim. Other chemicals may have the property of desensitizing the receptor. For example, hydrogen sulfide (H_2S) has the prominent "rotten egg" odor at low concentrations. However, at high concentrations the olfactory senses become paralyzed, and the exposed individual can be quickly overcome with the toxic effect (Beaulieu and Beaulieu 1985, p. 14). High concentrations of H_2S can also cause respiratory arrest.

Long-term chronic health effects may be experienced by humans in various situations. For example, chronic bronchitis has been convincingly linked to long-term inhalation of sulfur dioxide, one of the more prominent urban air pollutants. (Hodgson and Levi 1987, pp. 189–190). Emphysema, asbestosis, silicosis, and berylliosis have all been associated with exposure to dusts and/or fumes.

Dermal Absorption. Absorption of toxicants through the epidermal layer of the skin and into the bloodstream is hindered by the densely packed layer of rough, keratinized,* epidermal cells. Absorption of chemicals occurs much more readily through scratched or broken skin. There are significant differences in skin structure from one region of the body to another (palms of hands vs. facial skin), and these differences further influence dermal absorption.

Absorption of chemicals by the skin is roughly proportional to their lipid solubility and can be enhanced by application of the chemical in an oily vehicle and rubbing the resulting preparation into the skin. Some lipid-soluble compounds can be absorbed by the skin in quantities sufficient to produce systemic effects. For example, carbon tetrachloride can be absorbed by the skin in amounts large enough to produce liver injury (ICAIR 1985, p. 4-3).

The *NIOSH Pocket Guide to Chemical Hazards* (HHS 1994) and the ACGIH handbook of TLVs and BEIs (ACGIH 1994–1995) provide guidance regarding dermal exposure to hazardous materials. (*See also* HHS 1985, p. 2-2)

Toxic Actions

Toxic chemicals can be categorized according to their physiological effect upon the exposed species. The categories often overlap, but can be (somewhat simplistically) separated into groups of irritants, asphyxiants, CNS depressants, and systemic toxicants.

* The layer of keratin is a tough, fibrous protein containing sulfur and forming the outer layer of epidermal structures such as hair, nails, horns, and hoofs.

Irritants. Chemicals that cause effects such as pain, erythema, swelling of the skin, eyes, respiratory tract, or gastrointestinal tract are considered irritants, causing a local effect at the point of entry to the body. An example is sodium hydroxide (caustic) dust on perspiration-moist skin. The pH of the fluid is quickly increased above normal, resulting in irritation. Mechanical friction, such as the rubbing of shirt cuffs or collar, compounds the irritating effect. The effect may be as simple as a mild stinging sensation to the more serious blistering of the skin. Ammonia vapors or spray can irritate the mucous membranes of the respiratory tract, causing tearing and stinging in the nasal passages and throat.

Asphyxiants. Chemical asphyxiants are those that deny oxygen to cells of the host organism, thereby slowing or halting metabolism. Simple, or mechanical, asphyxiants displace the available oxygen in an air space to the point of producing an atmosphere unable to support life (less than 16% oxygen). Oxygen starvation may occur in a confined space where methane gas (CH_4) displaces oxygen to the extent that the oxygen content of the atmosphere falls to less than 16%. Conversely, CO is a gas that chemically ties up the hemoglobin in blood after inhalation. With hemoglobin unable to transport oxygen to the cells and carbon dioxide from the cells, the tissues cannot maintain natural metabolic functions, and death occurs.

Central Nervous System (CNS) Depressants. Inhalation of most organic solvent vapors and anesthetic gases or the introduction of narcotics to the body in the form of alcohol or depressant drugs causes a deadening of the nervous system. A worker who inhales trichloroethylene vapor during a workshift might not have the neuromuscular coordination to safely drive an automobile. The giddiness and drunkenness can be mistaken for the effects of elevated blood alcohol concentration.

Systemic Toxicants. Systemic toxicants are chemical compounds that exhibit their effect dramatically upon a specific organ system and possibly far from the site of entry. There is considerable overlap between the systemic toxicants and the other categories. For example, the organic solvent carbon tetrachloride (CCl_4) is definitely a CNS depressant as well as an irritant and can cause irreversible liver or kidney damage.

Mercury vapor does not seem to produce irritation upon inhalation, but causes serious impairment to nerve endings. Chronic inhalation of mercury vapor can result in serious disease of the nervous system, including insanity.

An agent that has the potential to induce the abnormal, excessive, and uncoordinated proliferation of certain cell types, or the abnormal division of cells, is termed a carcinogen or potential carcinogen. Inhalation of asbestos fibers has been firmly linked to the production of lung cancer and mesothelioma (cancer of the linings of lung tissues).

A chemical that causes mutations or changes in the genetic codes of the DNA in chromosomes is called a mutagen. Formaldehyde vapor causes these changes in the bacterial organisms *Salmonella* sp. This characteristic is the basis for the "Ames test," a bacterial procedure used for indication of mutagenicity of suspect substances. Mutagenic toxins may affect future generations.

A teratogen is a toxicant that produces physical defects in unborn offspring. A suspect substance may be administered to a test animal to determine if it will cause congenital abnormalities in a fetus produced by the test animal (Beaulieu and

Beaulieu 1985, pp. 15–17). The birth defects of a teratogen are not passed to future generations.

Risk Assessment and Standards

The EPA and other regulatory agencies have, over the years, frequently opted for risk-based standards because of the court-imposed need to "show harm" when a particular standard is challenged. As noted in the "Introduction" to this chapter, this insistence upon a rational basis (i.e., a showing of harm) for environmental or exposure standards has caused the standards-setting process to be time consuming, laborious, and frustrating. In 1990, it became apparent that Congress was then steering the EPA back toward more reliance upon technology-based standards (*Environment Reporter* March 9, 1990, pp. 1840–1841). The 1990 Clean Air Act Amendments (CAAA) require the EPA to assign maximum achievable control technology (MACT) standards to the newly listed hazardous air pollutants. Yet Section 303 of the CAAA also establishes a Risk Assessment and Management Commission, which is to "make a full investigation of the policy implications and appropriate uses of risk assessment and risk management in regulatory programs under various Federal laws to prevent cancer and other chronic human health effects which may result from exposure to hazardous substances" (42 USC 7412). Thus, the search continues for approaches to rationalize standards in human health effects.

The congressional focus upon technology-based standards is an expression of the frustration of that body with the slow pace of the standards-setting process, the endless arguments growing from the "how-clean-is-clean" issues, and the inherent flaws in biological research (conversion of test animal data to human exposure application — more on this later in this chapter). Nevertheless, the courts can be expected to lend a sympathetic ear to pleas for rationality in standards, and risk-based standards and some of the verdicts will be with us for years to come.

Risk Assessment. The risk assessment process for evaluation of a hazardous waste site is a specific example of the more general risk assessment processes used in developing risk-based standards. The risk assessment process usually consists of the following four steps:

- Toxicological evaluation
- Dose–response evaluation
- Exposure assessment
- Risk characterization

(*See also* Ehrhardt et al. 1986; U.S. EPA 1986)

Toxicological Evaluation. The toxicological evaluation should answer the question, "Does the chemical have an adverse effect?" It is a qualitative evaluation of the scientific data to determine the nature and severity of actual or potential health hazards associated with exposure to a chemical substance. This step involves a critical evaluation and interpretation of toxicity data from epidemiological, clinical, animal, and *in vitro** studies. Factors that should be considered during the toxicologi-

* Studies conducted in cells, tissues, or extracts from an organism, i.e., not in the living organism.

cal evaluation for each contaminant include routes of exposure, types of effects, reliability of data, dose, mixture effects, and the strength of evidence supporting the conclusions of the toxicological evaluation. The toxicological evaluation should also identify any known quantitative indices of toxicity such as the No Observable Adverse Effect Level (NOAEL), Lowest Observable Adverse Effect Level (LOAEL), carcinogenic risk factors, etc. (ICAIR 1985, p. 8-2).

The dose–response relationship is the most fundamental concept in toxicology. The product of the dose–response evaluation is an estimate of the relationship between the dose of a chemical and the incidence of the adverse effect in the human population actually exposed or in test organisms in the laboratory.

Dose–Response Evaluation. Once the toxicological evaluation indicates that a chemical is likely to cause a particular adverse effect, the next step is to determine the potency of the chemical. The dose–response curve describes the relationship that exists between the degree of exposure to a chemical (dose) and the magnitude of the effect (response) in the exposed organism. By definition, no response is seen in the absence of the chemical being evaluated. At low dose levels, response may not be evident, but as the amount of chemical exposure increases, the response becomes apparent and increases. Thus, a steep curve indicates a highly toxic chemical; a shallow curve indicates a less toxic substance. The toxicity values derived from this quantitative dose–response relationship can be used to estimate the incidence of adverse effects occurring in humans at different exposure levels. Depending upon the mechanism by which the chemical acts, the curve may rise with or without a threshold. Figure 4.1 illustrates the NOAEL and LOAEL described earlier. The TD_{50} and TD_{100} points indicate the doses associated with 50 and 100% occurrence of the measured toxic effect.

Figure 4.2 illustrates threshold and no-threshold dose–response curves. In both cases, the response normally reaches a maximum, after which the dose–response curve becomes flat.

The dose–response evaluation for noncarcinogenic chemicals provides an estimation of the NOAEL or LOAEL. The NOAEL may then be assumed to be the basis for establishing an "acceptable daily intake" (ADI). In practice, the NOAEL is adjusted by safety and uncertainty factors which are an attempt to account for the "unknowns" involved.

Mathematical models of the dose–response relationship for carcinogenic chemicals are used to derive estimates of the probability or range of probabilities that a carcinogenic effect will occur under the test conditions of exposure. These procedures are greatly more complex, involving three categories of data reliability. In most cases it is assumed that there is no threshold dose for carcinogens, i.e., no exposure is considered acceptable. (*See also* ICAIR 1985, Chapters 3 and 6)

Exposure Assessment. An exposure assessment is conducted to estimate the magnitude of actual and/or potential human exposures, the frequency and duration of these exposures, and the pathways by which humans are potentially exposed. The objectives of a site-specific exposure assessment are to identify actual or potential

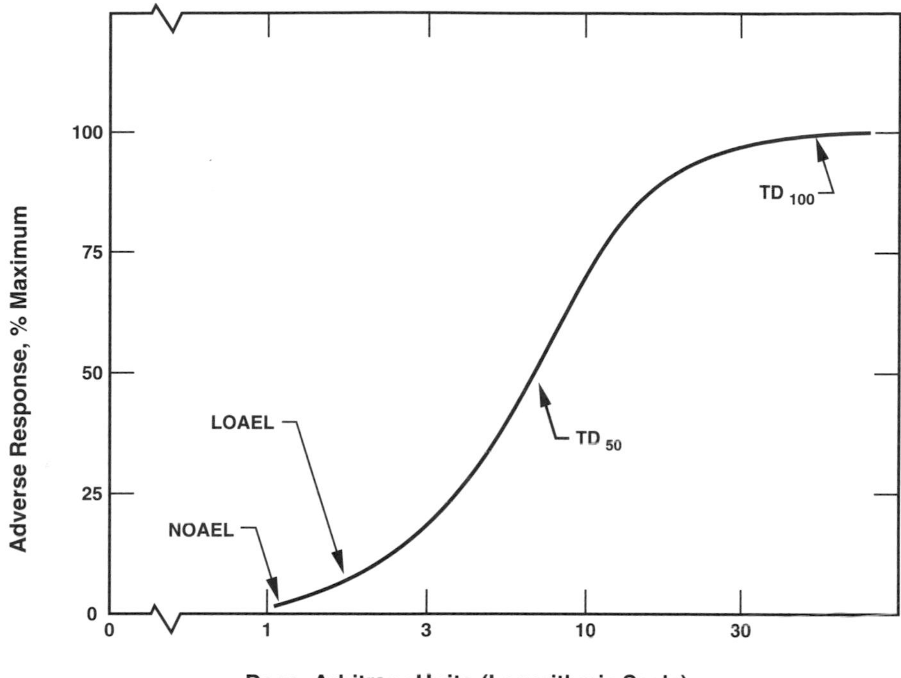

FIGURE 4.1 Hypothetical dose–response curves. (Adapted from ICAIR Life Systems, Inc. 1985. *Toxicology Handbook.* Prepared for EPA Office of Waste Programs Enforcement, Washington, D.C. TR-693-21A.)

routes of exposure, characterize the population exposed, and determine the extent of potential exposure at a site. The product of the exposure assessment process is an estimation of exposure levels or doses incurred (past, present, or future) for chemicals of concern at the site. In the more general case, the extent of exposure may be known and carefully controlled (ICAIR 1985, p. 8-2).

Risk Characterization. The final step in risk assessment, risk characterization, is the process of estimating the incidence of an adverse health effect under the conditions of exposure described in the exposure assessment. It is performed by integrating the information developed during the toxicity assessment (toxicological evaluation and dose–response evaluation) and the exposure assessment to yield a complete characterization of risk for a given hazardous waste site. Figure 4.3 diagrammatically illustrates the process.

The final risk assessment should include a summary of the risks associated with the exposure situation and such factors as the weight of evidence associated with each step of the process, the estimated uncertainty of the component parts, the distribution of risk across various sectors of the population, and the assumptions contained within the estimates.

The primary reason for interest in the details of a dose–response relationship for carcinogens is the need to estimate the risk to humans at low doses. Those responsible

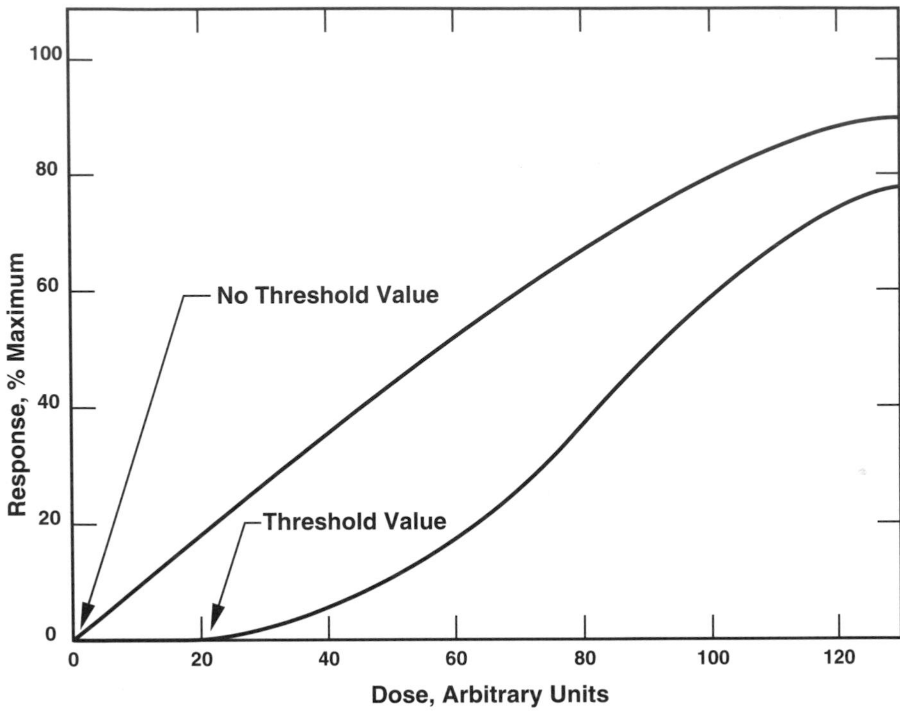

FIGURE 4.2 Hypothetical dose–response curves. (Adapted from ICAIR Life Systems, Inc. 1985. *Toxicology Handbook.* Prepared for EPA Office of Waste Programs Enforcement, Washington, D.C. TR-693-21A.)

for promulgating risk-based standards want to know how small amounts of a chemical will affect lifetime disease incidence in humans. Typically, the only information is scant epidemiological data, together with results of animal experiments, both at high doses. Regulation, and the rationale thereof, would be much simpler if certain aspects of the dose–response relationship could be conclusively demonstrated. For example, if it could be conclusively demonstrated that there is a "threshold" dose below which there is no response, then exposure up to that threshold would evidently contribute no risk (Zeise et al. 1986, p. 1).

Thus, a risk-based standard may involve an exhaustive review of limited, questionable, or inappropriate exposure data; the need to extrapolate from observable effects at very high concentration exposure to very low concentration exposure criteria; the similar requirement to extrapolate from animal to human exposure criteria; and application under significantly different conditions than those prevailing in the data collection situation. This process, then, becomes the basis for establishing a standard at the predetermined risk level, i.e., one incidence per 100,000, 1,000,000, 10,000,000, etc. It is an imperfect process, vulnerable to assault, and frequently difficult to defend. There is little doubt that the technology-based standard is a more straightforward (and, therefore, more appealing to the lawmaker/regulator) process. (*See also* Zeise et al. 1986, pp. 43, 124–125; ICAIR 1985, Chapter 8; U.S. EPA 1986,

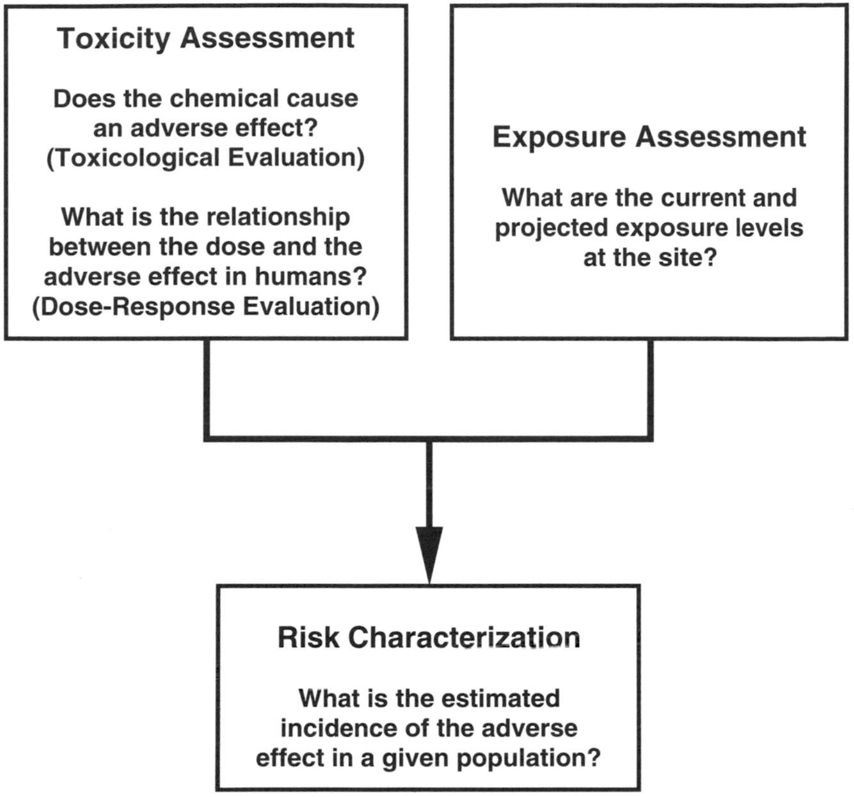

FIGURE 4.3 Risk assessment process at hazardous waste sites (EPA).

Chapters 4–7; Hodgson and Levi 1987, pp. 281–283; Krieger et al. 1995, pp. 123–133; Kester et al. 1995, Chapter 12)

Other Hazards

Explosion and Fire. There are many potential causes of explosions and fires at uncontrolled hazardous waste sites, including:

- chemical reactions that produce explosion, fire, or heat.
- ignition of explosive or flammable chemicals.
- ignition of materials due to oxygen enrichment.
- agitation of shock- or friction-sensitive compounds.
- sudden release of materials under pressure.

Explosions and fires may arise spontaneously even at well-managed facilities. Such events are more likely to result from carelessness or poor practice on active sites or cleanup activities on abandoned sites. Examples include activities such as moving drums, mixing incompatible chemicals, or introducing an ignition source (such as electrical, electrostatic, or friction-generated spark) into an explosive or flammable environment. At hazardous waste sites, explosions and fires not only pose the obvious hazards of intense heat, open flame, smoke, and flying objects, but may cause the release of toxic chemicals into the environment. Such releases are a threat to workers on the site and to the general public living or working nearby (HHS 1985, p. 2-2). Regulated treatment, storage, and disposal sites are specifically designed and operated to prevent such incidents. (*See also* Dawson and Mercer 1986, pp. 62–73; Meyer 1989, Chapter 13)

Ionizing Radiation. Radioactive materials emit one or more of three types of harmful radiation: alpha, beta, and gamma, frequently identified by the Greek alphabet characters α, β, and γ. Alpha radiation has limited penetration ability and is usually stopped by clothing and the outer layers of the skin. Alpha radiation poses little threat outside the body, but can be hazardous if alpha emitters are inhaled or ingested. Beta radiation can cause harmful "beta burns" to the skin and damage the subsurface blood system. Beta emitters are also hazardous if inhaled or ingested. Gamma radiation easily passes through clothing and human tissue and can cause serious, permanent damage to the human body (HHS 1985, p. 2-2).

As will be covered in Chapter 13, radioactive waste (radwaste) has traditionally been managed under separate statutory and regulatory authorities and has not been considered a subset of regulated hazardous waste. New EPA regulations for the management of "mixed waste" are being developed to deal with wastes meeting both hazwaste and radwaste definitions and having both characteristics. The distinction is thus blurred, and new approaches to regulation and management of these wastes will be forthcoming.

Several major health hazards may result from exposure to radiation, including burns or damage to internal organs, accumulation in the body until toxic levels are reached, malignancies, sterility, and/or harmful mutations. Acute exposure can result from improper handling of radioactive materials or improper disposal or storage in nonsecure facilities. Chronic exposure can potentially result from leaching of landfills, volatilization of radioactive materials, or proximity of subjects to radiation sources. (*See also* Dawson and Mercer 1986, pp. 65–67; Corbitt 1989, pp. 9.87–9.111; Nebel and Wright 1993, pp. 489–490)

Biomedical Hazards. As discussed in Chapter 12, the AIDS epidemic has brought the management of biomedical wastes sharply into the forefront. Wastes from health care, research, and biomedical manufacturing facilities may contain a variety of other infectious and/or pathogenic wastes.* Infectious wastes are those materials that contain disease-causing organisms or matter. Wastes that are infectious or contain infectious materials pose a hazard to handlers and the public if they are not isolated and/or disposed of in a manner that destroys the viability of the infectious matter. These wastes are now recognized as a subset of hazardous wastes and have

* There is inconsistency in the terminology used to define these wastes. The descriptors infectious, pathogenic, biomedical, toxic, and medically hazardous have all been used to describe infectious wastes.

become the subject of federal, state, and local regulatory activity. (*See also* U.S. EPA 1986; Munter et al. 1995, pp. 226–229)

Additional Hazards Associated With Hazardous Waste Management. Hazardous wastes and hazardous waste facilities may subject workers to a variety of other hazards, including physical hazards such as injury by heavy equipment, confined spaces, heat stress, engulfment, container handling, and electrical energy; exposure hazards such as oxygen deficiency, irritation, or corrosiveness; transportation incidents; and workplace violence. These hazards are the subject of Chapter 15, wherein their prevention and management will be explored in some detail. In most cases, such exposures are limited to workers in direct contact or close proximity to the wastes. However, on- or offsite spills, uncontrolled releases, inadequate site security, or transportation accidents can subject the public to harmful exposures to these hazards. (*See also* Dawson and Mercer 1986, pp. 68–70; HHS 1985, p. 2-2; Danby 1995, Chapter 9)

Regulatory Application of Health Standards and Criteria

Technology-Based Standards

Technology-based standards are best described as those having their rationale grounded in treatment and/or control technologies, gradations of primitive to sophisticated processes, cost-effectiveness, economic feasibility, esthetics, and political considerations. Some examples include:

- The Clean Water Act requirements for definition and application of best practicable control technology currently available for classes and categories of point sources (other than publicly owned treatment works)
- The Clean Water Act requirements for definition and application of secondary treatment for publicly owned treatment works, and the inclusion, by definition, of oxidation ponds, lagoons, and trickling filters as secondary treatment
- The Resource Conservation and Recovery Act (RCRA) treatment standards for land disposal restricted wastes include those expressed as specified technologies
- The 1990 CAAA which require MACT by sources of hazardous air pollutants

Risk-Based Standards

Standards and criteria derived from risk analyses of the nature outlined earlier in this chapter and based upon a predetermined level of risk to the receptor population are referred to as risk-based standards. Some examples include:

- The Safe Drinking Water Act charges the EPA with promulgating primary drinking water standards containing maximum contaminant levels (MCLs) for public water supplies. The MCLs are to be established for each

contaminant found in public water supplies that may have adverse human health effects, at levels having no known or anticipated adverse human health effect, with an adequate margin of safety.
- The RCRA land disposal restrictions also include a large number of standards that are health related or risk based.
- The Superfund cleanup standards which require that remedial actions attain a level of control which renders impacted waters at least as clean as the MCLs of the Safe Drinking Water Act and the water quality criteria of the Clean Water Act.

RCRA Standards

As will be seen in subsequent chapters, RCRA embodies both technology-based and risk-based standards. The requirements for impermeable liners for land disposal facilities; for storage of hazardous wastes in nonreactive containers; for burning of hazardous waste fuels in high-temperature furnaces; for 99.99%, or 99.9999%, destruction and removal efficiencies (DRE) in thermal units; and the land disposal restrictions, in general, are technology-based standards.

If concentrations of the 40 toxicity characteristic wastes (40 CFR 261.24) are equal to or more than 100 times the National Interim Primary Drinking Water Standards, the waste is hazardous and must be managed as such. Such risk-based standards are most prevalent in permits for treatment, storage, and disposal facilities; in groundwater monitoring requirements for land disposal facilities; and in remedial requirements.

Congress and the EPA have attempted to craft the RCRA regulatory approach in risk-based rationales, but the large numbers and quantities of chemicals and mixtures involved, together with the varieties of generator/source operations, have made that approach exceedingly difficult. As a result, the RCRA (the act and the program) has focused upon regulatory mechanisms which, in large measure:

- attempt to identify wastes which are hazardous to human health and the environment, and capture them in a "cradle-to-grave" management system.
- create physical and space barriers which isolate the public from contact with the identified hazardous wastes during generation, transportation, storage, treatment, and/or disposal.
- minimize the generation of hazardous wastes.
- encourage the reuse and recycling of hazardous wastes and the treatment to nonhazardous or reduced hazard condition.
- ensure secure disposal of wastes which cannot otherwise be safely managed.

TOPICS FOR REVIEW OR DISCUSSION

1. A dose–response curve that passes through the origin indicates what with respect to acceptable dose?
2. Identify four categories of physiological effects imposed by chemical constituents of hazardous wastes.
3. In the hazardous waste lexicon, what is meant by the term "toxicity hazard"?
4. Which of the routes of exposure is considered least likely to be a factor to workers on industrial sites? Why?
5. The risk assessment process for evaluation of a hazardous waste site usually consists of:

   a. ________________________
   b. ________________________
   c. ________________________
   d. ________________________

6. Carbon tetrachloride, a widely distributed pollutant, may cause damage to what human organs?
7. Identify some of the physiological effects upon humans of exposure to mercury.
8. The current regulatory scheme for hazardous waste management generally relies upon risk-based or technology-based standards. Briefly explain each. What are the arguments favoring each?

REFERENCES

American Conference of Governmental Industrial Hygienists (ACGIH). 1994-1995. *Threshold Limit Values for Chemical Substances and Physical Agents and Biological Exposure Indices*. ACGIH, Cincinnati, OH.

Beaulieu, Harry J., and Diane L. Beaulieu, 1985. *Toxicology*. National Environmental Health Association, Denver, CO.

Corbitt, Robert A. 1989. *Standard Handbook of Environmental Engineering*. McGraw-Hill, New York.

Danby, John G. 1995. "Health and Safety Training for Hazardous Waste Activities." *Accident Prevention Manual for Business and Industry — Environmental Management*. National Safety Council, Itasca, IL.

Dawson, Gaynor W., and Basil W. Mercer. 1986. *Hazardous Waste Management*. John Wiley & Sons, New York.

Ehrhardt, Robert F., Philip J. Stapleton, Rebecca L. Fry, and Deborah J. Stocker. 1986. "How Clean is Clean? — Clean-up Standards for Groundwater and Soil." Prepared by Dames and Moore for the Groundwater Task Force of the Edison Electric Institute.

Enger, Eldon D., J. Richard Kormelink, Bradley F. Smith, and Rodney J. Smith. 1989. *Environmental Science: The Study of Interrelationships*. Wm. C. Brown Publishers, Dubuque, IA.

Environment Reporter, March 9, 1990, pp. 1840–1841. Bureau of National Affairs, Washington, D.C.

Hodgson, Ernest, and Patricia E. Levi. 1987. *A Textbook of Modern Toxicology*. Elsevier Science Publishing Company, New York.

ICAIR Life Systems, Inc. 1985. *Toxicology Handbook*. Prepared for EPA Office of Waste Programs Enforcement, Washington, D.C. TR-693-21A.

Kamrin, Michael A. 1989. *Toxicology*. Lewis Publishers, Chelsea, MI.

Kester, Janet E., Holly A. Hattemer-Frey, Joseph W. Gordon, and Gary R. Krieger. 1995. "Risk Assessment." *Accident Prevention Manual for Business and Industry — Environmental Management*. National Safety Council, Itasca, IL.

Kreiger, Gary R., Mark J. Logsdon, Christopher P. Weis, and Joanna Moreno. 1995. "Basic Principles of Environmental Science." *Accident Prevention Manual for Business and Industry — Environmental Management*. National Safety Council, Itasca, IL.

Meyer, Eugene. 1989. *Chemistry of Hazardous Materials*. Prentice-Hall, Englewood Cliffs, NJ.

Munter, Florence, Stephen W. Bell, Robert Hollingsworth, Joseph W. Gordon, and Charles N. Lovinski. 1995. "Hazardous Wastes." *Accident Prevention Manual for Business and Industry — Environmental Management*. National Safety Council, Itasca, Il.

Nebel, Bernard J. and Richard T. Wright. 1993. *Environmental Science*. Prentice-Hall, Englewood Cliffs, NJ.

Sittig, Marshall. 1985. *Handbook of Toxic and Hazardous Chemicals and Carcinogens,* Second Edition. Noyes Publications, Park Ridge, NJ.

U.S. Department of Health and Human Services (HHS). 1994. *NIOSH Pocket Guide to Chemical Hazards*. Public Health Service, Superintendent of Documents, Government Printing Office, Washington, D.C.

U.S. Department of Health and Human Services (HHS). 1985. *NIOSH/OSHA/USCG/EPA Occupational Safety and Health Guidance Manual for Hazardous Waste Site Activities*. Superintendent of Documents, Government Printing Office, Washington, D.C.

U.S. Department of Health and Human Services (HHS). 1990 (Draft). *Health Assessment Guidance Manual*. Agency for Toxic Substances and Disease Registry, Atlanta, GA.

U.S. Department of Health and Human Services (HHS). (Earlier editions — U.S. Department of Health, Education, and Welfare). *Registry of Toxic Effects of Chemical Substances*. Superintendent of Documents, Government Printing Office, Washington, D.C.

U.S. Environmental Protection Agency (EPA). 1986. *Managing and Tracking Medical Wastes*. Office of Solid Waste and Emergency Response, Washington, D.C. EPA 530-SW-89-022.

U.S. Environmental Protection Agency (EPA). 1989. *Risk Assessment Guidance for Superfund — Volume I — Human Health Evaluation Manual (Part A)*. Office of Emergency and Remedial Response, Washington, D.C. EPA 540/1-89/002.

Zeise, Lauren, Richard Wilson, and Edmund A. C. Crouch. 1986. *The Dose Response Relationships for Carcinogens: A Review*. John F. Kennedy School of Government, Harvard University, Cambridge, MA.

5 HAZARDOUS WASTE SOURCES/GENERATORS

OBJECTIVES

At completion of this chapter, the student should:

- have familiarity with some of the common industrial sources of hazardous waste and the Resource Conservation and Recovery Act (RCRA) approach to regulation of wastes from specific industries/processes.
- understand the role that the generator plays in the "cradle-to-grave" management of hazardous wastes and the basic requirements RCRA imposes upon generators.
- understand the RCRA focus on controls based upon the three classifications of generators, i.e., nature and composition of a waste, environmental and health impacts of a waste, and/or quantity of waste produced.

INTRODUCTION

In the previous chapters, we have shown that the increasing numbers of hazardous waste incidents brought about increasing public alarm and pressure upon Congress and the state legislatures to take decisive action to protect human health and the environment. We have also shown that Congress has, through original enactments and subsequent amendments, steadily strengthened and tightened RCRA and the Comprehensive Environmental Response Compensation and Liability Act (CERCLA) in its effort to achieve timely control and remediation of hazardous waste impacts. We have illustrated the wide variety of hazardous waste abuses and disposal practices that have helped to shape the statutory and regulatory structures.

We have shown the interrelationships of hazardous waste releases to the atmosphere, to publicly owned wastewater treatment facilities, to surface streams, to the land surface, and to the earth's crust. We have shown the routes of movement through the environment and the mechanisms of human and environmental exposure. With this background overview, we may now begin to consider the generic approaches to management and control, as well as those embodied in the RCRA and CERCLA.

Enactment of RCRA, in 1976, enabled the U.S. Environmental Protection Agency (EPA) and the delegated (or "primacy") states to develop programs to implement the cradle-to-grave management of hazardous wastes. Remediation of abandoned hazardous waste sites, and those for which "responsible parties" could not be found, was not provided for until enactment of CERCLA in 1980. Although subsequent amendments of both acts have blurred this historical distinction with some overlapping authorities, practitioners have come to think of hazardous wastes as being either RCRA (currently generated) or CERCLA (residual) wastes. In this chapter, we will overview RCRA-specific management of hazardous waste generator activities. We will defer discussion of the management of wastes contributed by site remediation activities to Chapter 9.

The Generator Defined

The "generator" is the first element of the RCRA cradle-to-grave concept, which includes generators, transporters, treatment plants, storage facilities, and disposal sites. The RCRA regulations define a generator as:

> any person, *by site*, whose act or process produces hazardous waste identified or listed in Part 261 of this chapter or whose act first causes a hazardous waste to become subject to regulation. (40 CFR 260.10)

In more practical terms, the generator is the *creator* of a hazardous waste who must analyze all solid wastes produced to determine if they meet the RCRA Subtitle C definitions or listings of hazardous wastes. The RCRA definition is generally unambiguous with respect to conventional industrial sources, but can become less clear in the event of an accidental release. In site remediation activity, identification of the *creator* of the waste can become a highly contentious issue and /or the basis for major litigation (more on this in Chapter 11). Once a waste has been identified as a hazardous waste, it becomes subject to the Subtitle C regulations, and the generator assumes very significant responsibilities for the correct management thereof.

The Three Classifications of Generators

Congress and the EPA initially recognized that large numbers of generators, particularly small businesses, produce relatively minor quantities of hazardous wastes and, accordingly, created two classes of generators. The generator of more than 1000 kg of hazardous waste per month or more than 1 kg of *acutely** hazardous waste per month was designated a "generator" (frequently spoken of as a "large quantity generator") and is subject to the full content of the 40 CFR 262 regulation. Those generating less than 1000 kg of hazardous wastes or less than 1 kg of acutely hazardous waste were classified as small quantity generators (SQGs) and were exempted from most of the generator requirements of the RCRA regulations.

Because of concerns that wastes exempted from regulation by the SQG exclusion could be causing significant environmental harm, Congress amended the defi-

* Acutely hazardous wastes are wastes that the EPA has determined to be so dangerous that small amounts are regulated in a manner similar to larger amounts of other hazardous wastes. They are, specifically, F020-F023 and F-26-F028 identified in 40 CFR 261.31 and the "p" wastes listed in 40 CFR 261.33.

nition of SQGs in the Hazardous and Solid Waste Amendments of 1984 (HSWA). SQGs were redefined as producers of more than 100 kg and less than 1000 kg of hazardous waste per month and no more than 1 kg of acutely hazardous waste. The SQG was made subject to new restrictions, which are summarized herein.

A new classification, the Conditionally Exempt Small Quantity Generator, was defined as producing less than 100 kg of hazardous waste and less than 1 kg of acutely hazardous waste per month. This category of generator is exempt from most generator requirements. (*See also* Phifer and McTigue 1988, pp. 9–10); U.S. EPA 1986, Chapter 2)

The RCRA Subtitle C regulations recognize three categories of generators:

- *Large quantity generators* (generators) are defined as those facilities that generate more than 1000 kg of *hazardous waste* or more than 1 kg of *acutely hazardous waste* per month.
- *Small quantity generators* (SQGs) are defined as *producing* more than 100 kg, but less than 1000 kg of *hazardous waste* per month or less than 1 kg of *acutely hazardous waste* per month, or as *accumulating* less than 6000 kg of hazardous waste at any one time or less than 1 kg of acutely hazardous waste at any one time.
- *Conditionally exempt small quantity generators* are those which generate less than 100 kg of *hazardous waste* per month and which accumulate less than 1 kg of *acutely hazardous waste* per month, or which *accumulate* less than 1000 kg of *hazardous waste* at any time or less than 1 kg of *acutely hazardous waste* at any one time.

Wastes Generated

In 1991, the latest year for which generator biennial reports have been tabulated, 23,426 large quantity generators produced 306 million tons of RCRA hazardous waste (U.S. EPA 1994a). The EPA has, on record, 266,000 large and small quantity generators (U.S. EPA 1993). As discussed earlier, the *reported* quantities of RCRA-regulated hazardous waste *generated* in the United States have remained in the range of 250 to 300 million metric tons per year through most of the 1980s and early 1990s.

The *Toxic Release Inventory* (TRI) ranks the total release quantities of TRI chemicals by Standard Industrial Code (SIC) 21 through 39, thereby providing some sense of the relative contributions of hazardous waste by type of industry (*see* Table 5.1). Again, as discussed in Chapter 3, the TRI *release* statistics are not comparable to RCRA hazardous waste *generation* quantities reported by the EPA.

A few examples of basic industries and the types of hazardous wastes produced are listed in Appendix A to illustrate the wide variety and complexity of the wastes. The student should consult specific industry trade publications for details regarding industry-specific wastes produced.

These few examples are inadequate to suggest the numbers and kinds of hazardous chemical constituents in hazardous wastes which must be managed. There are approximately 800 listed wastes, in 40 CFR 261, and countless more of characteristic

Table 5.1 Quantities of TRI Releases and Transfers by Industry Type, 1992

SIC Code	Industry	Releases	Transfers	Total
20	Food products	38,568,497	45,946,998	84,515,495
21	Tobacco mfg.	1,991,033	38,779	2,029,812
22	Textile mill products	21,467,273	12,811,012	34,278,285
23	Apparel	1,576,282	900,946	2,477,228
24	Lumber and wood	32,373,513	6,894,349	39,267,862
25	Furniture and fixtures	55,053,507	15,457,044	70,510,551
26	Paper products	233,048,527	69,501,680	302,550,207
27	Printing and publishing	40,479,331	11,629,747	52,109,078
28	Chemical products	1,527,344,618	1,222,093,683	2,749,438,301
29	Petroleum refining	82,733,063	573,913,393	656,646,456
30	Rubber and plastics	134,412,512	48,101,422	182,513,934
31	Leather products	10,495,995	9,959,680	20,455,675
32	Stone, glass, clay	25,654,866	19,423,734	45,078,600
33	Primary metals	345,229,090	1,019,262,106	1,364,491,196
34	Fabricated metals	101,202,243	278,420,845	379,623,088
35	Machinery, nonelectrical	33,670,024	54,950,859	88,620,883
36	Electrical	52,216,161	346,823,099	399,039,260
37	Transport equipment	135,987,336	187,868,342	323,855,678
38	Measuring, photo	32,984,291	28,086,864	61,071,155
39	Miscellaneous	18,249,532	14,912,086	33,161,618
	Multiple SIC in 20-39	217,833,016	380,305,768	598,138,784
	No SIC in 20-39	14,711,382	11,735,747	26,447,129
Totals		3,157,282,092	44,359,038,183	47,516,320,275

Source: U.S. EPA 1994b, pp. 208–209.

wastes. The traditional intensity of industrial and business competition engenders the introduction of new products and, thus, new wastes to be managed. This historical burgeoning of waste generation, the health concerns and environmental degradation, the public and political pressures that arise, the ever-increasing costs of waste management, and liability concerns have brought about intensified efforts to reduce quantities of wastes generated and to reuse and recycle wastes much more effectively. (*See also* Dawson and Mercer 1986, pp. 119–129; U.S. EPA 1986, Table 2 and Appendix B; Phifer and McTigue 1988, Chapter 3; Nebel and Wright 1993, Chapter 14)

Regulatory Requirements

Generators and SQGs are subject to regulations contained in 40 CFR 262. These regulations require:

- obtaining an EPA identification number.
- safe management of wastes during accumulation.
- proper preparation of wastes prior to transport.
- manifesting of hazardous waste.
- record keeping and reporting.

Each requirement is discussed in the following with different requirements for the three categories of generators noted where appropriate.

EPA ID Number

One of the ways by which EPA and the primacy states monitor and track generator activity is the assignment of a unique identification number to each generator, transporter, and operator of a treatment, storage, and disposal facility (TSDF). Without this number the generator is barred from treating, storing, disposing of, transporting, or offering for transportation any hazardous waste. Furthermore, the generator is forbidden from offering his or her RCRA-defined hazardous waste to any transporter or TSDF that does not also have an EPA ID number. Generators and SQGs obtain ID numbers by "notifying" the EPA of hazardous waste activity using a standard EPA notification form. Conditionally exempt SQGs are not required to obtain ID numbers. (*See also* U.S. EPA 1990, Chapter 2)

Pretransport Regulations

Pretransport regulations specify actions which the generator must take to ensure that hazardous wastes are packaged, labeled, marked, and (if appropriate) placarded prior to offering the wastes for transportation. The pretransport requirements (40 CFR 262, Subpart C) refer to elements of the U.S. Department of Transportation (DOT) regulations for transporting hazardous materials (49 CFR 172, 173, 178, and 179).* These regulations require:

- proper packaging to prevent leakage of hazardous waste, during both normal transport conditions and potentially dangerous situations, e.g., a drum of waste dropped from a truck bed or loading dock.
- labeling, marking, and placarding of the packaged waste to identify the characteristics and dangers associated with transporting wastes.

A thorough examination of these detailed and exacting regulations would greatly exceed the scope of this text. The student or practitioner contemplating or having responsibilities for pretransport preparation of hazardous waste shipments must complete the training required by 49 CFR 172, Subpart H. The general thrust of the

* The DOT regulations for transportation of hazardous materials were significantly modified in 1990. The modifications implement the HM 181 "Performance Oriented Packaging Standards" which bring American hazardous materials shipping standards nearer to accord with international standards.

52478 **Federal Register** / Vol. 55, No. 246 / Friday, December 21, 1990 / Rules and Regulations

Sym-bols	Hazardous materials descriptions and proper shipping names	Hazard class or Division	Identifica-tion Numbers	Pack-ing group	Label(s) required (if not excepted)	Special provisions	(8) Packaging authorizations (§173.***)			(9) Quantity limitations		(10) Vessel stowage requirements	
							Excep-tions	Non-bulk pack-aging	Bulk packag-ing	Passenger aircraft or railcar	Cargo aircraft only	Vessel stow-age	Other stowage provisions
(1)	(2)	(3)	(4)	(5)	(6)	(7)	(8A)	(8B)	(8C)	(9A)	(9B)	(10A)	(10B)
	Accellerene, see p-Nitrosodimethylaniline												
	Accumulators, electric, see Batteries, wet *etc.*												
D	Accumulators, pressurized, pneumatic *or* hydraulic *(containing non-flammable gas).*	2.2	NA1956		NONFLAM-MABLE GAS.		306	306	None	No Limit	No Limit	A	
	Acetal	3	UN1088	II	FLAMMABLE LIQUID.	T7	150	202	242	5 L	60 L	E	
	Acetaidehyde	3	UN1089	I	FLAMMABLE LIQUID.	A3, B16, T20, T26, T29	None	201	243	Forbidden	30 L	E	
A	Acetaidehyde ammonia	9	UN1841	III	CLASS 9.		155	204	241	200 kg	200 kg	A	34
	Acetaidehyde oxime	3	UN2332	II	FLAMMABLE. LIQUID.	T8	150	202	242	5 L	60 L	A	
	Acetic acid, glacial *or* Acetic acid solution, *more than 80 per cent acid, by mass.*	8	UN2789	II	CORROSIVE	A3, A6, A7, A10, B2, T8.	154	202	242	1 L	30 L	A	12, 21, 48
	Acetic acid solution, *more than 10 per cent but not more than 80 per cent acid, by mass.*	8	UN2790	II	CORROSIVE	A3, A6, A7, A10, B2, T8.	154	202	242	1 L	30 L	A	112
	Acetic anhydride	8	UN1715	II	CORROSIVE	A3, A6, A7, A10, B2, T8.	154	202	242	1 L	30 L	A	40
	Acetone	3	UN1090	II	FLAMMABLE LIQUID.	T8	150	202	242	5 L	60 L	B	
	Acetone cyanohydrin, stabilized	6.1	UN1541	I	POISON	2, A3, B9, B14, B74, B76, B77, N34, T38, T43, T45.	None	227	244	Forbidden	30 L	D	25, 40, 49, M2
	Acetone oils	3	UN1091	II	FLAMMABLE LIQUID.	T7, T30	150	202	242	5 L	60 L	B	
	Acetonitrile, see Methyl cyanide												
	Acetyl acetone peroxide with more than 9% by mass active oxygen.	Forbid-den											
	Acetyl benzoyl peroxide, solid, or more than 40% in solution	Forbid-den											
	Acetyl bromide	8	UN1716	II	CORROSIVE	B2, T12, T26	154	202	242	1 L	30 L	C	8, 40
	Acetyl chloride	3	UN1717	II	FLAMMABLE LIQUID. CORROSIVE.	A3, A6, A7, N34, T18, T26.	None	202	243	1 L	5 L	B	40
	Acetyl cyclohexanesulfonyl peroxide, more than 82 per cent wetted with less than 12 per cent water.	Forbid-den											
	Acetylene, dissolved	2.1	UN1001		FLAMMABLE GAS.		None	303	None	Forbidden	15 kg	D	25, 40, 57
	Acetylene (liquefied)	Forbid-den											
	Acetylene silver nitrate	Forbid-den											
	Acetylene tetrabromide, see Tetrabromoethane												
	Acetyl iodide	8	UN1898	II	CORROSIVE	B2, T9	154	202	242	1 L	30 L	C	8, 40
	Acetyl methyl carbinol	3	UN2621	III	FLAMMABLE LIQUID.	B1, T1	150	203	242	60 L	220 L	A	
	Acetyl peroxide, *see* Diacetyl peroxide, *etc.*												
	Acetyl peroxide, solid, or more than 25 percent in solution	Forbid-den											
	Acid butyl phosphate, see Butyl acid phosphate												
	Acid, sludge *see* Sludge acid												
	Acridine	6.1	UN2713	III	KEEP AWAY FROM FOOD.		153	213	240	100 kg	200 kg	A	
	Acrolein dimer, stabilized	3	UN2607	III	FLAMMABLE LIQUID.	T1	150	203	242	60 L	220 L	A	40

FIGURE 5.1 DOT hazardous materials table (49 CFR 172.101).

requirements can be ascertained by examining the hazardous materials table column headings (Figure 5.1) and the "Eight-Step Procedure" prepared by the DOT Transportation Safety Institute, which is provided as Appendix B to this chapter.

In brief, the marking requirements include the requirement for individual containers to display a "Hazardous Waste" marking of the format shown in Figure 5.2. The marking must include a proper DOT "shipping name" which uses the standardized language of 49 CFR 172.101 and 172.102. The labels on individual containers

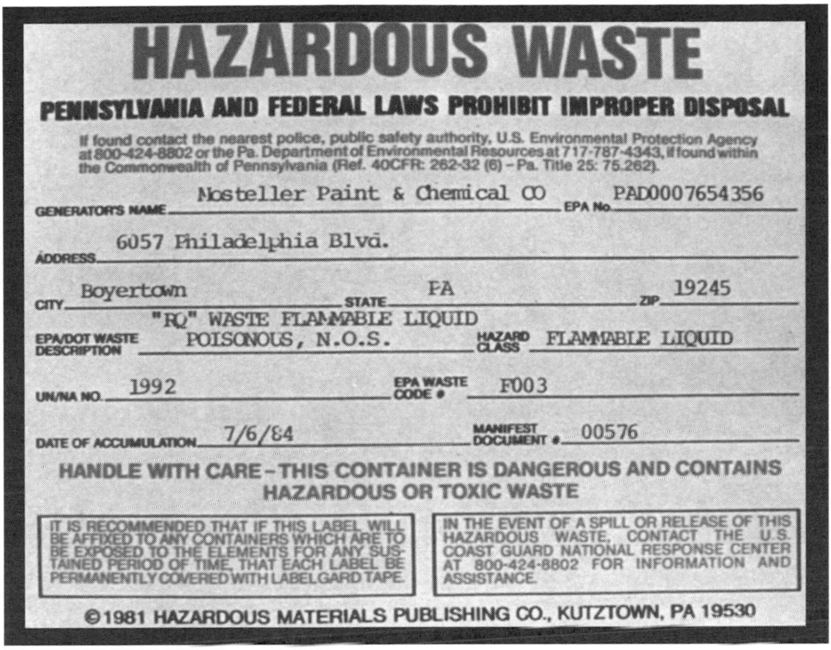

HAZARDOUS WASTE

PENNSYLVANIA AND FEDERAL LAWS PROHIBIT IMPROPER DISPOSAL

If found contact the nearest police, public safety authority, U.S. Environmental Protection Agency at 800-424-8802 or the Pa. Department of Environmental Resources at 717-787-4343, if found within the Commonwealth of Pennsylvania (Ref. 40CFR: 262-32 (6) – Pa. Title 25: 75.262).

GENERATOR'S NAME Mosteller Paint & Chemical CO EPA No. PAD0007654356

ADDRESS 6057 Philadelphia Blvd.

CITY Boyertown STATE PA ZIP 19245

EPA/DOT WASTE DESCRIPTION "RQ" WASTE FLAMMABLE LIQUID POISONOUS, N.O.S. HAZARD CLASS FLAMMABLE LIQUID

UN/NA NO. 1992 EPA WASTE CODE # F003

DATE OF ACCUMULATION 7/6/84 MANIFEST DOCUMENT # 00576

HANDLE WITH CARE – THIS CONTAINER IS DANGEROUS AND CONTAINS HAZARDOUS OR TOXIC WASTE

IT IS RECOMMENDED THAT IF THIS LABEL WILL BE AFFIXED TO ANY CONTAINERS WHICH ARE TO BE EXPOSED TO THE ELEMENTS FOR ANY SUSTAINED PERIOD OF TIME, THAT EACH LABEL BE PERMANENTLY COVERED WITH LABELGARD TAPE.

IN THE EVENT OF A SPILL OR RELEASE OF THIS HAZARDOUS WASTE, CONTACT THE U.S. COAST GUARD NATIONAL RESPONSE CENTER AT 800-424-8802 FOR INFORMATION AND ASSISTANCE.

©1981 HAZARDOUS MATERIALS PUBLISHING CO., KUTZTOWN, PA 19530

FIGURE 5.2 Marking hazardous waste shipment.

must accurately display the correct hazard class as prescribed by Subpart E of Part 172. A hazard class label is shown in Figure 5.3. Bulk shipments, whether motorized or containerized, must display the correct placard. A placard is shown in Figure 5.4.

The labeling, marking, and placarding requirements grow from the need for emergency responders to have the best possible knowledge of the materials involved in any actual or potential release situation. Efforts are in progress to achieve international consistency of marking, labeling, and placarding conventions.

Accumulation of Waste

A generator may accumulate hazardous waste onsite for 90 days or less, provided the following accumulation-related requirements are met:

- *Proper Storage* — The waste must be properly stored in containers or tanks marked with the words "hazardous waste" and the date when accumulation began (Figure 5.5).
- *Emergency Plan* — A contingency plan and procedures to implement it must be developed. Generators are required to have a written emergency plan, but SQGs are not.*,**

* The generator requirements for contingency planning and a training program are by reference to 40 CFR 265, Subparts B, C, and D, and to 40 CFR 265.16, contained in 40 CFR 262.34. Those new to the RCRA program and subject to the generator regulations should study 40 CFR 262.34 and the referenced material in 40 CFR 265 very carefully.

** The small quantity generator is, however, required to meet minimal emergency planning requirements set forth in 40 CFR 262.34(d).

FIGURE 5.3 DOT hazard label.

- *Personnel Training* — Facility personnel must be trained in the proper handling of hazardous waste. Generators are required to have an established training program (40 CFR 265.16). SQGs are exempt from this requirement, but must ensure that employees handling hazardous wastes are familiar with proper procedures.

The 90-day accumulation period allows a generator to collect enough waste to make transportation more cost-effective. If the generator accumulates hazardous waste onsite for more than 90 days, the generator becomes subject to the Subtitle C requirements for storage facilities, including the requirement for permitting. The regulations provide for a one-time, 30-day extension under extenuating circumstances.

SQGs may store waste onsite for up to 180 days (or up to 270 days if the waste must be transported for 200 or more miles for offsite treatment, storage, or disposal), providing certain criteria are met. The onsite quantity of waste may not exceed 6000 kg at any time. Conditionally exempt SQGs must not accumulate more than 1000 kg of hazardous waste, nor more than 1 kg of acutely hazardous waste. In either case, if accumulation limits are exceeded, the generator becomes subject to the full generator regulatory requirements.

The Manifest

The Uniform Hazardous Waste Manifest (Figure 5.6) is the instrument which enables the tracking of, and accounting for, hazardous wastes in the cradle-to-grave

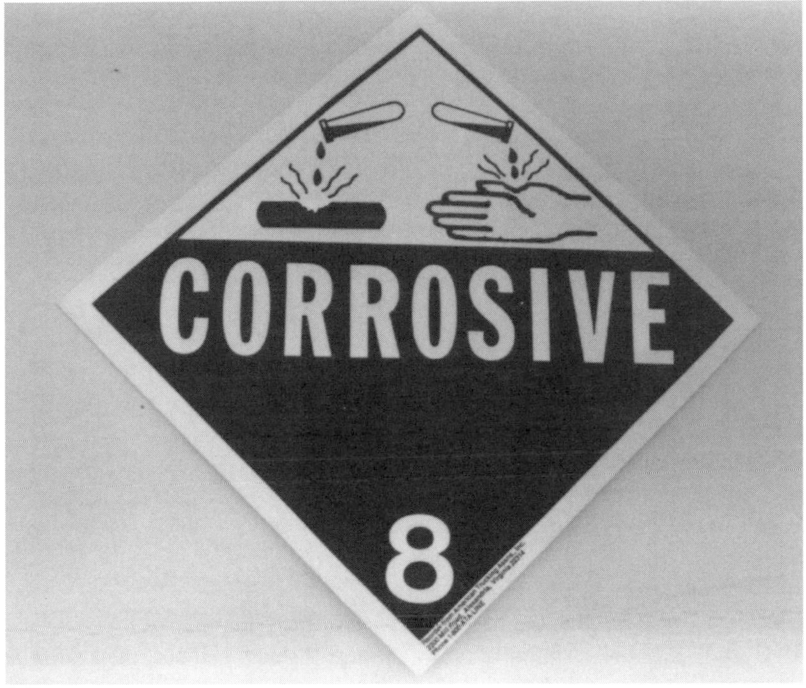

FIGURE 5.4 DOT hazard placard.

system. Through the use of the manifest, generators and/or regulators can track the movement of hazardous waste from the point of generation to the point of ultimate treatment, storage, or disposal. RCRA manifests document:

- the name and EPA identification number of the generator, the transporter, and the facility where the waste is to be treated, stored, or disposed.
- a telephone number at which emergency response information may be accessed at all times (24 hours per day) while the shipment is enroute (*See* 49 CFR 172, Subparts C and G).
- the DOT description, including proper shipping name, of the waste being transported.
- the quantities of waste being transported.
- the address of the TSDF to which the generator is sending the waste.*

The EPA regulations pertaining to manifests do not cover some DOT requirements that pertain to "shipping papers," particularly with respect to emergency response requirements. The Uniform Hazardous Waste Manifest serves the purpose of a shipping paper for hazardous waste shipments. Thus, generators or generator

* It is good practice to also designate the name and address of an alternate TSDF. If for any reason the shipment is not accepted by the designated facility, the transporter must return the shipment to the shipper unless an alternate destination has been designated.

FIGURE 5.5 Dating accumulation container, Arizona Department of Environmental Quality.

representatives should become fully familiar with the 40 CFR 262, Subpart B and Appendix and 49 CFR 172, Subparts C and G prior to preparation of hazardous waste manifests.

The multiple-copy form is initially completed and signed by the hazardous waste generator. The generator retains Part 6 of the manifest, sends Part 5 to the EPA or the appropriate state agency,* and provides the remaining parts of the manifest to the transporter. The transporter retains Part 4 of the manifest and gives the remaining parts of the manifest to the TSDF upon arrival. The TSDF retains Part 3 and sends Parts 1 and 2 to the generator and the regulatory agency (or agencies), respectively. Throughout this transition, the hazardous waste shipment is generally considered to be in the custody of the last signatory on the manifest.

If the generator does not receive Part 1 of the manifest form from the designated facility within 35 days from the date the waste was accepted by the initial transporter, the generator is required to initiate appropriate tracer activity. If the generator does not receive Part 1 by the 45th day, the generator must file an exception report with the EPA regional office. The report must detail the efforts of the generator to locate the waste. SQGs that do not receive a copy of the signed manifest from the designated facility within 60 days must explain the exception on a copy of the original manifest and send it to the EPA regional administrator.

* Both the EPA and the state regulatory agency must receive copies in some situations.

Please print or type
(Form designed for use on elite (12-pitch) typewriter.)

Form Approved. OMB No. 2050-0039. Expires 9-30-91

UNIFORM HAZARDOUS WASTE MANIFEST

1. Generator's US EPA ID No.

Manifest Document No.

2. Page 1 of

Information in the shaded areas is not required by Federal law.

GENERATOR

3. Generator's Name and Mailing Address

A. State Manifest Document Number

B. State Generator's ID

4. Generator's Phone (   )

5. Transporter 1 Company Name

6. US EPA ID Number

C. State Transporter's ID

D. Transporter's Phone

7. Transporter 2 Company Name

8. US EPA ID Number

E. State Transporter's ID

F. Transporter's Phone

9. Designated Facility Name and Site Address

10. US EPA ID Number

G. State Facility's ID

H. Facility's Phone

HM	11. US DOT Description (*Including Proper Shipping Name, Hazard Class, and ID Number*)	12. Containers No.	12. Containers Type	13. Total Quantity	14. Unit Wt/Vol	I. Waste No.
	a.					
	b.					
	c.					
	d.					

J. Additional Descriptions for Materials Listed Above

K. Handling Codes for Wastes Listed Above

15. Special Handling Instructions and Additional Information

16. **GENERATOR'S CERTIFICATION:** I hereby declare that the contents of this consignment are fully and accurately described above by proper shipping name and are classified, packed, marked, and labeled, and are in all respects in proper condition for transport by highway according to applicable international and national governmental regulations.

If I am a large quantity generator, I certify that I have a program in place to reduce the volume and toxicity of waste generated to the degree I have determined to be economically practicable and that I have selected the practicable method of treatment, storage, or disposal currently available to me which minimizes the present and future threat to human health and the environment; **OR**, if I am a small quantity generator, I have made a good faith effort to minimize my waste generation and select the best waste management method that is available to me and that I can afford.

Printed/Typed Name | Signature | Month Day Year

TRANSPORTER

17. Transporter 1 Acknowledgement of Receipt of Materials

Printed/Typed Name | Signature | Month Day Year

18. Transporter 2 Acknowledgement of Receipt of Materials

Printed/Typed Name | Signature | Month Day Year

FACILITY

19. Discrepancy Indication Space

20. Facility Owner or Operator: Certification of receipt of hazardous materials covered by this manifest except as noted in Item 19.

Printed/Typed Name | Signature | Month Day Year

EPA Form 8700-22 (Rev. 9-88) Previous edition obsolete.

ORIGINAL — RETURN TO GENERATOR

7-BLS-C6

FIGURE 5.6 Sample uniform hazardous waste manifest form.

Record Keeping and Reporting Requirements

Generators are subject to extensive record keeping and reporting requirements by 40 CFR 262, Subpart D. Generators who transport hazardous waste offsite must submit an annual report to the EPA regional administrator on EPA Form 8700-13A. The report covers generator activities during the previous year and requires detailed accounting of wastes generated and their disposition. Generators must keep copies of each signed manifest for three years from the date signed, a copy of each exception report filed, each annual report, and copies of analyses and related determinations made in accord with the generator regulations (40 CFR 262). Generators that treat, store, or dispose of their hazardous waste onsite must also "notify" the EPA of hazardous waste activity, obtain an EPA ID number, apply for a permit, and comply with the permit conditions. They too must submit an annual report which contains a description of the type and quantity of hazardous waste the facility handled during the year and the method(s) of treatment, storage, or disposal used.

Exports and Imports of Hazardous Wastes

Export of hazardous waste from the United States to another country is prohibited unless:

- notification of intent to export has been provided to the EPA at least 60 days in advance of shipment.
- the receiving country has consented to accept the waste.
- a copy of the EPA "Acknowledgement of Consent" accompanies the shipment.
- the hazardous waste shipment conforms to the terms of the receiving country's consent (40 CFR 262.52).

Any person who imports hazardous waste from another country into the United States must comply with the requirements of 40 CFR 262, i.e., *the importer becomes the generator*, for RCRA regulatory purposes. (*See also* U.S. EPA 1986, Chapters 4 and 6; Phifer and McTigue 1988, Chapter 4)

Generator Responsibilities for Restricted Waste Management

One of the major impacts of HSWA is the restriction on land disposal for certain hazardous wastes. HSWA Section 3004 restricts the land disposal of hazardous waste beyond specified dates unless the wastes are treated to meet treatment standards. These requirements are found in 40 CFR 268. The land disposal restrictions are frequently referred to as "LDRs" or the "land ban."

In addition to the above requirements, Congress directed the EPA to evaluate the underground injection of spent solvents, dioxins, and California List wastes. Unless these practices were found to be protective of human health and the environment, disposal by underground injection was to be prohibited effective August 8, 1988. Congress also required the EPA to determine, by May 8, 1990, the conditions under which underground injection of each hazardous waste should be allowed. The standards applicable to underground injection of restricted wastes are set forth in 40 CFR 148. The land disposal restrictions will be reviewed in more detail in Chapter 7.

Generator Requirements

The generator must determine whether or not the waste generated is hazardous, as defined in 40 CFR 261. If the waste is hazardous, the generator must then determine if the hazardous waste is restricted. Even though the LDRs apply to the *disposal* of hazardous wastes, the EPA has structured the regulations so that the determination of whether a waste is restricted occurs at the point of generation. By evaluating a waste at the point of generation, subsequent dilution of the waste to meet the concentration limits (with a few exceptions, a forbidden practice) is prevented. Alternatively, a generator may use knowledge of the waste to determine if it is subject to the LDRs; however, documentation substantiating this determination must be kept in the generator's files (McCoy and Associates 1994, p. 11.1).

If the hazardous waste is determined to be a restricted waste, the generator must ensure that the waste is managed in compliance with the LDRs, whether onsite or offsite. Generators of hazardous wastes must:

- conduct waste analyses to determine if a waste is restricted; analytical methods are prescribed by the EPA publication SW 846 — *Test Methods for Evaluating Solid Waste, Physical/Chemical Methods* (U.S. EPA 1985a).
- assign the proper EPA hazardous waste code numbers to the waste.
- prepare a waste analysis plan if the waste is treated onsite in accumulation units [40 CFR 268.7(a)(4)].
- prepare the required notifications and certifications required for onsite or offsite waste management (40 CFR 268.4 thru 268.8).
- follow prescribed procedures if seeking an extension to the effective date for a restriction (40 CFR 268.5), petitioning for a no-migration exemption (40 CFR 268.6), or petitioning for a treatability variance (40 CFR 268.44).
- comply with the record keeping requirements pertaining to the LDRs (40 CFR 268.7).
- comply with the storage requirements of 40 CFR 268.50(a), the limits placed upon dilution of wastes by 40 CFR 268.3, and the prescribed deactivation of characteristic wastes in 40 CFR 268.42 (adapted from McCoy and Associates 1994, Chapter 11).

The LDRs do not apply to wastes generated by conditionally exempt SQGs. The LDRs are lengthy, detailed, and complex. The McCoy and Associates document referenced previously is an excellent source for precise and detailed guidance regarding the LDRs.

APPENDIX A

Some Basic Industries and Types of Hazardous Waste Produced

Industry	Wastes produced
Chemical manufacturing	• Spent solvents and still bottoms White spirits, kerosene, benzene, xylene, ethyl benzene, toluene, isopropanol, toluene diisocyanate, ethanol, acetone, methyl ethyl ketone, tetrahydrofuran, methylene chloride, 1,1,1-trichloroethane, trichloroethylene • Ignitable wastes not otherwise specified

Chemical manufacturing (continued)	• Strong acid/alkaline wastes Ammonium hydroxide, hydrobromic acid, hydrochloric acid, potassium hydroxide, nitric acid, sulfuric acid, chromic acid, phosphoric acid • Other reactive wastes Sodium permanganate, organic peroxides, sodium perchlorate, potassium perchlorate, potassium permanganate, hypochlorite, potassium sulfide, sodium sulfide • Emission control dusts and sludges • Spent catalysts • Ignitable paint wastes Ethylene dichloride, benzene, toluene, ethyl benzene, methyl isobutyl ketone, methyl ethyl ketone, chlorobenzene
Construction	• Ignitable wastes not otherwise specified • Spent solvents Methyl chloride, carbon tetrachloride, trichlorotrifluoroethane, toluene, xylene, kerosene, mineral spirits, acetone • Strong acid/alkaline wastes Ammonium hydroxide, hydrobromic acid, hydrochloric acid, hydrofluoric acid, nitric acid, phosphoric acid, potassium hydroxide, sodium hydroxide, sulfuric acid
Metal manufacturing	• Spent solvents and solvent still bottoms Tetrachloroethylene, trichloroethylene, methylene chloride, 1,1,1-trichloroethane, carbon tetrachloride, toluene, benzene, trichlorofluoroethane, chloroform, trichlorofluoromethane, acetone, dichlorobenzene, xylene, kerosene, white spirits, butyl alcohol • Strong acid/alkaline wastes Ammonium hydroxide, hydrobromic acid, hydrochloric acid, hydrofluoric acid, nitric acid, phosphoric acid, nitrates, potassium hydroxide, sodium hydroxide, sulfuric acid, perchloric acid, acetic acid • Spent plating wastes • Heavy metal wastewater sludges • Cyanide wastes • Ignitable wastes not otherwise specified

Some Basic Industries and Types of Hazardous Waste Produced (continued)

Industry	Wastes produced
Metal manufacturing (continued)	• Other reactive wastes Acetyl chloride, chromic acid, sulfides, hypochlorites, organic peroxides, perchlorates, permanganates • Used oils
Paper industry	• Halogenated solvents Carbon tetrachloride, methylene chloride, tetrachloroethylene, trichloroethylene, 1,1,1,-trichloroethane, mixed spent halogenated solvents • Corrosive wastes Corrosive liquids, corrosive solids, ammonium hydroxide, hydrobromic acid, hydrochloric acid, hydrofluoric acid, nitric acid, phosphoric acid, potassium hydroxide, sodium hydroxide, sulfuric acid • Paint wastes Combustible liquid, flammable liquid, ethylene dichloride, chlorobenzene, methyl ethyl ketone, paint waste with heavy metals • Solvents Petroleum distillates

Source: U.S. EPA 1985b.

APPENDIX B

DOT Eight-Step Procedure for Preparation of Hazardous Materials Shipments

Procedure	Ref.	Notes
1. Determine proper shipping name, hazard, class/division, ID number and packaging group	172.101(2), (3), (4), and (5)	
2. Is this material regulated by 49 CFR?	172.101(2) and (1)	
a. As a hazardous material?	Appendix A	
b. As a hazardous substance?	Appendix B	
c. Marine pollutant?	172.101	
d. By highway mode?	Col. (1)	
e. As a poison inhalation hazard?	Col. (7)	

DOT Eight-Step Procedure for Preparation of Hazardous Materials Shipments (continued)

Procedure	Ref.	Notes
3. Determine proper packaging		
a. Determine if an exception is authorized for the particular hazardous materials.	172.101(8)(A) and reference to sections indicated	
b. If no exception is authorized, determine the specific packaging requirements.	172.101(8)(B) or (C) and reference to section listed	
c. Determine the maximum net quantity of the hazardous material that may be shipped in one package by passenger-carrying and/or cargo-only aircraft as appropriate.	172.101(9)(A) and (B)	
d. Ensure that completed package meets general packaging requirements.	173.24, 173.24a, and 173.24b	
e. Determine DOD packaging, if appropriate.		
f. Determine special provisions.	172.101(7)	
4. Mark the package	Subpart D of Part 172 commencing at 172.300	
5. Label the package:		
a. With appropriate table label(s) unless excepted	172.101(6)	
b. With appropriate additional or multiple labeling requirements	172.402, 404, and 406	
6. Prepare shipping papers with shipper's certification and signatured	172.200, 201, 202, 203, and 204	
7. Provide emergency response information	Subpart G of 172 commencing at 172.600	
8. Provide or placard as appropriate	Subpart F of 172 commencing at Section 172.500	

Source: U.S. DOT 1992.

TOPICS FOR REVIEW OR DISCUSSION

1. Why are regulatory agencies (and their regulatory issue) so concerned with limiting the time over which hazardous wastes may be stored or accumulated?
2. What is the main purpose of the Hazardous Waste Manifest system?
3. How do the RCRA regulations apply the descriptors "hazardous waste" and "acutely hazardous waste" in making the distinctions between "conditionally exempt small quantity generator," "small quantity generator," and "generator"?
4. Why is it important to assign standardized shipping names for hazardous materials being shipped in commerce?
5. To what publication should one refer to determine the correct shipping name for a hazardous waste?
6. RCRA regulations (40 CFR 262.34) allow a SQG to accumulate waste onsite for 180 days (or 270 days if the waste must be transported more than 200 miles to the treatment, storage, or disposal site). What regulatory circumstance would cause the storage period to be automatically shortened?
7. The operator of a satellite accumulation point, as described by the RCRA regulations (40 CFR 262.34), accumulates U005 waste in excess of 1 qt, and fails to begin accumulating the waste in another container. Is the facility now out of compliance? Explain.
8. A SQG is not *required* to prepare and implement a contingency plan. What emergency planning is required?

REFERENCES

Dawson, Gaynor W., and Basil W. Mercer. 1986. *Hazardous Waste Management.* John Wiley & Sons, New York.

McCoy and Associates. 1994. *The RCRA Land Disposal Restrictions — A Guide to Compliance, 1993.* Elsevier Science Publishing Company, New York.

Nebel, Bernard J., and Richard T. Wright. 1993. *Environmental Science The Way The World Works,* Fourth Edition. Prentice-Hall, Englewood Cliffs, NJ.

Phifer, Russell W., and William R. McTigue, Jr. 1988. *Handbook of Hazardous Waste Management for Small Quantity Generators.* Lewis Publishers, Chelsea, MI.

U.S. Department of Transportation. 1992. *Intermodal Transportation of Hazardous Materials for Industry — Student Workbook.* Transportation Safety Institute, Oklahoma City.

U.S. Environmental Protection Agency. 1985a. *Test Methods for Evaluating Siolid Waste.* Office of Solid Waste, Superintendent of Documents, Government Printing Office, Washington, D.C. EPA SW-846 (Update II — April 1985).

U.S. Environmental Protection Agency. 1985b. *Does Your Business Produce Hazardous Waste?* Office of Solid Waste and Emergency Response, Washington, D.C. EPA 530-SW-010.

U.S. Environmental Protection Agency. 1986. *Understanding the Small Quantity Generator Hazardous Waste Rules: A Handbook for Small Business.* Office of Solid Waste and Emergency Response, Washington, D.C. EPA 530-SW-86-019.

U.S. Environmental Protection Agency. 1990. *RCRA Orientation Manual, 1990 Edition.* Superintendent of Documents, Government Printing Office, Washington, D.C.

U.S. Environmental Protection Agency. 1993. *Catalog of Hazardous Waste Database Reports*. Solid Waste and Emergency Response, Washington, D.C. EPA 530-B-94-001.

U.S. Environmental Protection Agency. 1994a. *The Biennial RCRA Hazardous Waste Report (Based on 1991 Data) Executive Summary*. Solid Waste and Emergency Response, Washington, D.C. EPA 530-S-94-1994.

U.S. Environmental Protection Agency. 1994b. *1992 Toxics-Release InventoryPublic Data Release*. Office of Pollution Prevention and Toxics, Washington, D.C. EPA 745-R-94-001.

6 TRANSPORTATION OF HAZARDOUS WASTES

OBJECTIVES

At completion of this chapter, the student should:

- understand the advantages/disadvantages of the modes of transportation of hazardous wastes.
- be familiar with the requirements for action by transporters in the event of a release during transportation.
- understand the general nature of the regulations imposed upon transport of hazardous wastes by the Resource Conservation and Recovery Act (RCRA) and the Hazardous Materials Transportation Act (HMTA) regulations and their relationship to each other.

INTRODUCTION

Activity associated with transportation of hazardous wastes from the generator or source to intermediate destinations and to final disposition has been fraught with mismanagement of the wastes and has frequently been involved in major threats to the environment and public safety. In pre-RCRA times, small, locally based, refuse haulers provided immediate and cheap removal of hazardous waste accumulations on a "no questions asked" basis. The most marginal of trucking operations could survive by removing unwanted wastes and disposing of them with abandon.

In the late 1970s to early 1980s period, as RCRA became viable, many hazardous waste generators sought to avoid the new financial burdens of lawful waste management by hasty disposal of accumulated wastes. During this period, "midnight dumping" schemes became common. Truckers outfitted tankers with dumping valves so that liquid wastes could be dumped "on-the-run." Trailers loaded with drums of wastes were simply abandoned in random locations. Rural areas and deserts were littered and stained with all manner of hazardous wastes.

As RCRA regulations were implemented and the manifest system began to function, these practices were brought under control of the respective authorities. As the regulatory agencies gained recognition and experience, most of the marginal transporters were "weeded out," and transportation became a vital link in the cradle-to-grave management strategy. Although illegal transportation activities have continued to require the attention of law enforcement agencies, much of the regulatory focus has shifted to accident prevention, emergency response activity, surveillance of import–export activity, and tracking of wastes from source to ultimate disposition.

In this chapter, we will overview basic hazardous waste transportation operations and cover the pertinent regulatory structures of the U.S. Environmental Protection Agency (EPA) and the U.S. Department of Transportation (DOT). Statistical data on transportation of hazardous *waste* is difficult to obtain. In the following discussions, it is frequently necessary to generalize in terms of hazardous *materials* which, in the DOT lexicon, include hazardous *wastes*.

Modes and Scope of Hazardous Waste Transportation

A 1981 report, prepared for the EPA, estimated that 96% of the 264 million tons of hazardous wastes generated each year were disposed of at the site where they were generated and that most of the hazardous waste shipped offsite was transported by truck (Westat, Inc. 1981).* These shipments were usually over routes of 100 miles or less (ICF, Inc. 1984, p. 2). By 1989, the National Solid Wastes Management Association (NSWMA) stated that trucks traveling over public highways moved 98% of the hazardous waste that is treated offsite. Rail freight moved the remainder (NSWMA 1989, p. 11). By 1993, the EPA counted 20,800 transporters of hazardous waste (U.S. EPA 1993). Shipments of hazardous waste by inland waterways and by air are infrequent and are not considered here.

Another important perspective can be gained from the statistics for hazardous *materials* transportation. Rail transportation moves about 8% of hazardous materials shipped, but 57% of the *ton-miles* of hazardous materials shipped (U.S. Office of Technology Assessment 1986, p. 46). Moreover, the student should have clearly in mind the fact that most "hazardous materials" become hazardous *wastes* when released to the environment. At that occurrence, the hazardous waste regulations of RCRA, CERCLA, and the state and local jurisdictions apply.

Enactment of the Hazardous and Solid Waste Amendments of 1984 (HSWA) brought more than 100,000 new small quantity generators (SQGs) under regulation. Most of the SQGs have had no alternative to shipment of their hazardous wastes offsite for disposition. Thus, HSWA may have instigated some increase in transportation of wastes to treatment, storage, and disposal facilities (TSDF). The addition of 25 new chemical constituents to Table 1, 40 CFR 261.24, in 1990, is said to have brought 17,000 new generators under RCRA regulation. In 1993, the EPA counted 266,000 generators, of which approximately 240,000 are SQGs (U.S. EPA 1993). Thus, very large numbers of generators have no options other than to transport hazardous wastes offsite for ultimate disposition; very large numbers of shipments involve small quantities and originate at small operations not accessible by rail; transportation of hazardous wastes is a major waste management activity and a major source of potential incident/release/exposure concerns.

* Reliable current statistics on quantities treated onsite are difficult to obtain. In general, ever-tightening regulatory control, liability concerns, and availability of commercial treatment options have tended to cause wastes to be shipped offsite for treatment. Conversely, accelerating Superfund and RCRA site remediation activities involve more onsite treatment of hazardous wastes.

Highway Shipment of Hazardous Wastes

As noted previously, most hazardous waste transportation is accomplished via truck. Since implementation of RCRA regulations, most waste haulers generally fit one of three categories:

- Generators transporting their wastes to TSDFs
- Contract haulers collecting wastes from generators and transporting the wastes to TSDFs
- TSDFs collecting wastes from generators and transporting the wastes to their facilities

The highway transport mode is regarded as the most versatile. Tank trucks can access most industrial sites and TSDFs, while rail shipping requires expensive sidings and is suitable only for large quantity shipments. Cargo tanks are the main carriers of bulk hazardous *materials* (U.S. Office of Technology Assessment 1986, Chapter 3); however, large quantities of hazardous *wastes* are shipped in 55-gallon drums.

Cargo tanks are usually made of steel or aluminum alloy, but can be constructed of other materials such as titanium, nickel, or stainless steel. They range in capacity from about 2000 to 9000 gallons, depending upon road weight laws and the properties of the materials to be transported. Federal road weight laws usually limit motor vehicle weights to 80,000 pounds gross. The DOT specifications for cargo tanks used in bulk shipment of the common types of hazardous materials carried and example cargos are listed in Table 6.1. Figure 6.1 shows a DOT specification MC-406 tank trailer used for hauling combustible and flammable wastes. Figure 6.2 is an example of an MC-310 tank trailer for hauling corrosive wastes. These specification cargo tanks have been superseded by new specifications DOT 406, 407, and 412. However, the earlier specifications can continue in use after required modifications. The user must stay current with respect to 49 CFR 178 Continuing Qualifications requirements and schedules.

Railway Shipment of Hazardous Wastes

Rail shipments account for about 8% of the tonnage of hazardous materials transported annually, with about 3000 carloads shipped daily. The portion of these shipments that are hazardous *wastes* is apparently not known. Rail tank car specifications for transportation of pressurized hazardous materials are DOT 105, 112, and 114; for unpressurized shipments the numbers are DOT 103, 104, 111, and 115. Capacities for tank cars carrying hazardous materials are limited to 34,500 gallons or 263,000 pounds gross weight (49 CFR 179).

Accidents/Incidents Involving Hazardous Waste Shipments

Accident and transportation release statistics from the late 1970s and early 1980s provide insight to the relative hazards posed by the highway and rail modes of hazardous *materials* transportation. These data indicate that highway transport expe-

Table 6.1 Cargo Tank Table

Cargo Tank Specification Number	Types of Commodities Carried	Examples
MC-406 (MC-300, 301, 302, 303, 305)[a]	Combustible and flammable liquids of low vapor pressure	Fuel oil, gasoline
MC-407 (MC-304)	Flammable liquids, Poison B materials with moderate vapor pressure	Toluene, diisocyanate
MC-412 (MC-310, 311)	Corrosive	Hydrochloric acid, caustic solution
MC-431 (MC-330)	Liquified compressed gases	Chlorine, anhydrous ammonia, propane, butane
MC-438	Refrigerated liquified gases	Oxygen, methane

[a] The number in parentheses designates older versions of the specifications; the older versions may continue in service until required phase out, but all newly constructed cargo tanks must meet current specifications.

Source: 49 CFR 172.101 and 178.315-178.343.

FIGURE 6.1 DOT specification MC-406 cargo tank for transporting combustible and flammable materials

FIGURE 6.2 DOT specification MC-310 cargo tank for transporting corrosive materials.

rienced twelve times the number of incidents involving hazardous materials, four times the number of fatalities, and twice the number of injuries as occurred in rail transport. However, rail accidents released approximately 50% greater quantities than did highway accidents involving hazardous *materials* (Blackman 1985, Chapter 2). Total transportation incidents* involving hazardous wastes show significant increases from 1989 to 1993 (Table 6.2). However, numbers of hazardous waste

Table 6.2 Transportation Incidents[a] Involving Hazardous Wastes — Rail and Highway

	Incidents		Accidents/Derailments		Deaths	
Year	**Hazwaste**	**Hazmat**	**Hazwaste**	**Hazmat**	**Hazwaste**	**Hazmat**
1989	149	7,558	15	342	0	8
1990	194	8,883	10	299	0	8
1991	202	9,110	13	303	0	10
1992	413	9,351	17	284	0	15
1993	575	12,815	7	264	0	15

[a] "Incidents" do not equate with "accidents." A release incident can occur without an accident, and, conversely, an accident can occur without a release.

Source: Chemical Waste Transportation Institute, 1994.

* *See* Glossary entry for "incident."

FIGURE 6.3 Highway transportation incident.

incidents involving accidents or derailments show no particular trends. No transportation incident-related deaths were reported during the period. Hazardous *materials* incidents are shown for comparison.

Hazardous materials transportation incidents tend to be spectacular, dangerous, freakish, and unpredictable (Figure 6.3). Rail accidents, as noted, involve containers of up to 34,500 gallons or 130 tons vs. the 9000 gallon/40 ton limits for highway transportation. The greater quantity per container, chemical incompatibilities between rail tank car shipments, and the difficult accessibility encountered in rural locations leads to unmanageable fires which are frequently allowed to "burn themselves out" (Figures 6.4 and 6.5).

Incidents involving truck shipment of hazardous materials, when they occur in urban areas, are more likely to endanger human lives and property (Figure 6.6). Fires in populated areas typically must be controlled expeditiously in order to limit exposure and property damage.

Regulatory Structures

Department of Transportation Regulations

In general, the DOT regulations deal with container and equipment specifications, packaging, categorization of wastes, and the determination of proper shipping descriptions. The EPA regulations provide the tracking mechanisms that are intended to maintain the cradle-to-grave management system.

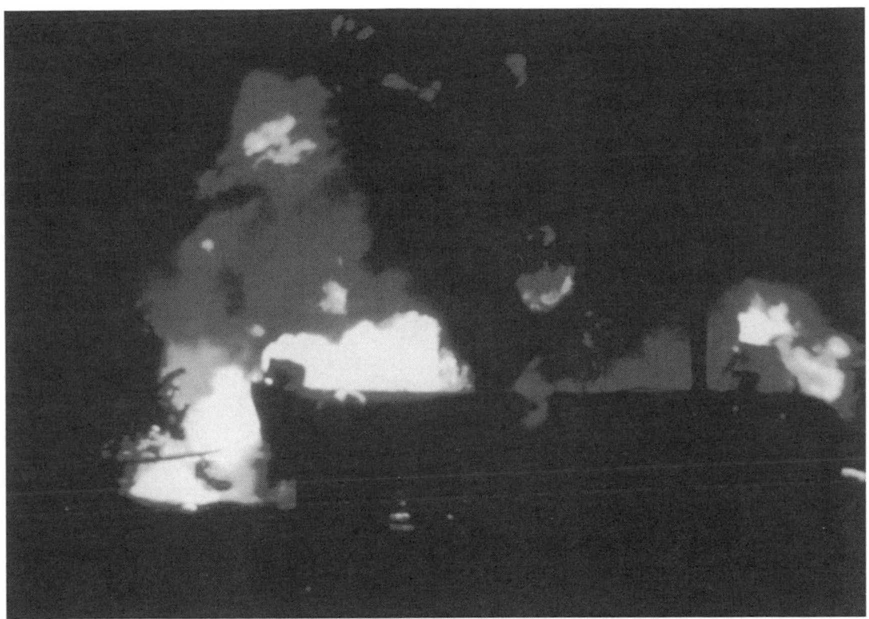

FIGURE 6.4 Rail transportation "incident" [Environsafe Services of Ohio, Inc. (ESOI), P.O. Box 167571, Oregon, OH 43616-7571].

As noted in Chapter 5, the DOT regulations dealing with transportation of hazardous materials are found at 49 CFR 171 thru 179 and are referred to as the HM 181* "Performance Oriented Packaging Standards." The content and detail of these regulations greatly exceed the scope of these chapters, but the general thrust can be understood by examining the column headings of the 49 CFR 172.101 Hazardous Materials Table (Chapter 5, Figure 5.1) and Appendix B of Chapter 5. The elements pertaining to transporters of hazardous materials focus on emergency response information and requirements, training of the "hazmat employee,"** and specialized training for drivers.

The transporter must maintain the emergency response information contained on the manifest in a manner that ensures that it is immediately accessible to emergency responders. For example, drivers of cargo tank vehicles must keep the manifest on the seat adjacent to the driver's seat or in the "pocket" of the door on the driver's side of the cab. Similar requirements apply to train crews and bridge personnel on vessels. If the transporter makes use of a transfer facility, the emergency response information must be maintained in a location that is immediately accessible to the personnel operating the facility.

* The DOT, as do other agencies, assigns a "docket number" to new regulatory proposals. The proposed regulations are referred to by docket number throughout the promulgation process. Upon final publication of the rule package, the DOT continues to refer to the implemented program by that number. Thus, the implementation of the Performance Oriented Packaging Standards continues to be referred to as HM 181.

** Similarly, the training requirement of 49 CFR 172, Subpart H is referred to as "the HM 126F training."

FIGURE 6.5 Rail transportation incident morning after (ESOI).

FIGURE 6.6 Highway transportation incident illustrating a threat to urban areas.

DOT immediate notification requirements for hazardous materials incidents are applicable to discharges of hazardous wastes. Notice is given by calling the National Response Center, operated by the U.S. Coast Guard (800 424 8802). Specifically, the National Response Center must be notified when:

- a person is killed or injured to the extent that hospitalization is required.
- estimated damage exceeds $50,000.
- the fire, spill, breakage, or contamination involves disease-causing agents or radioactive material.
- there is an evacuation of the general public for one hour or more.
- the spill exceeds a Superfund reportable quantity.
- a life-threatening situation exists (49 CFR 171.15).

The HM 126F hazmat employee training requirement is prescribed in 49 CFR 172, Subpart H. The training is required for any employee who performs any function having to do with the safety of a hazardous material shipment (*see* 49 CFR 171.8 for the definition of "hazmat employee" and "hazmat employer"). The required training consists of three categories, which are:

1. *General Awareness/Familiarization Training* — The hazards associated with hazmat transportation, the hazard classes of HM 181, and hazard communication requirements
2. *Function-Specific Training* — The packaging, labeling, marking, and placarding of hazardous materials shipments, i.e., the Performance Oriented Packaging Standards
3. *Safety Training* — Including the emergency response, personal protective clothing and equipment, and methods and procedures for avoiding accidents and exposure

The standards also include driver training requirements and specialized training for drivers of vehicles transporting explosives, radioactive materials, or cryogenic gases. The hazmat employee must repeat the training at two-year intervals; drivers must be trained annually.

RCRA Regulations for Hazardous Waste Transporters

The RCRA transporter regulations (40 CFR 263) define "transporter," provide the tracking mechanisms that are intended to maintain the cradle-to-grave management systems for hazardous waste management, and impose cleanup and reporting requirements that apply in the event of the discharge of hazardous waste(s) during transport.

The transporter is defined as any person engaged in the offsite transportation of hazardous waste within the United States if such transportation requires a manifest. This definition covers transportation by air, highway, rail, or water. The transporter regulations do not apply either to the onsite transportation of hazardous waste by generators who have their own treatment or disposal facilities nor to TSDFs trans-

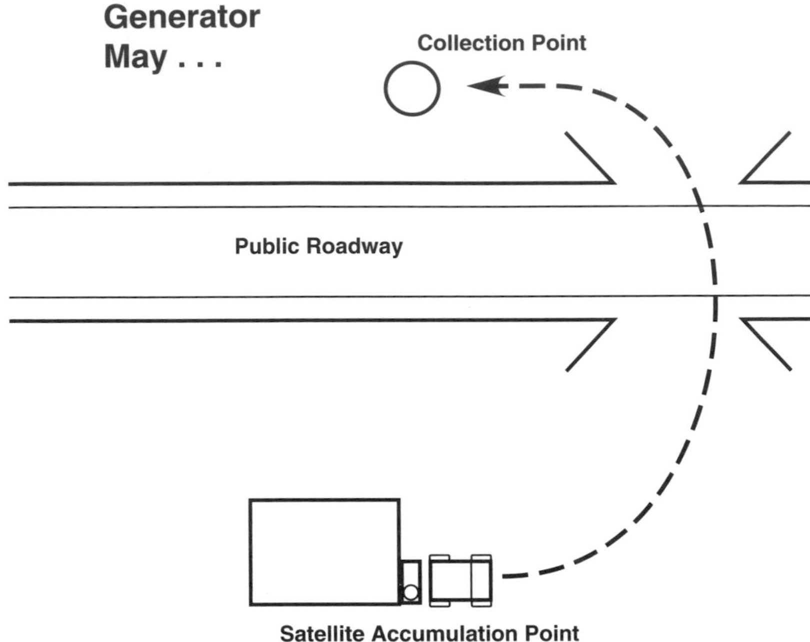

FIGURE 6.7 Onsite transportation of hazardous waste.

porting wastes within a facility (U.S. EPA 1990, p. III-26). *However*, both generator and TSDF owners and operators must avoid transporting wastes over public roads that pass through or alongside their facilities (Figures 6.7 and 6.8).

Under some circumstances, transporters can become subject to the generator regulations by importing hazardous waste into the United States, by mixing hazardous wastes of different DOT shipping descriptions by placing them into a single container, or by being responsible for cleanup of a discharge of hazardous wastes or commercial chemical product that occurred during transport. In such circumstances, the transporter must comply with the generator regulations (40 CFR 263.10).

A transporter may store hazardous wastes at a transfer station for up to ten days without being subject to other than the transporter regulations. If the storage time exceeds ten days, the transporter becomes a storage facility and must comply with the regulations pertaining to such a facility, including the requirements for obtaining a permit.

Transporters must comply with RCRA Subtitle C regulations which require:

- obtaining an EPA identification number.
- complying with the manifest system.
- handling hazardous waste discharges.

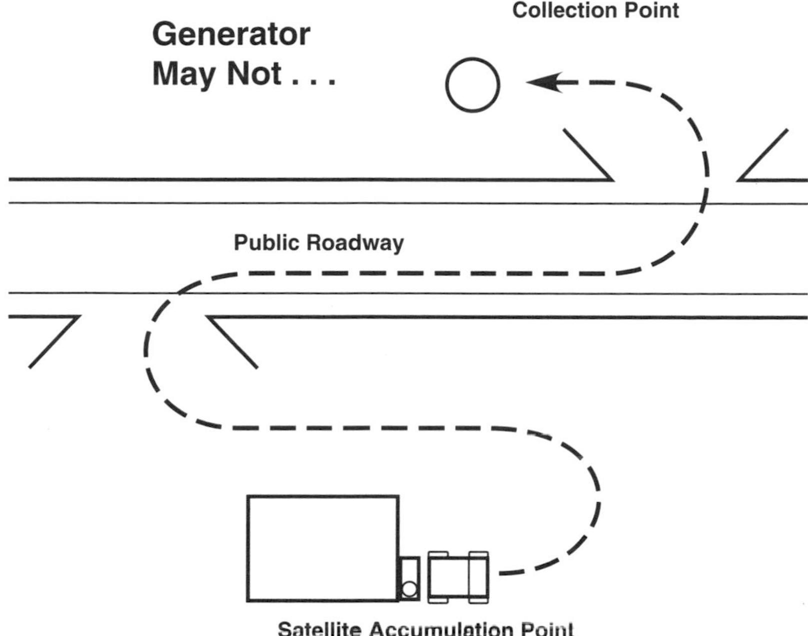

FIGURE 6.8 Offsite transportation of hazardous waste.

EPA ID Number

As discussed in the previous chapter, the EPA ID number is essential to the EPA and the primacy states in tracking transporter activity. Without this unique number, the transporter is forbidden to handle hazardous waste. Moreover, a transporter may not accept hazardous waste from a SQG or generator nor transfer hazardous waste to a TSDF unless they have EPA ID numbers.* A transporter obtains an ID number by "notifying" the EPA of hazardous waste activity using a standard EPA notification form.

The Manifest

The RCRA Subtitle C regulations prohibit transporters from accepting hazardous waste shipments from shippers without a manifest.** The function of the manifest system was described in the previous chapter. The transporter who accepts manifested hazardous wastes is required to sign and date the manifest and return a signed copy to the generator or previous transporter. The transporter is

* Transporters may, however, accept hazardous waste shipments from conditionally exempt SQGs.
** An exception is the provision for delivery of reclaimed wastes from SQGs [*see* 40 CFR 263.20(h)].

responsible for the shipment until the manifest is signed by the owner or operator of the receiving facility.

The transporter is required to deliver the entire quantity of waste accepted from either the generator or another transporter to the facility listed on the manifest or to the alternate facility if one is listed on the manifest. If the waste cannot be delivered as the manifest directs, the transporter must inform the generator and receive further instructions. The transporter must have the owner or operator of the TSDF sign and date the manifest at the time of delivery to the TSDF. The transporter retains Copy 4 of the manifest and gives the remaining three parts of the manifest to the TSDF owner or operator. The transporter must retain a copy of the manifest for three years from the date the hazardous waste is accepted by the *initial transporter*.

Handling Hazardous Waste Discharges

In the event of a discharge of hazardous waste during transport, special requirements established by the EPA and DOT must be followed by the driver/transporter. A discharge of hazardous waste is defined as "the accidental or intentional spilling, leaking, pumping, pouring, emitting, emptying, or dumping of hazardous waste into or on any land or water" (40 CFR 260.10).

EPA and DOT regulations pertaining to hazardous waste release events include provisions authorizing federal, state, or local government officials, acting within the scope of their official duties, to permit the immediate removal of hazardous wastes by transporters who do not have EPA ID numbers and without a manifest. Within 15 days following the incident, the transporter must obtain a temporary ID number and file a report, including a manifest, with the DOT. The EPA has also exempted all persons involved in treatment or containment actions during an immediate response to the discharge of hazardous wastes or materials from permitting requirements. All regulations for the final disposition of wastes must be followed after the emergency has been concluded.

EPA regulations similarly require transporters to clean up any discharges that occur during transport or take actions required or approved by appropriate government officials to mitigate human health or environmental hazards (Office of Technology Assessment 1986, p. 247). Such cleanups are characteristically hazardous, not only to those doing the cleanup work, but to nearby residents, to other users of the transportation system, and to the environment. It is rarely possible to achieve a totally satisfactory cleanup. Liquid wastes, liquid-borne solid wastes, and water from fire-fighting operations are often dispersed through storm drains and the soil, to the extent that it cannot be retrieved. Atmospheric releases are rarely controlled in a timely manner.

Great advances have been made in response techniques and in cleanup procedures, but much more effort is needed in prevention of transportation-related hazardous material/waste releases. Figures 6.9 through 6.15 provide some sequences of transportation-related cleanup operations. (*See also* Roberts 1985; Wentz 1989, pp. 263–267)

FIGURE 6.9 Release from a transportation incident [Arizona Department of Environmental Quality (DEQ)].

FIGURE 6.10 Release from a transportation incident (Arizona DEQ).

FIGURE 6.11 Cleanup following a transportation incident (Arizona DEQ).

FIGURE 6.12 Cleanup following a transportation incident (Arizona DEQ).

FIGURE 6.13 Release from a transportation incident (Arizona DEQ).

Import–Export Activity

International movement of hazardous wastes is a matter of growing interest and concern to responsible officials in the United States, Mexico, Canada, and other nations. Documented shipments to and from Mexico and Canada are a small, but growing fraction of the quantities generated and managed in each nation. Table 6.3 summarizes those quantities for the years 1987 through 1994.

Significant effort on the part of U.S. (state and federal) and Mexican officials has been committed to improvement of tracking and accountability for hazardous wastes in the border areas. Indeed, the "increases" in U.S.–Mexican shipments, indicated in Table 6.3, may reflect some combination of improving awareness, surveillance, inspection, documentation, and enforcement pertaining to hazardous waste shipments. Nevertheless, much of the waste generated on the Mexican side is never accounted for, and an occasional U.S. shipper attempts illegal movement of wastes to Mexico.

FIGURE 6.14 Cleanup following a transportation incident (Arizona DEQ).

FIGURE 6.15 Cleanup following a transportation incident (Arizona DEQ).

Table 6.3 Transborder Shipment of Hazardous Waste — U.S., Mexico, and Canada (Metric Tons)

Year	From Mexico[a]	To Mexico[a]	From Canada[b]	To Canada[b]
1987		10,710	43,203	129,476
1988	990	15,615	66,304	144,613
1989	1,940	28,101	103,707	154,304
1990	3,261	39,209	136,752	143,411
1991	5,795	57,091	223,079	135,161
1992	6,806	72,178	174,682	123,998
1993	11,146	71,593	229,648	173,416
1994	7,108			

Note: Canadian definition of "hazardous waste" includes recyclables, gases, and biomedical wastes which are not included in the U.S. definition.

[a] Data from unpublished EPA databases.

[b] Data from Environment Canada manifest database.

Researchers of the UCLA School of Public Health have documented border area industrial waste management problems since 1989. They report that, the 1983 U.S.–Mexico Agreement* notwithstanding, EPA records for 1988 show that only 1% (7 of 748) of the maqulidora** industries operating in northern Baja California and Sonora requested shipment of hazardous wastes to the United States (Perry et al. 1990). The Baja industries are estimated to generate 100,000 tons of hazardous waste per year. By the end of 1990, the Secretaria de Desarrollo Urbano y Ecologia (SEDUE)*** found that only 14.5% of the maquilas legally recycled or returned their residues to the United States (Castillo and Perry 1992). The researchers suggest a variety of options for improved coordination, tracking, and accountability of hazardous wastes in the border areas (Perry et al. 1990). (*See also* Perry and Klooster 1992, Chapters 4, 5, and Executive Summary)

Two recent federal criminal prosecutions,† growing from the attempted illegal shipment of waste polychlorinated biphenyls (PCBs) to Mexico, confirm the necessity for vigorous monitoring and enforcement of waste management statutes in the border area. To this end, the EPA provides technical and enforcement training to the U.S. Customs Service personnel, and the two agencies conduct joint training exercises at border patrol facilities. In recent years, the county, state, and federal environmental and law enforcement agencies have greatly improved cooperation and coordination of border area investigative activity.

* U.S.–Mexican Agreement of Cooperation for the Protection and Improvement of the Environment in the Border Area (1983), Annex III.

** *See* "maquiladora" entry in the Glossary.

***The federal environmental agency in Mexico.

† *U.S.* v. *Daniel G. Rodriguez-Castro* and *U.S.* v. *Weaver Electric Company, Inc.* (U.S. EPA 1994b).

TOPICS FOR REVIEW OR DISCUSSION

1. Discuss situations in which hazardous chemicals, in transit, burn or release flammables in rural and urban areas. When might it be advisable to attempt control, and why? When might it be best to let the fire burn itself out, and why?
2. There are six circumstances requiring notification of the National Response Center regarding a hazardous *materials* incident. What are they?
3. Discuss the advantages and disadvantages of highway vs. rail shipment of hazardous materials/wastes.
4. There are several missteps that can cause a transporter of RCRA hazardous wastes to become subject to generator or storage facility (or both) requirements. What are they?
5. Why is the admonition of Figure 6.8 important or significant?

REFERENCES

Blackman, William C., Jr. 1985. "Environmental Impacts of Policies Toward the Rail- and Motor-Freight Industries in the United States." Doctoral Dissertation, Graduate School of Public Affairs, University of Colorado, Denver.

Castillo, Victor M., and Diane Perry. 1992. "Environmental Implications of the Free Trade Agreement in the Maquiladora Industry." *Transboundary Resources Report,* Summer 1992. Environmental Committee of the Tijuana-San Diego Region/United Nations Association of San Diego County, Centro Cultural de Tijuana, Baja, California, Mexico.

Chemical Waste Transportation Institution. 1994. Unpublished database. Washington, D.C.

ICF, Inc. 1984. *Assessing the Costs Associated with Truck Transportation of Hazardous Wastes.* U.S. Environmental Protection Agency, Office of Solid Waste, Washington, D.C.

National Solid Waste Management Association (NSWMA). 1989. *Managing Hazardous Waste: Fulfilling the Public Trust.* NSWMA, Washington, D.C.

Perry, Diane M., and Daniel J. Klooster. 1992. *The Maquiladora Industry: Generation, Transportation and Disposal of Hazardous Waste at the California-Baja California, U.S.–Mexico Border: Second Maquiladora Report.* School of Public Health, University of California, Los Angeles.

Perry, Diane M., Roberto Sanchez, William H. Glaze, and Maria Mazari. 1990. "Binational Management of Hazardous Waste: The Maquiladora Industry at the US–Mexico Border." *Environmental Management* 14(4): 441–450.

Roberts, Alan I. 1985. "Transport of Hazardous Waste." *Transfrontier Movements of Hazardous Waste.* Organization for Economic Cooperation and Development, Paris.

U.S. Environmental Protection Agency. 1990. *RCRA Orientation Manual, 1990 Edition.* Superintendent of Documents, Government Printing Office, Washington, D.C.

U.S. Environmental Protection Agency. 1993. *Catalog of Hazardous Waste Database Reports.* Solid Waste and Emergency Response, Washington, D.C.

U.S. Environmental Protection Agency. 1994b. *Enforcement Accomplishments Report FY 1993.* Office of Enforcement, Washington, D.C. EPA 300-R-94-003.

U.S. Office of Technology Assessment. 1986. *Transportation of Hazardous Materials.* Superintendent of Documents, Government Printing Office, Washington, D.C.

Wentz, Charles A. 1989. *Hazardous Waste Management.* McGraw-Hill, New York.

Westat, Inc. 1984. *National Survey of Hazardous Waste Generators and Treatment Storage and Disposal Facilities Regulated Under RCRA in 1981.* U.S. Environmental Protection Agency, Office of Solid Waste, Washington, D.C.

7 TREATMENT AND DISPOSAL METHODS AND PROCESSES

OBJECTIVES

At the completion of this chapter, the student should:

- have overview knowledge of historical and traditional methods of treatment and disposal of hazardous wastes and the environmental impacts of each.
- have knowledge of past and present practices of land treatment and disposal, the environmental impacts thereof, and the Resource Conservation and Recovery Act (RCRA) land disposal restrictions.
- have overview knowledge of nonpoint-source water quality impacts of hazardous waste treatment and disposal operations.
- understand the air quality implications, residue management, and waste destruction capabilities of burning vs. incineration and the RCRA approach to each.
- understand some of the classic reuse and recycling processes as a basic management approach and as an introduction to Chapter 8.
- understand the basic differences between treatment, immobilization, and destruction and the processes associated with each category.
- be familiar with history and practice of ocean dumping and underground injection and with concerns regarding potential environmental impacts of each.

INTRODUCTION

In the two previous chapters, we overviewed first the generation of hazardous wastes, then the transportation thereof. We now take up the technologies, practice, and regulatory requirements associated with the ultimate disposition of hazardous wastes. Where appropriate, we will follow the pattern of previous chapters by beginning a topic with a discussion of "generic" practice or technology and follow with the regulatory requirements of the RCRA.

As before, the format for a generic discussion of treatment and disposal is shaped by the RCRA format which groups treatment, storage, and disposal functions together as the "final link in the cradle-to-grave hazardous waste management." The rationale for grouping *treatment* and *disposal* together is fairly clear.

Some recollection of the early practices and "horror stories" in Chapter 1 should serve to refresh our understanding of the abuses that were associated with accumulation of hazardous wastes. It is clear throughout the Subtitle C regulations that Congress intended that accumulation of hazardous wastes be controlled very rigorously. Thus, the grouping of treatment, *storage*, and disposal facilities (TSDF) as the final link, and as the entities requiring operating permits, became a regulatory format. For instructional purposes, it has become an entire way of thinking about the final disposition of hazardous waste.

The original RCRA legislation establishes two categories of TSDFs based upon permit status. Section 3005(a) of the act specifies that TSDFs must obtain a permit to operate. In recognition of the fact that several years would be required for the U.S. Environmental Protection Agency (EPA) to issue permits to all operating facilities, Congress included Section 3005(e) which established "interim status." TSDFs which were in existence on November 19, 1980, and which met certain conditions, were allowed to continue operating until their permit is issued or denied. Such facilities are said to have interim status and are regulated by 40 CFR 265. The second category consists of those facilities having permits. Permitted facilities are regulated by 40 CFR 264.

Both interim status and permit standards consist of two types of requirements:

- Administrative and nontechnical requirements which are nearly identical for interim status and permitted facilities
- Technical and unit-specific requirements which embody significant differences for interim status and permitted facilities

Large numbers of interim status facilities continue to operate legally without fully approved permits, and it is expected that this situation will prevail for several more years. The 40 CFR 264 "finally permitted" standards, which will eventually apply to all TSDFs, are more stringent than the Part 265 "interim status" standards. However, they are only a blueprint for the permit writer who must develop "best engineering judgment" standards for the specific facility. Accordingly, we will overview the interim status standards and, where appropriate, point out additional Part 264 requirements for permitted facilities.

Treatment, storage, and disposal (TSD) practice involves a large variety of units and technologies. Thus, the TSDF regulations are far more extensive than for generators and transporters. We will attempt to overview only the most important generic topics and salient features of the regulations. The student is encouraged to explore the technical literature and the RCRA Subtitle C regulations for details.

Administrative and Nontechnical Requirements

The administrative and nontechnical requirements are intended to ensure that owners and operators establish the necessary procedures and plans to operate the TSDF according to established practice and to handle any emergencies or accidents. These requirements are found in Subparts A through E of 40 CFR Parts 264 and 265.

Subpart A — Facilities That Are Subject To The Regulations

In general, all owners or operators of facilities engaged in the treatment, storage, or disposal of hazardous wastes must comply with the TSD regulations. Exceptions include:

- a farmer disposing of waste pesticides from his own operations.
- the owner or operator of a totally enclosed treatment facility.
- the owner or operator of an elementary neutralization unit or a wastewater treatment unit.
- a person responding to or cleaning up a hazardous waste spill or release.
- facilities that legitimately reuse, recycle, or reclaim hazardous waste.
- generators, including small quantity generators (SQGs), accumulating wastes within the time periods specified in 40 CFR 262.
- a transporter storing manifested shipments for less than ten days (40 CFR 265.1).

Subpart B — General Facility Standards

As was covered in the previous chapters, all facilities handling hazardous wastes must obtain an EPA identification number.* Owners and operators of TSDFs must ensure that the wastes being handled are correctly identified and managed according to the regulations. They must ensure that facilities are secure and are operating properly. Personnel working in the facilities must be trained to perform their duties correctly, safely, and in compliance with all applicable laws, regulations, and codes. In order to satisfy these requirements, owners and operators must:

- *conduct waste analyses* prior to initiating treatment, storage, or disposal in accord with a written waste analysis plan. The plan must specify tests and test frequencies that will provide the owner or operator with sufficient information on the properties of the waste to manage the waste in accord with the laws, regulations, and codes.
- *install security measures* to prevent unknowing entry of people or animals onto the active portions of the TSDF (Figure 7.1). The facility must be surrounded by a barrier with controlled entry systems or 24-hour surveillance. Signs carrying the warning "Danger — Unauthorized Personnel Keep Out" must be posted at all entrances (Figure 7.2). Signs must be printed in English and also in other languages predominant in the area surrounding the facility. Precautions must be taken to avoid fires, explosions, generation of toxic gases, and any other events that would threaten human health, safety, and the environment.
- *conduct inspections* according to a written inspection schedule to assess the compliance status of the facility and detect potential problem areas.

* It may be conceptually useful to understand that *anyone* can apply for, and obtain, an EPA ID number. Issuance of the ID number by the EPA does not amount to a permit or certification. It is a means of identification that the holder will be called upon to provide should he/she ultimately engage in hazardous waste management activity.

FIGURE 7.1 Site security requirement (40 CFR 264/265.14) [Chemical Waste Management, Inc. (CWM), 107 South Motor Avenue, Azuza, CA 91702].

Observations made during the course of the inspections must be recorded in the facility's operating log and kept on file for three years. All problems noted must be remedied.

- *conduct training* to reduce the potential for mistakes that might threaten human health and the environment. The regulations specify that the employee "must successfully complete classroom instruction or on-the-job training that teaches them to perform their duties in a way that ensures the facility's compliance with the regulations." In addition, the Occupational Safety and Health Administration (OSHA) now requires TSDFs to implement a hazard communication plan, medical surveillance program, and a health and safety plan. Decontamination procedures (Chapter 15) must be in place, and employees must receive a minimum of 24 hours of safety training.
- *properly manage ignitable, reactive, or incompatible wastes.* Ignitable or reactive wastes must be protected from sources of ignition or reaction or be treated to eliminate the possibility. Owners or operators must ensure that treatment, storage, or disposal of ignitable, reactive, or incompatible waste does not result in damage to the containment structure and/or threaten human health or the environment. Separation of incompatible wastes must be maintained.
- *comply with location standards* to avoid siting a new facility in a location where flood or seismic events could affect a waste management unit. Bulk liquid wastes are also prohibited from placement in salt domes, salt beds, or underground mines or caves.

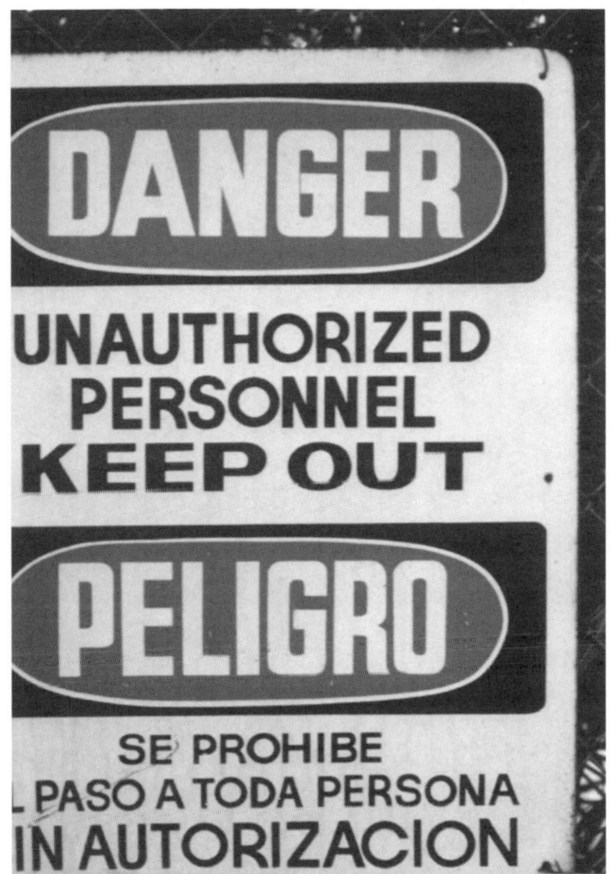

FIGURE 7.2 Sign requirement (40 CFR 264/265.14) (CWM).

- *prepare and comply with the construction quality assurance program requirements* which are applicable to foundations, dikes, soil liners, geomembranes, leachate detection, collection and removal systems, and final cover systems. These construction standards are extensive and will be covered in detail in the permitting process. (40 CFR Subpart B).

Subpart C — Preparedness and Prevention

Facilities must be designed, constructed, maintained, and operated to minimize the possibility of a fire, explosion, or any unplanned sudden or nonsudden release of hazardous waste constituents which could threaten human health or the environment. Facilities must be equipped with:

- *an internal communications or alarm system* which can provide immediate emergency instructions to facility personnel.
- *telephone or two-way radio* capable of summoning emergency assistance from local police, fire, and emergency response units.

FIGURE 7.3 Aisle space, drum stacking limitation (CWM).

- *portable fire extinguishers* and fire, spill control, and decontamination equipment.
- *water* at adequate volume and pressure to supply water hoses, foam-producing equipment, automatic sprinklers, or water spray systems.

All communications and emergency equipment must be tested as necessary to ensure proper operation in time of emergency. All personnel must have immediate access to the internal alarm or emergency communication system. Aisle space (Figure 7.3) must be maintained to allow unobstructed movement of personnel and equipment during an emergency.

Owners or operators of TSDFs must attempt to make arrangements to:

- *familiarize police, fire, and emergency response teams* with the facility, wastes handled and their properties, workstations, and access and evacuation routes.
- *designate primary and alternate emergency response teams* where more than one jurisdiction might respond.
- *familiarize local hospitals* with the properties of the hazardous wastes handled at the facility and the types of injuries or illnesses which could result from events at the facility.

Subpart D — Contingency Plan and Emergency Procedures

A contingency plan must be in effect at each TSDF and, by reference [262.34(a)(4)], at each generator facility. The plan must be designed to minimize hazards to human health or the environment from fires, explosions, or any release of hazardous waste constituents. The plan must be implemented immediately whenever there is a fire, explosion, or release which could threaten human health or the environment.

The contingency plan must:

- describe the actions which personnel must take to implement the plan.
- describe arrangements concluded with local police, fire, and hospital authorities; contractors; and emergency response teams to coordinate emergency services.
- list names, addresses, and phone numbers of all persons qualified to act as emergency coordinator for the facility.
- list emergency equipment, communication and alarm systems, and the location of each item.
- include an evacuation plan for facility personnel.

The contingency plan must be maintained at the facility and at all emergency response facilities that might be called upon to provide emergency services. It must be reviewed and updated whenever any item affecting the plan is changed. A key requirement is the designation of an emergency coordinator who is responsible for directing response measures and reducing the adverse impacts of hazardous waste releases.

Other regulatory programs related to hazardous waste management, releases of hazardous materials to the environment, or exposures of humans to toxic materials also require emergency response planning and/or preparation of contingency plans. These planning requirements are becoming more numerous, and the specifications are becoming more complex and sophisticated. Owners or operators of TSDFs and their emergency coordinators will increasingly find it necessary to devote time and resources to the contingency planning effort. Among the different regulatory programs, some planning requirements are similar, duplicative, overlapping, or redundant. Time and resource commitments, training, drills, and coordination requirements can be economized by combining the required plans in one document. Table 7.1 provides suggested components and regulatory references for accomplishing a consolidated and coordinated contingency plan.

Subpart E — Manifest System, Record Keeping, and Reporting

The operation of the manifest system has been previously described. The TSDF owner or operator receiving the waste is responsible for ensuring that the waste described on the manifest is the same as the waste on the truck. The intent is to ensure that there are no significant discrepancies in the amount (e.g., an extra drum) or type of waste (e.g., acid waste instead of paint sludge) that was shipped by the generator. If a significant discrepancy is discovered, the TSDF must reconcile the difference with the generator or transporter. If the difference cannot be cleared up, the EPA must be notified within 15 days of the incident. Subpart E includes extensive record keeping and reporting requirements (U.S. EPA 1990, pp. III-35, 36).

Table 7.1 Contingency Planning Consolidation and Coordination

Agency	Statute	Plan Requirement	Ref.
EPA	RCRA	Contingency Plan	40 CFR 262.34, 264 and 265, Subparts C and D
OSHA	SARA[a]	HazWOpER Emergency Plan	29 CFR 19210.120(l), (p), and (q)
EPA	CWA	Spill Prevention Control and Countermeasure Plan	40 CFR 112
OSHA	CAA	Chemical Process Safety Standard	29 CFR 1910.119
OSHA	OSHA	Emergency Action Plans	29 CFR 1910.38
EPA	CAAA	Risk Management Program for Chemical Accidental Release Prevention	40 CFR 68[b]

[a] SARA Title III includes emergency planning by state emergency response commissions (SERCs) and local emergency planning committees (LEPCs). RCRA facilities may be required, or may wish, to coordinate their contingency plans with those of the SERC or LEPC or both.

[b] Implementing regulations are in proposed form at the time of this writing.

General Technical Standards for Interim Status Facilities

The objective of the RCRA interim status technical requirements is to minimize the potential for environmental and public health threats resulting from hazardous waste treatment, storage, and disposal at existing facilities which are awaiting permitted status. The general standards cover three areas:

- Groundwater monitoring requirements (Subpart F)
- Closure, post-closure requirements (Subpart G)
- Financial assurance (Subpart H)

Subpart F — Groundwater Monitoring

Owners and operators of surface impoundments, landfills, and land treatment facilities that are used to manage hazardous waste must meet minimum groundwater monitoring requirements. The interim status facility requirements in 40 CFR 265.91 call for a monitoring system consisting of at least one well upgradient from the facility and three downgradient. The upgradient wells must provide data on groundwater that is not influenced by leakage from the waste management unit. The downgradient wells must be placed to intercept any waste migrating from the unit should a release occur.

Figure 7.4 illustrates a "one-up-and-three-down" layout of monitoring wells for a land disposal facility — the upper left well being the upgradient or background data well, the others being the downgradient wells. Figure 7.5 illustrates an

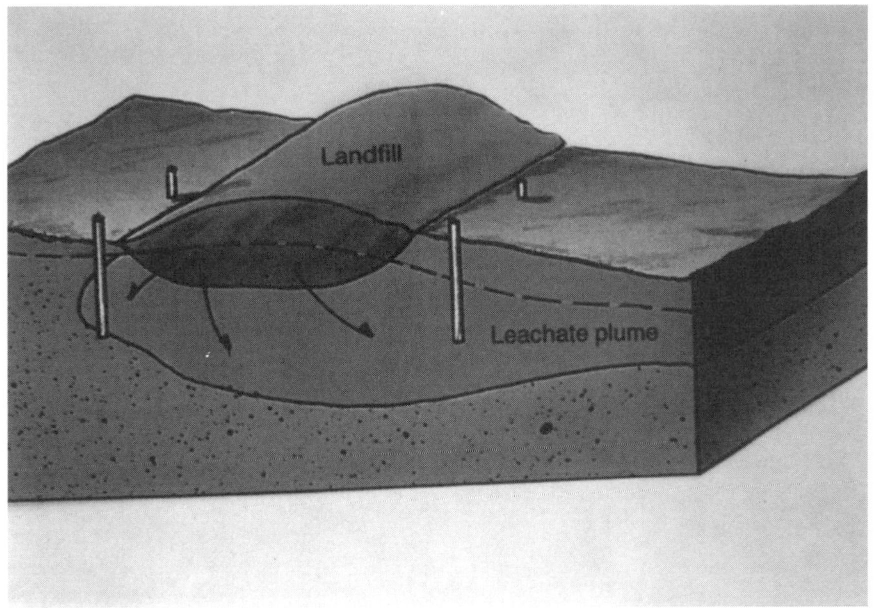

FIGURE 7.4 Groundwater monitoring well layout for a landfill disposal facility. (From Smart, Glenn R., and David K. Cook. 1988. "RCRA and CERCLA Groundwater Well Locations and Sampling Requirements." *Hazardous Materials Control* 1(3) May-June:26–33. With permission.)

important problem, i.e., the nearby stream at low stage may draw the contaminant plume into the base flow and away from the monitoring wells. Figure 7.6 illustrates a very common phenomenon — the creation of an artificial drawdown curve, which can alter the movement of the plume and generate misleading data from the monitoring well.

The one-up-and-three-down layout is generally understood to be a minimum pattern. As practitioners have gained in knowledge of plume behavior, older notions of vertical and transverse dispersion have given way to the understanding that contamination releases may move in very narrow plumes. Recent tracer tests and detailed plume studies have established that:

> Because of weak dispersion, the degree of concentration heterogeneity diminishes very little down-gradient, requiring a more dense network of wells. In some plumes, the difference between detecting or missing a concentration zone orders of magnitude above a regulatory limit is the difference in positioning in depth of the critical well by only a meter or two. (Ozbilgin et.al. 1992)

The permitted facility monitoring requirements of 40 CFR 264.97 speak in terms of "a sufficient number of wells, installed at appropriate locations and depths to yield ground-water samples from the uppermost aquifer that: (1) represent the quality of

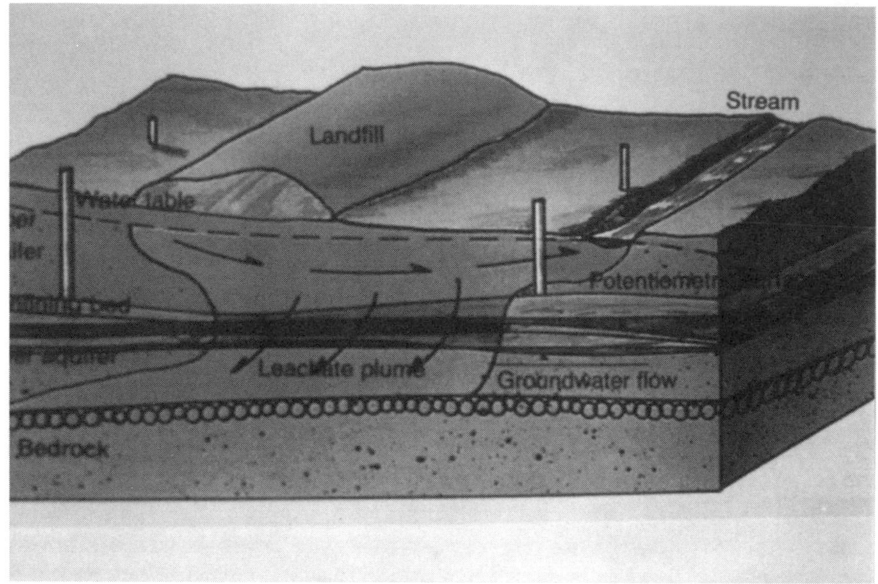

FIGURE 7.5 Natural drawdown interference with groundwater monitoring regime. (From Smart, Glenn R., and David K. Cook. 1988. "RCRA and CERCLA Groundwater Well Locations and Sampling Requirements." *Hazardous Materials Control* 1(3) May-June:26–33. With permission.)

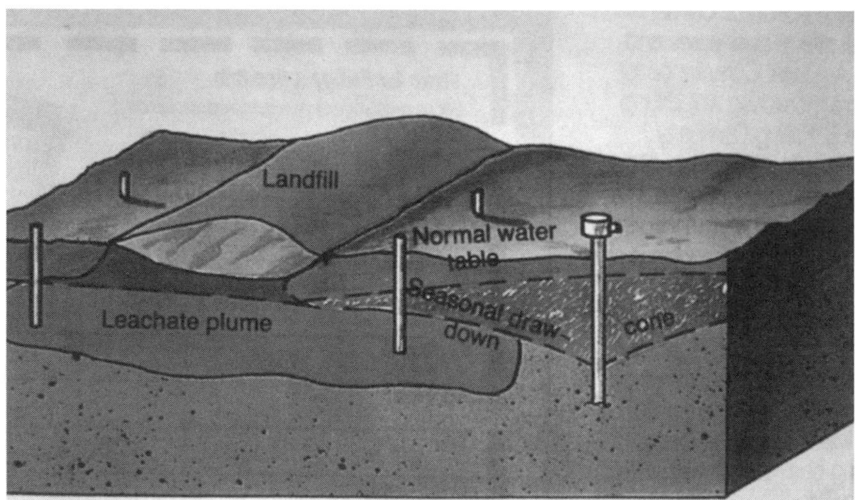

FIGURE 7.6 Artificial drawdown interference with groundwater monitoring regime. (From Smart, Glenn R., and David K. Cook. 1988. "RCRA and CERCLA Groundwater Well Locations and Sampling Requirements." *Hazardous Materials Control* 1(3) May-June:26–33. With permission.)

background water .... (2) represent the quality of ground water passing the point of compliance." Thus, the numbers, location, and depth of completion of monitoring wells has become a major resource consideration for owners and operators contemplating the permitting or closure of a land treatment or disposal facility.

Initially, the owner or operator obtains analytical data from quarterly samples of the wells to establish background concentrations of selected chemicals. The parameters for which monitoring is accomplished include:

- drinking water parameters.
- groundwater quality parameters.
- groundwater contamination parameters.

After one year of quarterly sampling, background levels are established and routine monitoring begins. The indicator parameters, used to assess groundwater quality and potential contamination, are monitored annually. The results of the routine monitoring are compared to background levels and are tested statistically to determine whether significant changes have occurred. The EPA or delegated state agency must be notified if the comparison indicates a change.

In the event that a significant increase (or decrease) in pH is detected for any of the indicator parameters, the owner or operator must implement a groundwater assessment program to determine the nature of the problem. If the assessment shows contamination by hazardous wastes, then the owner or operator must continue assessing the extent of groundwater contamination until the problem is ameliorated or until the facility is closed (U.S. EPA 1990, Chapter 4).

Specific groundwater monitoring parameters are prescribed for permitted facilities. The student or reader interested in further details of groundwater monitoring requirements for permitted facilities should examine Subpart F of 40 CFR 264.

Subpart G — Closure, Post-Closure

Closure is the period when wastes are no longer accepted, during which all waste processing must be completed and a final cap or cover is applied to the land treatment facility. All equipment, structures, and soil must be disposed of or decontaminated. The owner or operator is required to have a closure plan and keep it on file at the facility until closure is completed and certified to the EPA or state regulatory agency. The closure plan must include:

- a description of the closure process to be implemented.
- an estimate of the maximum amount of waste the facility will handle prior to closure.
- a description of the steps needed to decontaminate equipment and remove soils and debris during closure.
- a schedule for closure.

Once closure is completed, the owner or operator certifies that the facility has been properly closed. A survey plat indicating the location and dimensions of landfill cells or other disposal areas is submitted to the local land authority and to the EPA or state agency. The plat preserves a record of the exact location and dimensions of the hazardous waste activity for future reference. A notation must also be made on the deed to the property, notifying potential purchasers that the site was engaged in hazardous waste activity.

Following the closure, a 30-year post-closure period is established for facilities that do not "clean close" as described here. The post-closure care consists of at least the following:

- Groundwater monitoring and reporting
- Maintenance and monitoring of waste containment systems
- Continued site security

A post-closure plan, similar to the closure plan, must be on file at the site until post-closure care begins. The closure and post-closure plans may be amended at any time and must be amended if there is any change of circumstances that affects the plan. The closure timetable and the post-closure care period may be lengthened or shortened by the EPA or state agency.

Clean closure may be accomplished by the removal of all contaminants from impoundments and waste piles. At a minimum, owners and operators of surface impoundments and waste piles that wish to clean close must conduct soil analyses and groundwater monitoring to confirm that all wastes have been removed from the unit. The EPA and/or state agency may establish additional clean closure requirements on a case-by-case basis. Chapter 11, Figure 11.18 illustrates the extent of removal that may be necessary to clean close a former hazardous waste impoundment. A successful demonstration of clean closure eliminates the requirement for post-closure care of the site (U.S. EPA 1990, Chapter 4).

Subpart H — Financial Requirements

RCRA originally established financial requirements to assure that funds would be available to pay for closing a facility, for rendering post-closure care at disposal facilities, and to compensate third parties for bodily injury and property damage caused by accidents related to the operation of a TSDF. An obvious objective of Congress in establishing these requirements was avoidance of the necessity for cleanup under Superfund.

In the 1984 amendments, Congress mandated additional financial responsibility requirements, thereby emphasizing the importance of assured financial capability for completing needed remediation at TSDF sites. The financial requirements of Subpart H are:

- financial assurance for closure/post-closure.
- liability coverage for injury and property damage.

Owners and operators must meet the financial assurance requirements by preparation of cost estimates for closure and, if required, post-closure. The cost estimates must reflect the actual and projected costs for the conduct of the activities described

Table 7.2 Waste Management Options and Priorities

- Source reduction (process modification)
- Separation and volume reduction
- Exchange/sale as raw materials
- Energy recovery
- Treatment
- Secure ultimate disposal (landfill)

Source: Combs 1989.

in the closure plan. Similarly, cost estimates for post-closure operations must be projected for the full post-closure period.

The owner or operator must then demonstrate to the EPA or state agency the ability to pay the estimated amounts. The owner/operator may use any one or a combination of the following six mechanisms to comply with the financial assurance requirements:

- Trust fund
- Surety bond
- Letter of credit
- Closure/post-closure insurance
- Corporate guarantee
- Financial test

The Subpart H requirements for each of the mechanisms are extensive. The student or reader having particular interest in the details should examine 40 CFR 264/265, Subpart H.

Liability insurance requirements include coverage of $1 million (annual aggregate $2 million) per sudden accidental occurrence, such as a fire or explosion. Owners or operators must also maintain coverage of $3 million (annual aggregate $6 million) for nonsudden occurrences such as groundwater contamination. The liability coverage may be demonstrated using any of the six mechanisms allowed for assurance of closure and post-closure funds.

Hazardous Waste Treatment

Hazardous waste treatment is a rapidly developing industry full of experimentation and innovation. This innovation is being driven by the need for effective and economical processes for treating wastes rather than landfilling them without treatment. A hierarchy of general waste management options can be constructed as shown in Table 7.2. The most desirable option is source reduction through process modification (Combs 1989, p. XV-1). The less desirable options follow.

Source reduction approaches and waste exchanges will be discussed in Chapter 8. Overview discussions, examples, and regulatory requirements pertaining to separation and volume reduction practices, energy recovery, treatment and destruction methods, and secure ultimate disposal follow.

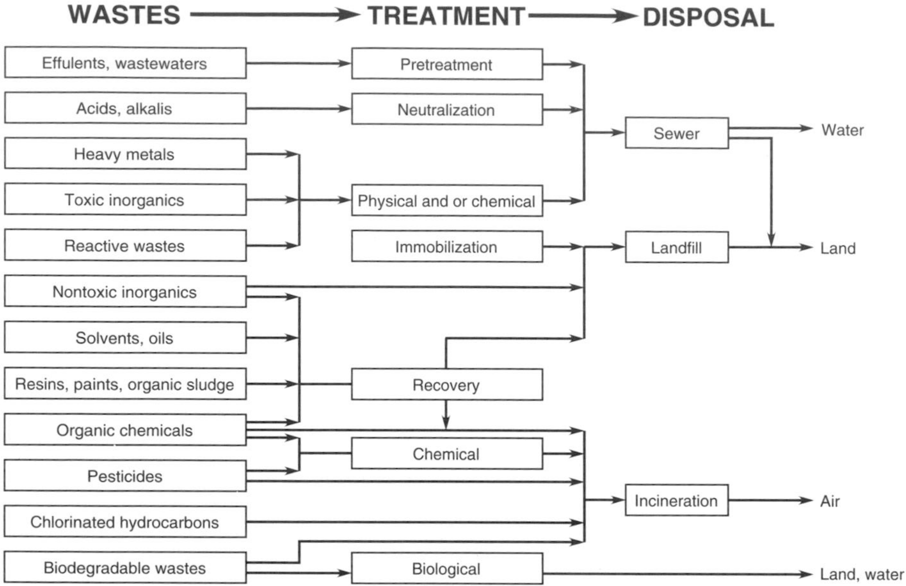

FIGURE 7.7 Treatment and disposal alternatives for industrial wastes. (Adapted from Wentz, Charles A. 1989. *Hazardous Waste Management.* McGraw-Hill, New York. With permission.)

The schematic of Figure 7.7 aligns types or categories of industrial wastes with the treatment processes and ultimate disposal usually applied. The volume of a waste destined for treatment or disposal can often be reduced by physical processes such as carbon adsorption, centrifugation, clarification, evaporation, solvent extraction, or stripping. Figure 7.8 shows a typical centrifuge layout. Figure 7.9 illustrates simple gravity separation in cone-bottom tanks. These processes make use of differences in specific gravity or mass to separate harmless or nonhazardous components from the hazardous components. The nonhazardous component may then be routed to further treatment, disposal, or recycling, as appropriate. The hazardous component must be destroyed, be rendered harmless, have toxicity reduced to acceptable levels, or be disposed of in a secure facility.

Uncontrolled burning for energy recovery is a common method of hazardous waste management, and the practice can be a potential threat to human health and the environment. Burners mix hazardous wastes with fuel oil or other fuel mixtures and burn the mix in low-temperature/low-pressure boilers or other combustion units. Some flammable wastes continue to be burned in disregard of federal, state, and local regulations and ordinances. Such low-temperature burning does not destroy most hazardous components of the waste and, in fact, causes their dispersion in the atmosphere.

Legitimate (and regulated) burning of hazardous waste fuel can be a useful disposition of the waste and an economical energy source. Cement kilns and industrial furnaces, having adequate operating temperatures, dwell times, and emission

FIGURE 7.8 Centrifuge — component of a hazardous waste solidification system (Casmalia Resources, Casmalia, CA 93429).

controls, have been allowed to burn some organic hazardous wastes. The EPA recently promulgated new regulations pertaining to combustion of hazardous wastes in boilers and industrial furnaces (BIFs), including cement kilns. These regulations and practices are a source of great contention, as will be discussed.

As indicated earlier, treatment technologies for hazardous wastes are available in ever-increasing numbers. These technologies and the commonly practiced recovery and disposal practices can be categorized as shown in Table 7.3.

Brief descriptions of the more commonly used treatment systems follow.

Activated Carbon Adsorption

Organic substances may be removed from aqueous or gaseous waste streams by adsorption* of the chemical substances onto a carbon matrix. The carbon may be used in either granular or powdered form, depending upon the application and the process economics. The effectiveness of activated carbon in removing hazardous constituents from aqueous streams is directly proportional to the amount of surface area of the activated carbon. The carbon is highly porous, having a total surface area

* Adsorption is a yet incompletely explained physical, surface accumulation phenomenon which refers to the ability of certain solids to attract and collect organic substances from the surrounding medium. Granular activated carbon, made from anthracite, is widely used to adsorb organic components from liquid and gaseous waste streams.

FIGURE 7.9 Gravity separation cones (ROMIC Chemical Corporation, 2081 Bay Road, Palo Alto, CA 94303).

in the range of 600 to 1000 m^2/g. Figure 7.10 diagrams a carbon adsorption system. The spent carbon is regenerated in ovens or by passing live steam through the carbon (Wentz 1989, pp. 172–173). A carbon regeneration system is diagrammed in Figure 7.11. (*See also* Wilson and Thompson 1988; Voice 1989)

Stripping

Air and steam stripping require mention in this brief introduction to hazardous waste treatment and disposal systems — not because of their particular effectiveness, but because strippers have been employed in so very many of the early site remediation efforts. Stripping is most frequently used to remove volatile organics from wastewaters or contaminated groundwater. Strippers generally involve towers containing cascades, trays, or manufactured media, with induced-draft air or live steam passing upward and contaminated water cascading or trickling downward over optimized surface areas. A countercurrent, packed-tower air stripper is diagrammed in Figure 7.12. Steam-stripping towers operate on a similar principle with live steam injected directly into the liquid waste.

In theory, the gas–liquid system reaches an equilibrium, based upon Henry's Law,* and the volatile contaminants are carried out, with the exhaust air stream or

* Henry's Law: At constant pressure, the weight of gas absorbed by a given volume of a liquid is proportional to the pressure at which the gas is supplied. For example, if a liter of water dissolves 5 g of a gas under 1 atm of pressure, it will dissolve 10 g of the same gas under 2 atm of pressure.

Table 7.3 Hazardous Waste Treatment, Recovery, and Disposal Processes

1. Physical Treatment Processes
   - A. Gas cleaning
     1. Mechanical collection
     2. Electrostatic precipitation
     3. Fabric filter
     4. Wet scrubbing
     5. Activated carbon adsorption
     6. Adsorption
   - B. Liquids–solids separation
     1. Centrifugation
     2. Clarification
     3. Coagulation
     4. Filtration
     5. Flocculation
     6. Flotation
     7. Foaming
     8. Sedimentation
     9. Thickening
   - C. Removal of specific components
     1. Adsorption
     2. Crystallization
     3. Dialysis
     4. Distillation
     5. Electrodialysis
     6. Evaporation
     7. Leaching
     8. Reverse osmosis
     9. Solvent extraction
     10. Stripping
2. Chemical Treatment Processes
   - A. Absorption
   - B. Chemical oxidation
   - C. Chemical precipitation
   - D. Chemical reduction
   - E. Combination and addition
   - F. Ion exchange
   - G. Neutralization
   - H. Pyrolysis
3. Biological Treatment Processes
   - A. Activated sludge
   - B. Aerobic lagoons
   - C. Anaerobic lagoons
   - D. Spray irrigation
   - E. Trickling filters
   - F. Waste Stabilization Ponds

Table 7.3 Hazardous Waste Treatment, Recovery, and Disposal Processes (continued)

4. Ultimate Disposal Processes
   - A. Deep well disposal
   - B. Dilution and dispersal
   - C. Incineration
   - D. Ocean dumping
   - E. Sanitary landfill
   - F. Land burial

Source: Dawson and Mercer 1986.

the spent steam, through the top of the unit. Some further treatment (carbon adsorption, incineration) must be applied to the exhaust vapors in order to capture and/or destroy the separated volatiles. A major problem with the early applications was the omission of this final stage and the uncontrolled release of the stripped volatiles to the atmosphere.

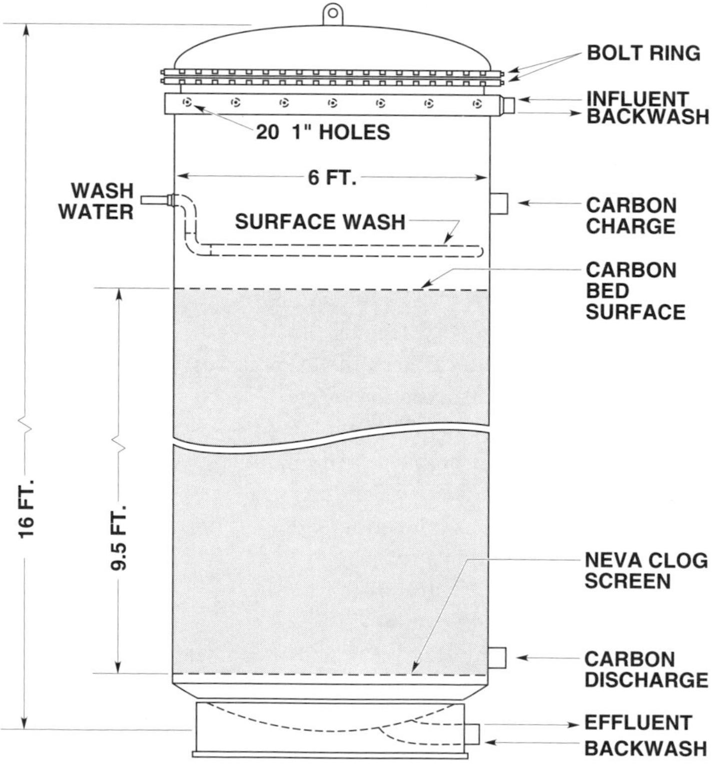

FIGURE 7.10 A carbon adsorption pressurized contactor.

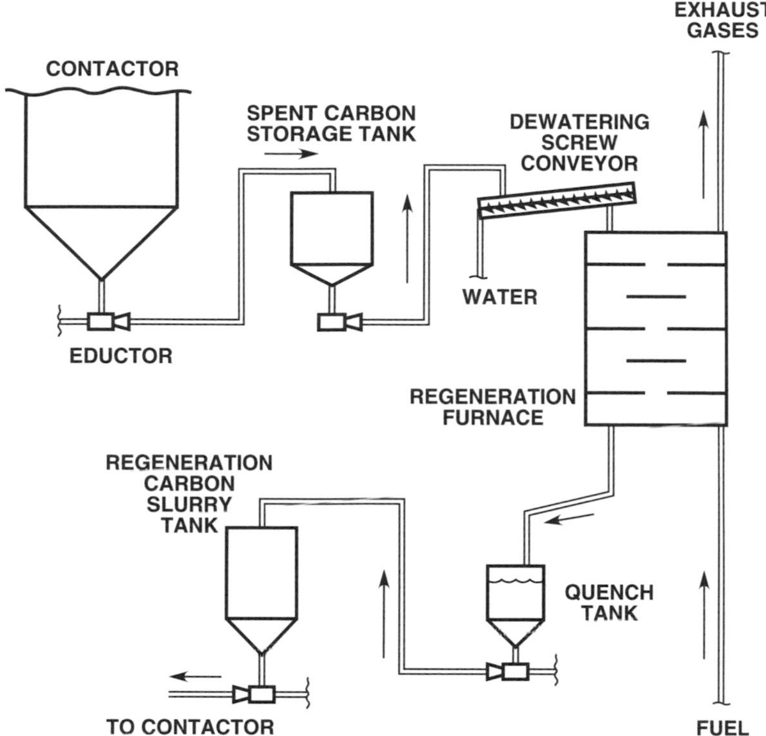

FIGURE 7.11 A carbon regeneration system.

Neutralization and Precipitation

Lime (quicklime or hydrated lime) can be used to treat liquid wastes containing heavy metals. Figure 7.13 illustrates a typical process. Both neutralization and precipitation are chemical processes in which a metal cation reacts with a hydroxide anion. In this process the addition of a hydroxide ion precipitates the metals. The coagulation of the precipitated metals is both a physical and chemical process. The attraction of cations for anions causes the formation of a floc. The mild turbulence in the stirred tank causes the small particles to collide, forming a sludge with a concentration of 20 to 50% solids (DuPont 1988). This process must then be followed by solidification or other processes specific to the sludge formed in order to render the sludge harmless to the environment.

Solidification

Metals and nonmetals can be solidified with pozzolan* and lime after the waste has been precipitated. Metal hydroxides and calcium salts will combine with fly ash

* An additive such as siliceous volcanic ash, or fly ash, originally used to improve the curing and strength properties of Portland cement concrete.

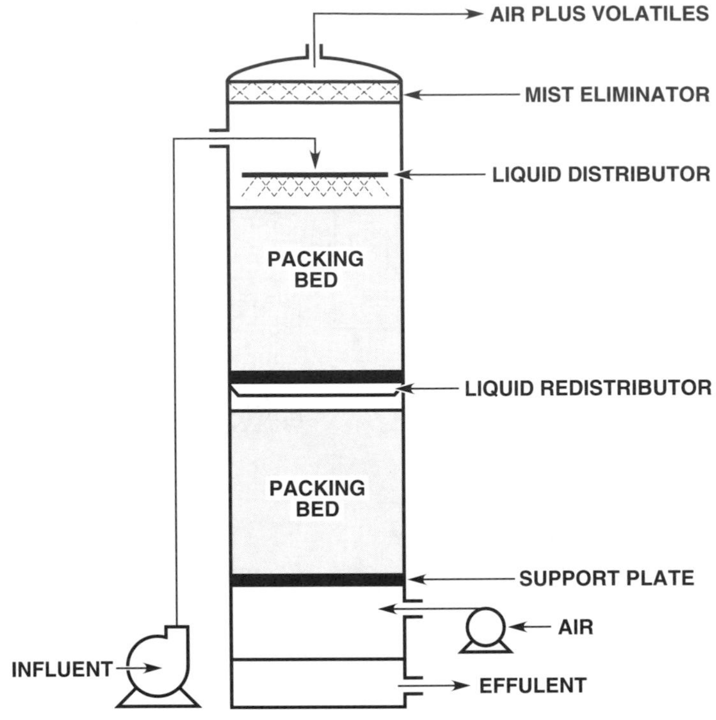

FIGURE 7.12 A countercurrent, packed-tower stripper.

and lime in the presence of water to form a cementitious product. A typical formulation is:

Final Solid = Lime + Fly Ash + Waste + Water

where lime is 5 to 15% by weight, fly ash is 50 to 65% by weight, waste is 8 to 19% by weight, and water is 10 to 60% of the original sludge by weight. For an organic sludge, a typical mixture ratio would be the same except for having water at 10 to 20% by weight (DuPont 1988).

Figures 7.14, 7.15, and 7.16 illustrate a typical solidification process — liquid waste storage and blending, lime and fly ash storage and dispensing, followed by mixing in a pugmill, respectively. The mixed matrix is then spread in drying beds where it solidifies. The solidified material may then be loaded and transported to a land disposal facility.

Oxidation and Reduction

The chemical processes of oxidation and reduction can be used to render hazardous wastes less hazardous or harmless. An *oxidation* reaction increases the

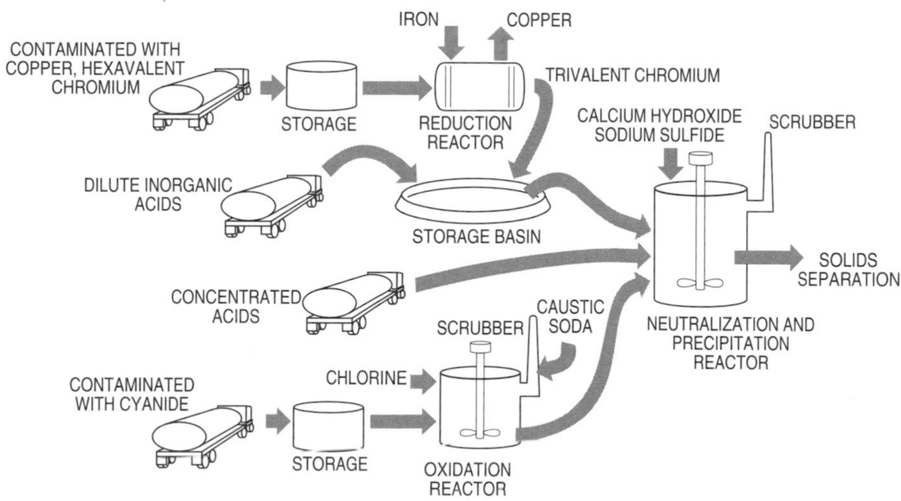

FIGURE 7.13 Schematic chemical treatment: neutralization, precipitation, and chemical oxidation/reduction.

FIGURE 7.14 Solidification process — liquid waste storage and blending (Casmalia Resources).

FIGURE 7.15 Solidification process — lime and fly ash storage and dispensing (Casmalia Resources).

FIGURE 7.16 Solidification process — pugmill mixing and related equipment (Casmalia Resources).

valence of an ion with a loss of electrons. A *reducing* reaction decreases the valence with a gain of electrons. Reactions that involve both oxidation and reduction are known as *redox* reactions.

Hexavalent chromium is a highly toxic component of various wastes, most notably those generated by the metal-finishing industry. “Hex chrome” is reduced to the comparatively innocuous trivalent chromium and can then be precipitated as chromic hydroxide, as shown in the following reactions which utilize sulfur dioxide and lime (Wentz 1989, p. 152):

$$SO_2 + H_2O \rightarrow H_2SO_3$$

$$2CrO_3 + 3H_2SO_3 \rightarrow Cr_2(SO_4)_3 + 3H_2O$$

$$Cr_2(SO_4)_3 + 3Ca(OH)_2 \rightarrow 2Cr(OH)_3 + 3CaSO_4$$

Cyanide-bearing wastewater, also commonly generated by the metal-finishing industry, is typically oxidized with alkaline chlorine or hypochlorite solutions. In this process, the cyanide is initially oxidized to a less toxic cyanate and then to carbon dioxide and nitrogen in the following reactions (Wentz 1989, p. 153):

$$NaCN + Cl_2 + 2NaOH \rightarrow NaCNO + 2NaCl + H_2O$$

$$2NaCNO + 3Cl_2 + 4NaOH \rightarrow 2CO_2 + N_2 + 6NaCl + 2H_2O$$

Oxidation of cyanide may also be accomplished with hydrogen peroxide, ozone, and electrolysis (Dawson and Mercer 1986, p. 333).

Biological Treatment

Biological treatment of municipal and industrial wastewaters (not to be confused with bioremediation — see Chapter 11) is generally used for removal of organic pollutants from wastewater. It is effective with wastewaters having low-to-moderate concentrations of simple organic compounds and lower concentrations of complex organics. The biota are generally ineffective in attacking mineral components and are useless against heavy metal constituents.

Biological treatment of toxic organic components requires considerably more sophisticated operational control than is necessary with nontoxic wastewaters. The microorganisms used in biological treatment processes can easily be destroyed by shock loading or rapid increases in the rate of feed. Acclimation and development of a functional population of biota may require considerable time, and the system is continuously subject to upset (Dawson and Mercer 1986, p. 335).

The biological treatment units (Figure 7.17) used for treatment of hazardous waste components in industrial wastewaters are similar in configuration and operation to those used in municipal sewage treatment works. They include activated sludge, trickling filters, aerated lagoons, oxidation ponds, and anaerobic digesters.

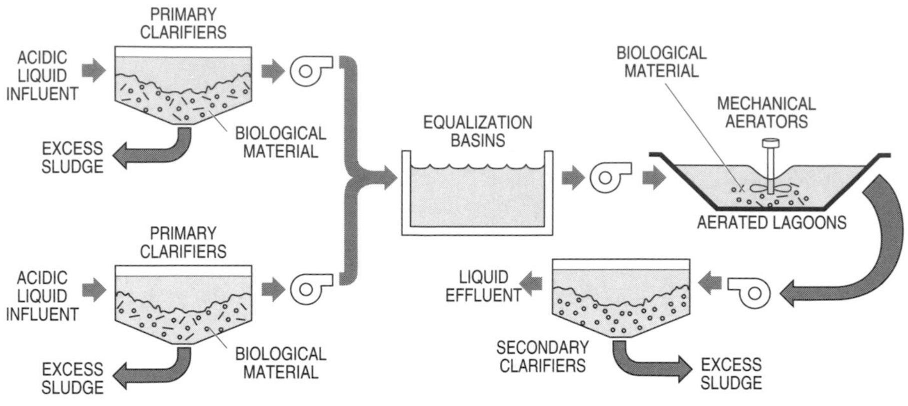

FIGURE 7.17 Schematic of a biological treatment of industrial waste.

Subpart Q — Chemical, Physical, and Biological Treatment

A list of some of the chemical, physical, and biological treatment processes which are regulated by 40 CFR 265, Subpart Q is provided in Table 7.3. Some of the more commonly used processes are described in the preceding paragraphs. There are many different types of treatment processes, and the processes are frequently waste specific. For these reasons, the EPA has not developed detailed regulations for any particular type of process or equipment. Instead, general requirements have been established to assure safe containment of hazardous wastes.

In the 40 CFR 268 land disposal restrictions, the EPA establishes extensive treatment standards for hazardous wastes, wastewaters, and waste extracts which must be met if the wastes are to be disposed of in land disposal facilities. The EPA also lists the treatment processes which have been demonstrated to be capable of achieving the standards, but does not specify that treatment be accomplished by that process (i.e., any process that can achieve the standard may be employed to treat the regulated waste). These regulatory requirements are overviewed in Section F of this chapter.

Thus, the EPA regulates hazardous waste *treatment* through the administrative and nontechnical requirements, the general standards, the specific standards of 40 CFR 264/265, the land disposal restrictions of 40 CFR 268, and the permitting requirements of 40 CFR 270. Finally, the EPA publishes "guidance" documents dealing with a wide range of hazardous waste management topics, including treatment. Several of them are referenced throughout this chapter.

Destruction of Hazardous Wastes by Incineration

Organic compounds can be destroyed by thermal processes and, after scrubbing, leave only nontoxic gases to be discharged to the atmosphere; inorganic residues of ash and scrubber sludge to be landfilled; and salt water to be injected in deep wells, evaporated, or diluted and discharged.

Heavy metals are not destroyed by any process (thermal or otherwise), but thermal processes will destroy sulfides and cyanides and leave all metals in the form of metal oxides. The ash and scrubber sludge can be stabilized, solidified, or converted to glassy slag which may be safely landfilled (Combs 1989).

In an incinerator, the basic stoichiometric combustion of organic waste materials (composed of carbon, hydrogen, and oxygen) can be illustrated by the following equations:

$$C + 1/2O_2 \rightarrow CO$$

$$C + O_2 \rightarrow CO_2$$

$$CO + 1/2O_2 \rightarrow CO_2$$

$$H_2 + 1/2O_2 \rightarrow H_2O$$

In real terms, the incinerator feed is not limited to just these three elements. Gas chromatographs of incinerator gases often indicate the presence of unexpected products of combustion. Inorganic materials may leave the incinerator either in the flue gas or in the residual ash and must be managed in an environmentally safe manner (Brunner 1988).

Combustion gases produced by a properly designed and operated incinerator burning chlorinated hydrocarbons are CO_2, H_2O, N_2, and HCl. All except HCl are completely nonhazardous. The HCl can be reacted with lime or caustic to produce nonhazardous salts which can be landfilled (Combs 1989).

Excess air is supplied in order to ensure that the combustion reaction is driven to completion. The major operating parameters for destruction of organic wastes in incinerators are:

- Turbulence (a function of design)
- Excess air (nominally 25 to 100%)
- Destruction temperature (1200 to 3000°F) (648 to 1649°C)
- Residence time (nominally 2 seconds)

In practice, operating temperatures of 1600 to 2200°F (871 to 1204°C) are required to ensure destruction of organic wastes at 2 seconds residence time.

As noted earlier, incineration of hazardous wastes is widely perceived as preferable to most treatment or destruction processes.* The drive to eliminate land disposal has sharpened the search for the ultimate incinerator. Several incinerator configurations and processes have been developed or are in development. Each variation is intended to meet a particular requirement, deal with a particular problem, or make use of an existing facility. Table 7.4 provides a list of the currently identified

* Incineration of hazardous waste has its detractors. In the early 1990s, environmental activists mounted vigorous opposition to the siting and/or permitting of new hazardous waste incinerators. The issue surfaced in the 1992 presidential campaign, and shortly after taking office, the Clinton administration announced the "combustion-waste minimization strategy" and suspended permitting of new incinerators. These issues are discussed in Chapter 8.

Table 7.4 Incineration Processes

Multiple hearth
Fluidized bed
Recirculating fluidized bed
Liquid injection
Fume
Rotary kiln
Cement kiln
Large industrial boiler
Multiple chamber
Cyclonic
Auger combustor
Two stage (starved air)
Catalytic
Oxygen enriched
Molten salt
Infrared (moving belt)

Source: Combs 1989.

processes. Figure 7.18 diagrams the rotary kiln incinerator, probably the most popular design in current use. Figure 7.19 is a view of a rotary kiln installation. Figure 7.20 diagrams a liquid injection incinerator, also a popular design.

As the land disposal restrictions were implemented, operators of BIFs, including cement kilns, many of which had been burning their own hazardous wastes, began operating as commercial burners. The practice was (and to some extent remains) fraught with uncertainty and contention. A central issue was the question of whether the wastes were legitimate hazardous waste fuels, or if the BIFs were being used as incinerators, i.e., "sham recycling." In 1990, the EPA published standards for BIFs in 40 CFR 266, Subpart H and began offering "interim status" to permit applicants while their permits were being processed. By July 1993, some 159 BIFs in 34 states and Puerto Rico had applied for permits. Further controversy arose over the standards, with incinerator operators protesting that BIFs were being given unfair competitive advantage in the less stringent standards. These and other issues, various petitions, legislative proposals, and related litigation were at a vigorous pitch when the EPA administrator, on May 18, 1993, announced a "temporary capacity freeze" as the centerpiece of a Hazardous Waste Minimization and Combustion Strategy. The freeze suspended new permitting for 18 months, and the agency announced that it intended to propose new regulations for hazardous waste incinerators and industrial boilers and furnaces within 18 months to 2 years. At the time of this writing, the 18 months have passed and no new standards have been proposed. A dozen or more incinerator permit applications were withdrawn following the announcement.

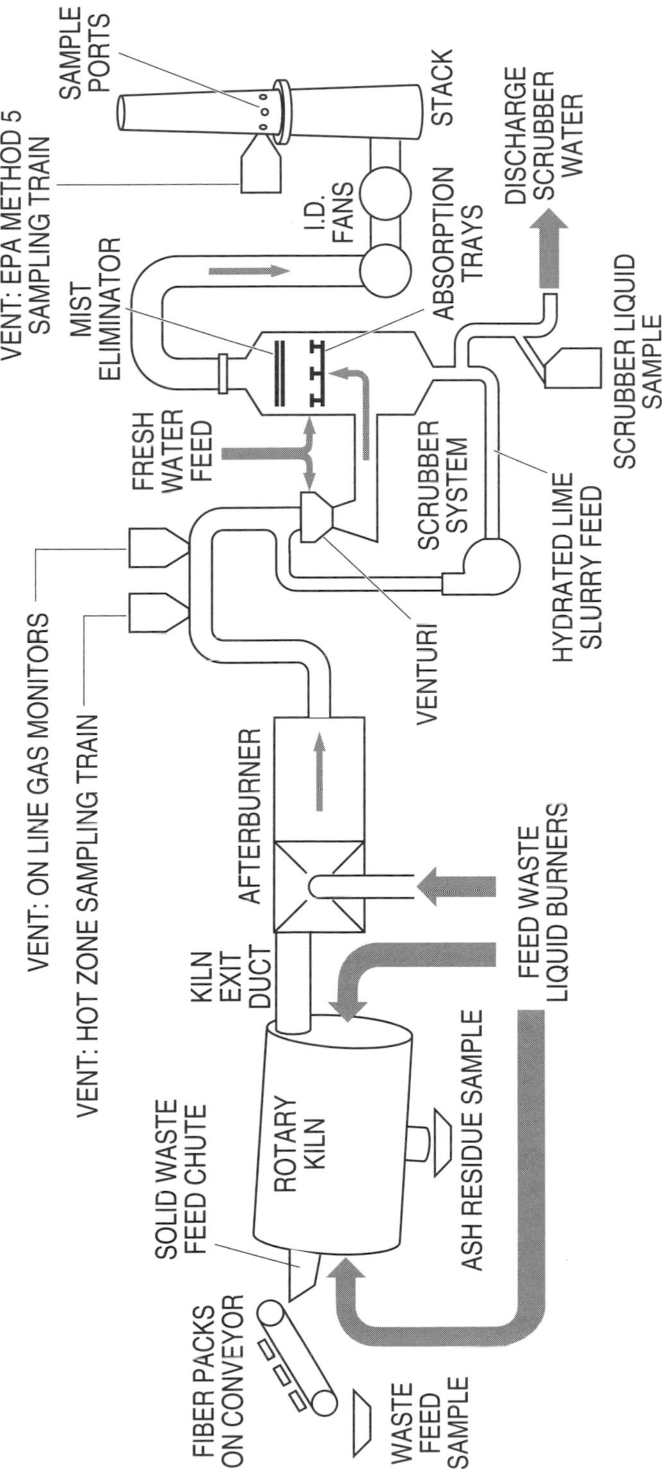

FIGURE 7.18 Schematic of a rotary kiln incinerator.

FIGURE 7.19 Rotary kiln incinerator layout [Environmental Systems Company (ENSCO), Little Rock, AR].

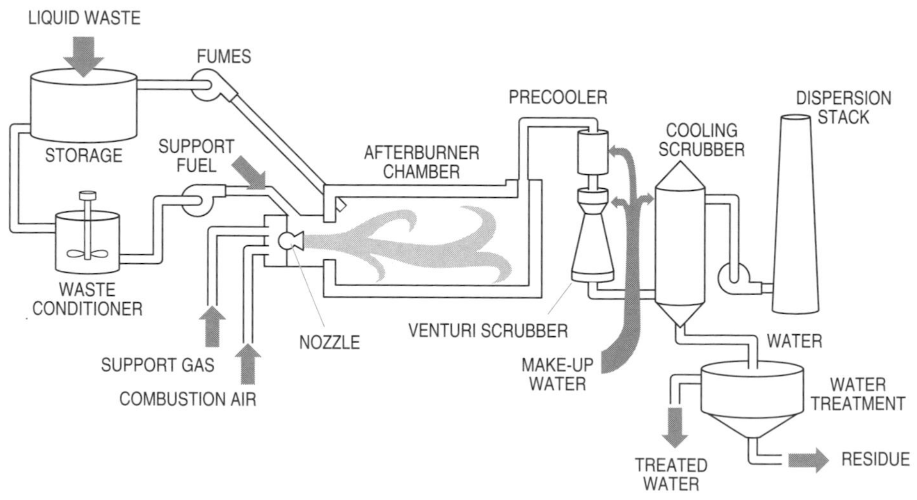

FIGURE 7.20 Schematic of a liquid injection incinerator.

Many of the emerging technologies for hazardous waste treatment and/or destruction fall into the classification of "other thermal processes." Most employ air/oxygen oxidation as a final step, but this is not always necessary. They are differentiated from incineration because they involve:

- extensive electrical energy input (plasma arc pyrolysis, microwave discharge, advanced electrical reactor, *in situ* vitrification).
- oxidation in the liquid phase (wet air and supercritical water oxidation).
- pyrolysis or vaporization which may or may not be followed by incineration of the off-gases in a second stage (pyrolysis, calcination, thermal desorption).

If the gases produced in the first stages of these processes are not destroyed by incineration in the second stage, then some other treatment process must follow, e.g., carbon adsorption (Combs 1989).

For an outstanding overview and update of hazardous waste incineration technology, the reader should review the work of Dempsey and Oppelt (1993). (*See also* Rappe et al. 1986, Sections I and II; U.S. EPA 1993a; Johnson and Cosmos 1989; Wentz 1989, Chapter 8; Barton et. al. 1992)

Subpart O — Incinerators

The interim status incinerator general operating requirements include:

- achieving normal steady-state combustion conditions before wastes are introduced.
- combustion and emission monitoring.

The owner or operator must analyze the waste that is to be incinerated. Special requirements, beyond those required under Subpart B, pertain to incinerators. The waste analysis must determine:

- heating value of the waste.
- total halogen and sulfur content.
- concentrations of lead and mercury, unless the facility can demonstrate that these elements are not present in the waste stream to be incinerated.

Interim status and permitted facilities burning dioxin-containing wastes must achieve 99.9999% destruction removal efficiency ("six-nines DRE") of dioxins.*

The trial burn is a temporary period during which the owner or operator demonstrates the efficiency of the incinerator in destroying a surrogate hazardous waste.

* Incineration of polychlorinated biphenyls (PCBs) is regulated under Toxic Substances Control Act (TSCA) authority (*see* 40 CFR 761.70).

Permitted facilities must conduct a trial burn or use alternate data to determine the operating methods for the incinerator that will result in meeting the following performance standards:

- 99.99% of each principal organic hazardous constituent (POHC) specified in the permit must be destroyed or removed by the incinerator (as above, 99.9999% destruction or removal of dioxins must be achieved).
- Hydrogen chloride (HCl) emissions must be controlled so that the rate of emission is no greater than the larger of either 1.8 kg/h or 1% of the HCl in the stack gas prior to entry to any pollution control equipment.
- Particulate emissions are limited to 180 mg/dry standard m^3 (0.08 grains/dry standard ft^3) of stack gas.

The permit will specify the composition of waste feed that may be incinerated. Different waste feeds may be incinerated only if a new permit or permit modification is obtained.

While incinerating hazardous waste, the combustion process and equipment must be monitored and inspected to avoid potential accidents or incomplete combustion. Incinerators may receive waste only after the destruction removal efficiency (DRE) has been achieved and the unit is complying with its operating requirements.

Subpart P — Thermal Treatment

Incineration is considered a type of thermal treatment process, although the intent with incineration is to destroy the waste. Less conventional methods of thermal treatment, such as molten salt combustion, calcination, wet air oxidation, and fluidized bed combustion, are regulated under this subpart. Owners or operators who thermally treat hazardous wastes (other than incinerators) must operate the unit following many of the requirements applied to the incinerator and consistent with the trial burn results.

Storage of Hazardous Wastes

As discussed earlier, the accumulation of hazardous waste has been one of the most troublesome of hazardous waste management issues for the regulatory agencies. Most of the early disasters and many of today's Superfund sites grew from the uncontrolled accumulation of hazardous wastes. Congress, in crafting the RCRA statutes, and the EPA, in the implementing regulations, have sought to impose rigorous controls and accountability upon all who accumulate and/or store hazardous wastes.

RCRA defines "storage" as the holding of hazardous waste for a temporary period, at the end of which the hazardous waste is treated, disposed of, or stored elsewhere. Throughout the Subtitle C regulations, the accumulation of hazardous waste beyond a prescribed period (90 days in most situations) is considered to be storage. The owner or operator of a facility in which waste is to be held for more than 90 days must apply for a permit before commencing accumulation and must comply with the regulations pertaining to storage facilities.

FIGURE 7.21 Typical abandoned drum scene [Environsafe Services of Ohio, Inc. (ESOI), P.O. Box 167571, Oregon, OH 43616-7571].

The 40 CFR 264/265, Subparts A through H, General Standards, previously overviewed, contain the major provisions applicable to storage facilities. Subparts I and J, the standards for the use of containers and tanks, pertain to all facilities that use them. Since the primary function of containers and tanks is storage, we include our overview of those subparts here. The requirements for container and tank management on interim status and permitted TSDFs are very similar. The minor differences will be pointed out in the following sections.

Subpart I — Containers

Whether viewing the most modern and well-operated hazardous waste facility or the most outrageous of abandoned hazardous waste dump sites, Americans have come to think of the standard 55-gallon drum when they think of hazardous waste (and vice versa). Figures 7.21 and 7.22 illustrate the point. The "drum" may be any one of several U.S. Department of Transportation (DOT)-specified 55-gallon containers, but they have collectively become the most frequently used (if not the standard) container for collection, storage, shipment, and disposal of liquid hazardous wastes.

Selection of the proper drum or container for wastes that are to be shipped requires adherance to the DOT regulations. The user consults the 49 CFR 172.101 Hazardous Materials Table (Chapter 5, Figure 5.1). Column 7 is checked for any applicable sprecial provisions, then packaging authorizations of Column 8 are consulted for the appropriate section of 49 CFR 173. The former 17-series steel drums are now designated as either 1A1 or 1A2. Figure 7.23 shows the location of the drum

FIGURE 7.22 Shipment of liquid hazardous waste in 55-gallon drums (CWM).

stamp information which must be in accord with the specification for the hazardous material to be contained.

Drums to be used in hazardous waste management must be in good condition; clean; and free of rust, dents, and creases prior to use. The regulations additionally require:

- containers holding hazardous waste to always be closed, except when wastes are added or removed.
- wastes in leaking or damaged containers to be recontainerized.
- ensuring the compatibility of the waste with the container (i.e., corrosive wastes should not be stored in metal containers).
- handling containers properly to prevent ruptures and leaks.
- preventing the mixture of incompatible wastes.
- conducting inspections to assess container condition.

Containers holding ignitable or reactive waste must be located at least 15 m (50 ft) from the facility property line.

Subpart J — Tanks

The Subpart J regulations apply to stationary tanks storing wastes that are hazardous under Subtitle C of RCRA (Figures 7.24 and 7.25). The regulations pertaining to underground storage tanks storing petroleum products (exempt from Subtitle C regulation) or hazardous *substances* are found in Subpart I of RCRA.

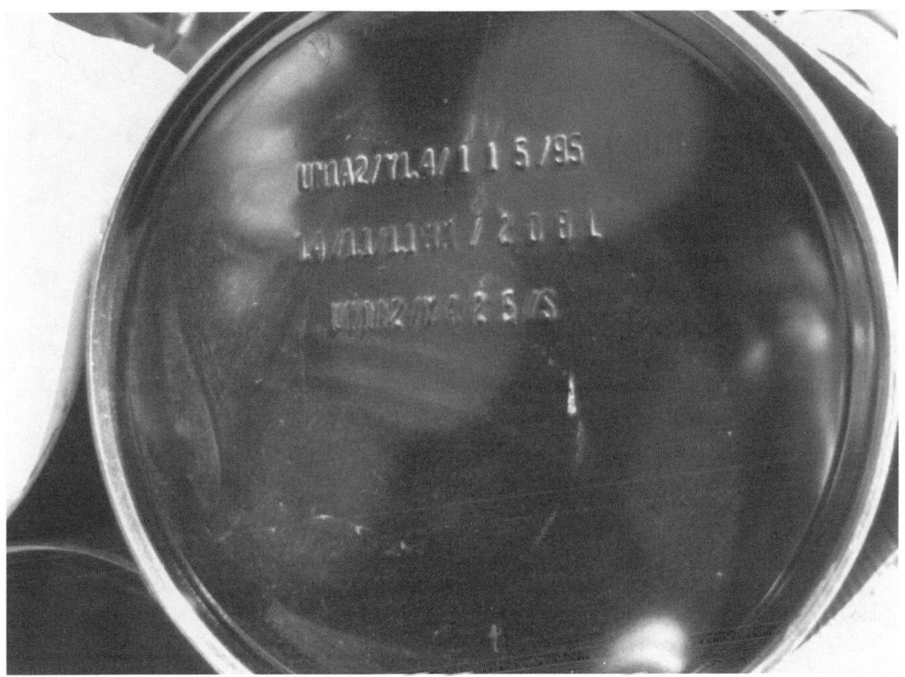

FIGURE 7.23 Drum stamp information.

Regulations governing hazardous waste tanks were substantially expanded under the 1984 Hazardous and Solid Waste Amendments (HSWA). There are five general operating requirements:

- *Tank assessment* must be completed to evaluate the structural integrity and compatibility with the wastes that the tank system is expected to hold. The assessment covers design standards, corrosion protection, tank tests, waste characteristics, and the age of the tank.
- *Secondary containment and release detection* is required unless the tank does not contain free liquids and is located in a building with impermeable floors. Secondary containment systems must be designed, installed, and operated to prevent the migration of liquid from the tank system and to detect and collect any releases that do occur. Containment systems commonly used include liners, vaults, and double-walled tanks. Figures 7.26, 7.27, and 7.28 illustrate acceptable containment systems.
- *Operating and maintenance requirements* necessitate the management of tanks to avoid leaks, ruptures, spills, and corrosion. This includes using freeboard or a containment structure to prevent and contain escaping wastes. A shutoff or bypass system must be installed to prevent liquid from flowing into a leaking tank. Figure 7.27 illustrates an all-too-common practice which is certain to be the eventual cause of disaster.
- *Response to releases* must include immediate removal of the remaining contents of leaking tanks. The area surrounding the tank must be visually inspected for leaks and spills. Based on the inspection, further migration

FIGURE 7.24 Hazardous waste storage tanks with secondary containment (CWM).

of the spilled waste must be stopped, and contaminated soils and surface water must be disposed of in accord with RCRA requirements. All major leaks must be reported to the EPA or state agency.

- *Closure and post-closure* requirements include the removal of all contaminated soils and other hazardous waste residues from the tank storage area at the time of closure. If decontamination is impossible, the tank storage area must be closed following the requirements for landfills.

RCRA facilities, whether subject to generator rules, in interim status, or finally permitted, are also subject to 40 CFR 264/265, Subparts AA and BB, covering atmospheric emissions from process vents and equipment leaks. Facilities which treat or store hazardous wastes in impoundments, tanks, or containers are subject to the newly published 40 CFR 264/265, Subparts CC, which impose air emission standards from the subject units. The new standards, published on December 6, 1994, are found at 59 FR 62896.

Subpart DD — Storage in Containment Buildings

In 1993, the EPA published final regulations, pertaining to storage of hazardous wastes in containment buildings, at 40 CFR 264/265, Subpart DD. All RCRA facilities which store bulk hazardous waste in "containment" buildings are subject to the new rules. They provide extensive structural specifications and exacting operating requirements, all of which are designed to ensure that:

FIGURE 7.25 Hazardous waste storage tanks with secondary containment (CWM).

- fugitive dusts are contained.
- liquid wastes are collected and completely and securely contained.
- there are no cracks or other structural defects which could permit release of hazardous waste constituents.
- tracking of wastes from the facility, by persons or equipment, is prevented.

The containment building design must be certified by a qualified, registered, professional engineer prior to operation of the unit.

At closure of the unit, the owner or operator must remove or decontaminate all waste residues and all contaminated equipment, subsoils, and structures. If, after removing all residues and making all reasonable efforts to decontaminate the facility, not all contaminated subsoils can be practicably removed or decontaminated, the closure and post-closure requirements that apply to landfills become applicable to the facility.

FIGURE 7.26 Secondary containment with additional containment for spillage from fill connection (CWM).

Land Disposal of Hazardous Wastes

Hazardous waste disposal practice has, historically, followed the path of least resistance. As discussed in Chapter 1, several factors have driven hazardous wastes onto and beneath the earth's surface. These factors include (1) the relatively low cost of land and land disposal procedures, (2) the environmental legislation of the 1970s and early 1980s which placed increasingly stringent controls on releases to the atmosphere and to "waters of the nation," and (3) widely held beliefs to the effect that land disposal was safe and proper.

The tragic consequences of these practices are now upon us, foursquare, and it is exceedingly important that the student understand the seriousness of the problem. It is even more important that he/she understand the procedures and practices that are necessary if new episodes of the old problem are to be avoided.

FIGURE 7.27 Invitation to disaster.

FIGURE 7.28 Secure landfill leachate detection and monitoring access gallery (CWM).

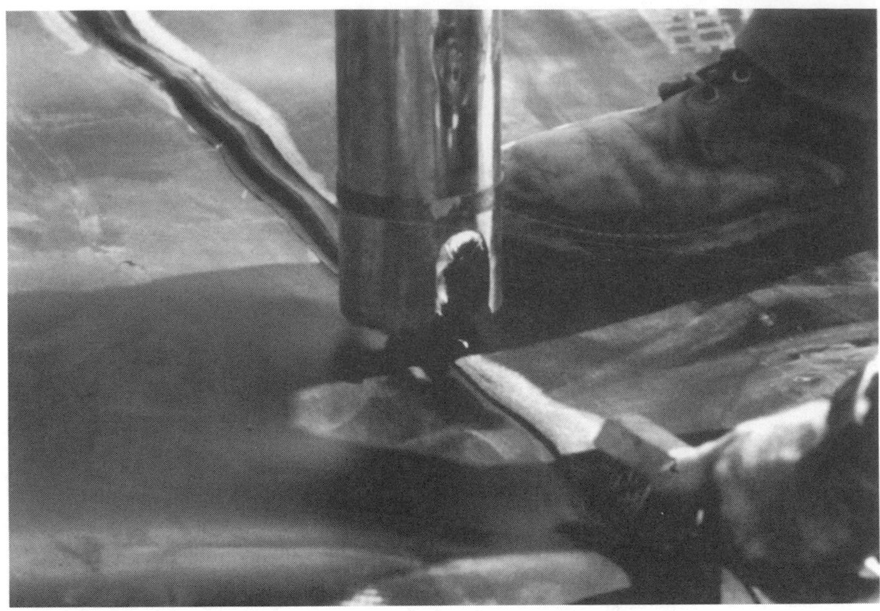

FIGURE 7.29 Land disposal liner sections being welded (Gundel Lining Systems, Inc., Houston, TX).

The four general types of land disposal facilities — landfills, waste piles, surface impoundments, and underground disposal — are discussed only briefly. The student is encouraged to examine the technical literature for details and for variations on the central theme.

Landfills

"Sanitary landfills" were developed for the disposal of municipal refuse as an orderly alternative to the open dump. Early practice called for the working face to be compacted and maintained at a 30 degree slope, with 6 in. of daily cover on the working face and with 2 ft of top cover over the daily cells (Ehlers and Steel 1958, pp. 197–203).

Codes, specifications, and administrators concerned themselves with control of insects, rodents, odors, and blowing refuse. Few operators of sanitary landfills gave thought to the effects of hazardous waste. Sites receiving liquid wastes usually designated a discharge area away from the compacted cells in order to avoid erosion of the cells. Dry hazardous wastes were legally mixed with domestic refuse, compacted, buried, and forgotten.

With large numbers of these sites now crowding the National Priority List (NPL; for remediation under Superfund), regulators, designers, and operators of landfills and "responsible parties" have become appropriately concerned that wastes be safely contained within secure landfills. Design and operating procedures have evolved to include elaborate safeguards against leakage and migration of leachates.

FIGURE 7.30 Liner bedding for protection from puncture (Laidlaw Environmental Services, Inc., 5295 South Garvey Road, Westmoreland, CA).

Most municipal landfills do not knowingly accept hazardous wastes, and landfill disposal of bulk liquids is banned by RCRA. Later in this chapter we will cover the RCRA land disposal restrictions which are increasingly stringent with regard to all forms of land disposal.

Secure landfills for hazardous waste disposal are now equipped with double liners, leakage detection, leachate monitoring and collection, and groundwater monitoring systems (Figure 7.28). Synthetic liners are a minimum 30 ml in thickness. Liner technology has improved greatly and continues to do so. Very large sections of liner fabric now minimize the numbers of joints. Adjacent sections are "welded" together to form leak-proof joints having a high degree of integrity (Figure 7.29). Liners are protected by sand bedding or finer material devoid of sharp edges or points which might penetrate the liner fabric (Figure 7.30). Another layer of bedding protects the inner liner from damage by machinery working the waste (Figure 7.31). Some states allow one of the liners to be of natural clays. The completed liner must demonstrate permeability of less than 10^{-6} cm per second and must include a leachate collection system.

Leachate detection and collection systems are equipped with access galleys or other means of leachate removal (Figure 7.32). The double-liner, leakage detection, and leachate collection systems are diagrammed in Figure 7.33.

Landfill caps are the subject of detailed guidance by the EPA. Figure 7.34 is a cross-sectional diagram of a typical cap design. The objective of the cap design is to protect the cells from erosion, to route potential runon around and away from the cap, and to prevent buildup of generated gases within the landfill.

FIGURE 7.31 Liner bedding for protection from puncture (Gundel Lining Systems).

FIGURE 7.32 Secure landfill leachate detection and monitoring access (Laidlaw Environmental Services).

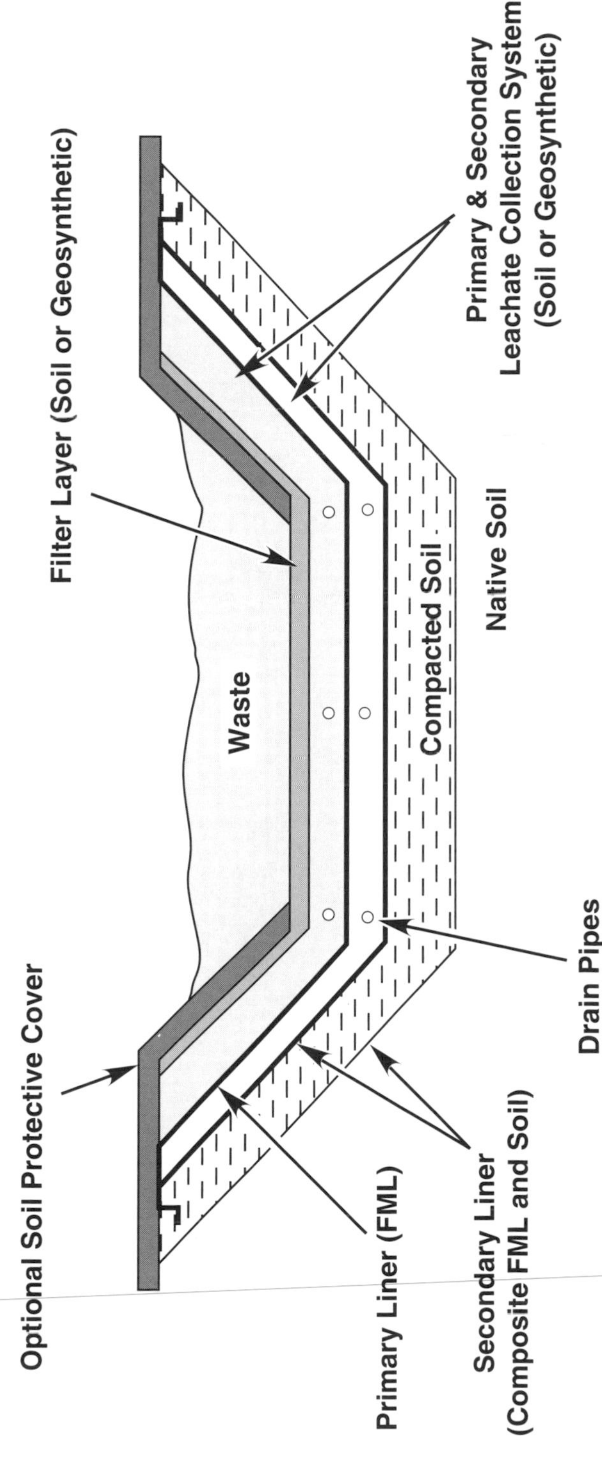

FIGURE 7.33 Schematic of a cross-section of a secure landfill double-liner system.

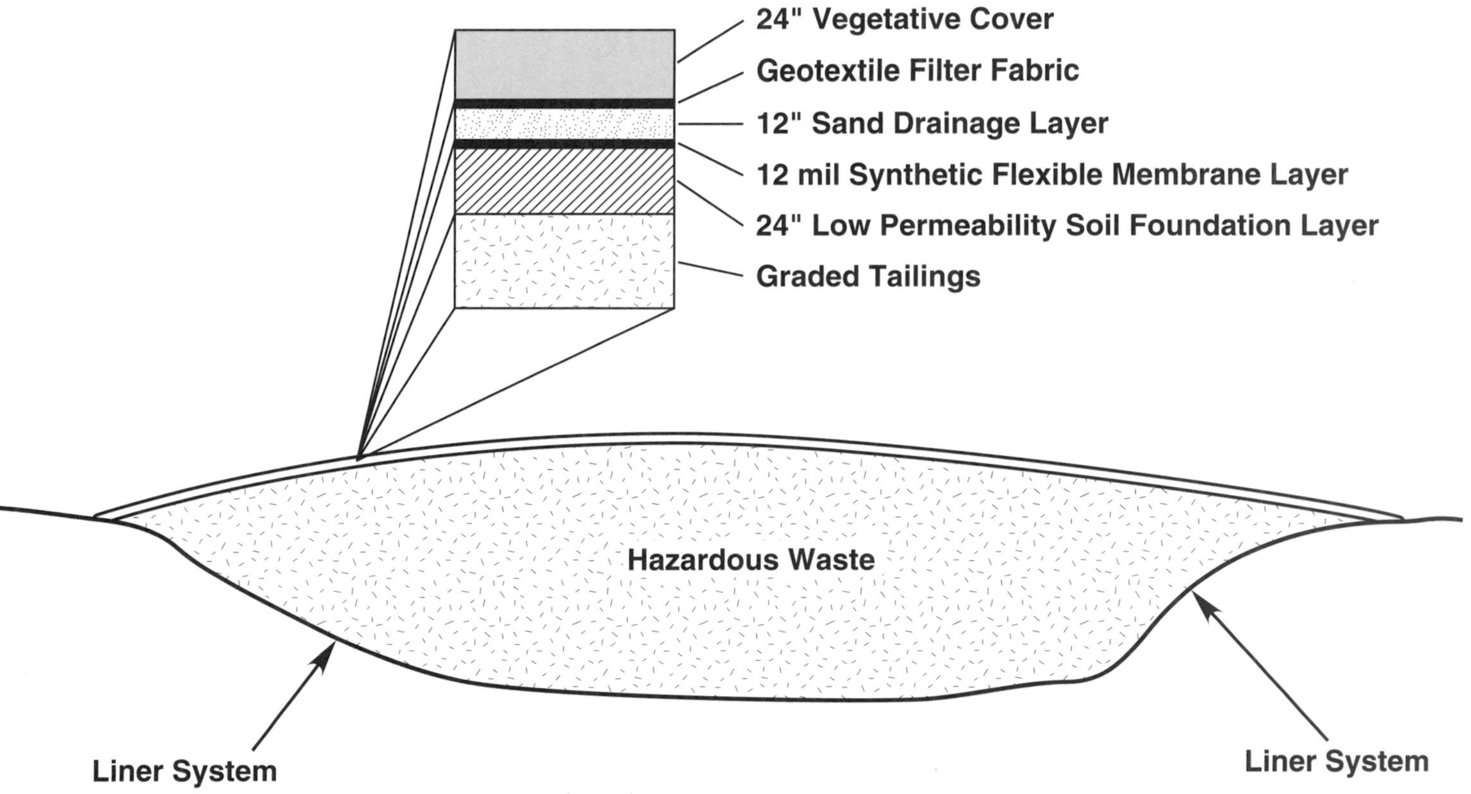

FIGURE 7.34 Schematic of a land disposal site cap designed for maximum resistance to infiltration.

Groundwater monitoring schemes are designed to provide upgradient (background) water quality data and to detect downgradient differences in critical water quality parameters. As was discussed earlier in this chapter, RCRA requires upgradient and downgradient patterns of monitoring well placement to detect leakage from landfills. (*See also* U.S. EPA 1981, 1982, 1987a, 1987b, 1988)

Subpart N — Landfills

Landfills have historically presented two general classes of problems. The first of these includes fires, explosions, production of toxic fumes, and related problems from the improper management of ignitable, reactive, and incompatible wastes. To deal with these problems, owners or operators are required to analyze their wastes to provide enough information for proper management. They must control the mixing of incompatible wastes in landfill cells. They may landfill ignitable and reactive wastes only when the wastes meet all applicable requirements of the land disposal restrictions of 40 CFR 268 and have been rendered unignitable or nonreactive (40 CFR 264/265.312).

The second general class of landfill problems concerns the contamination of surface and groundwaters. To deal with these problems, the interim status regulations require diversion of runon away from the active face of the landfill; treatment of any liquid wastes or semisolid wastes so that they do not contain free liquids; proper closure (including a cover) and post-closure care to control erosion and the infiltration of rainfall; and crushing or shredding most landfilled containers so that they cannot later collapse, thus leading to subsidence and breaching of the cover. Groundwater monitoring, as described in Subpart F, is required, as is the collection of rainwater and other runoff from the active face of the landfill. Segregation of waste, such as acids, that would mobilize, solubilize, or dissolve other wastes or waste constituents is required (U.S. EPA 1990, p. III-49).

In HSWA, Congress prohibited disposal of bulk and noncontainerized liquid hazardous waste and hazardous waste containing free liquids in landfills. Expanded or replaced interim status landfills are required to install doubler liners and leachate collection systems. Landfills permitted after November 1985 must also have two or more liners, two leachate collection systems (one above and one between liners), and must conduct groundwater monitoring.

Surface Impoundments

Prior to imposition of the RCRA regulations, surface impoundments were very frequently used for "treatment" of wastewaters having hazardous components. Some were of flow-through design, but many were described by their owners/operators as evaporation ponds or treatment ponds. Most were unlined, thereby allowing infiltration and ultimate groundwater contamination. In the case of the flow-through ponds, some degree of treatment may have been achieved by sedimentation and/or solidification of solids, surface emission of volatile organics, and/or oxygen transfer at the surface. Evaporation ponds lost most of their volatile organic compound (VOC) content to the atmosphere and may have achieved some degree of treatment via oxygen transfer at the surface and settling of solids. Many industrial waste impoundments were created by earthen dams that conveniently failed as the impounded content approached capacity.

In approximately the eastern half of the U.S., annual rainfall exceeds annual evaporation, so "evaporation" ponds in the eastern half of the country were losing liquid to the subsurface. Aerated impoundments, if properly managed, may have developed biota that were effective in attacking certain organic contaminants. However, the aeration accelerates the transfer of VOCs to the atmosphere, and the losses to the groundwater would have been similar to those discussed previously. Impoundments are similar to other biological systems in ineffectiveness with heavy metals, most inorganic, and some organic components of hazardous wastewaters.

In summary, it is questionable whether significant treatment beyond dispersion of pollutants into the atmosphere, surface streams, and the groundwater was achieved in and by these early facilities.

The EPA continues to recognize various configurations of surface impoundments as treatment units, and they continue to be widely used by industry. The RCRA requirements for double liners, leachate detection and removal systems, and groundwater monitoring have brought about improvements in protection of surface and groundwaters. The double-liner system for an impoundment facility is diagrammed in Figure 7.35. Such units do not contain, retain, nor reentrain VOCs released at the surface or stripped out by aeration. Moreover, sludges containing precipitated solids, expired aerobic biota, active anaerobic bacteria, inorganics including heavy metals, and remaining organics must be periodically removed and subjected to further management. RCRA guidance for design, construction, and operation of surface impoundments is discussed later. (*See also* U.S. EPA 1987a, 1987b)

Subpart K — Surface Impoundments

Hazardous waste surface impoundments are required to have at least one liner and be located on an impermeable base. New surface impoundments, replacements, or lateral expansions of surface impoundments for which permit application is made after November 8, 1984 must meet the minimum technological requirements added by the HSWA. These requirements are:

- the installation of two or more liners.
- a leachate collection system between the liners.
- groundwater monitoring as prescribed in Subpart F.

The requirements include preventing liquids from escaping due to overfilling or runon and prevention of erosion of dikes and dams. Liners must meet permit specifications for materials and thickness. During construction and installation, liners must be inspected for uniformity, damage, and imperfections.

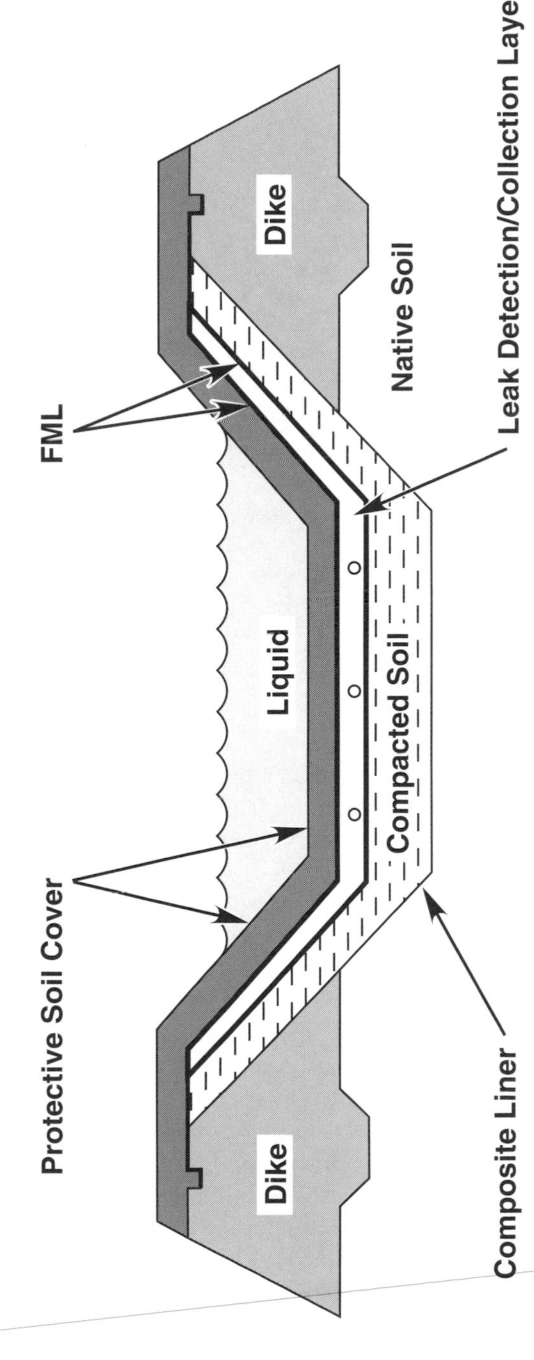

FIGURE 7.35 Schematic of a cross-section of a liquid waste impoundment double-liner system.

FIGURE 7.36 Hazardous waste pile showing fluff from auto-shredding operation.

Waste Piles

Essentially, the same considerations apply to waste piles as those discussed previously. Hazardous waste piles have arisen on many industrial sites. As in the previous discussions they were frequently referred to by their owner/operators as treatment piles. Indeed, the 40 CFR 264/265, Subpart L regulations continue to refer to them as storage or treatment units.

Such piles make their volatile components available for evaporation and are subject to wind and water erosion. They may be leached by percolation of rainfall and runon. As mentioned earlier, piles containing mineral or metal values may be leached with weak acid or caustic to recover the values. Unless carefully constructed over an impervious base, leachate tends to escape to the subsurface, contaminating groundwater or emerging as base flow in streams (Chapter 1, Figure 1.20).

Figure 7.36 shows piles of "fluff," the nonmagnetic materials discarded in auto-shredding operations. The fluff contains fabric, rubber, plastic, insulation, lead, and cadmium. It is usually saturated with oil and tends to autoignite. Samples of fluff usually fail the TCLP* toxicity test for lead and cadmium and, if so, must be managed as hazardous waste; they frequently contain trace amounts of PCBs from electrical components and insulation.

Aluminum dross, the ladle scum and dregs from aluminum salvage operations, is shown in Figure 7.37. The dross is allowed to accumulate in salvage yards where it is easily eroded by wind and runon/runoff. Some dross fails characteristic tests for various metals and, if so, must be managed as hazardous waste.

* *See* Glossary and/or 40 CFR 261.24.

FIGURE 7.37 Hazardous waste pile showing "dross" from aluminum salvage operation.

Accepted practice has been the transfer of the contents of waste piles to landfills when pile size or management became a problem. Recent determinations of TCLP toxicity require that dross and fluff piles be managed within acceptable RCRA management alternatives.* RCRA specifications for waste piles are similar to those for landfills and are discussed here.

Subpart L — Waste Piles

An owner or operator of a waste pile used for treatment or storage of a noncontainerized accumulation of solid, nonflowing hazardous waste is given a choice of compliance either with the waste pile or the landfill requirements. Waste piles used for disposal must comply with the requirements for landfills. The requirements for managing storage and treatment waste piles include protecting the pile from wind dispersion. The pile must be placed on an impermeable base that is compatible with the waste being stored. If hazardous leachate or runoff is generated, control systems must be imposed.

Underground Disposal

Several forms of underground disposal have been and are practiced. Of these, the most widely recognized, and the subject of the Subpart R regulations, are deep wells

* Some states, citing the variability in toxicity determinations on fluff and dross, have opted for "special waste" designations or other management options.

for injection of liquid hazardous wastes (Class I injection wells). A great variety of shallow "injection wells," most of them illegal, continue in operation throughout the nation and territories and are the sources of major groundwater quality problems. An excellent summary of the shallow well problem has been prepared for the EPA by the Cadmus Group (Cadmus Group, Inc., 1991). Other underground injection operations include disposal in salt formation deposits and worked-out salt mines and other open-pit and shaft mines. The latter are generally considered unsatisfactory, due to water and groundwater contamination problems, and will not be discussed further here.

Deep well injection has achieved some degree of acceptance in the U.S. and elsewhere. A 1993 EPA database shows some 84 Class I*,** injection wells in operation in the U.S. (U.S. EPA, 1993b). Of these, more than half are located along the Texas–Louisiana Gulf Coast, with 31 in Texas and 17 in Louisiana. The area has suitable injection zones and large numbers of hazardous waste generators.

Figure 7.38 is a cross-sectional diagram of a typical injection well. Advocates and practitioners rationalize the practice with the proposition that:

> liquid wastes can be injected into, and contained by, confined geologic strata not having other actual or potential uses of a more beneficial nature, thereby providing long-term isolation of the waste material from man's usable environment. The validity of this concept depends on two basic factors: (1) the presence of suitable receptor zones, and (2) the existence of adequate confinement. (Walker and Cox 1976, p. 2)

Capacity to accept an injected waste is a function of the amount of void space within the formation (its porosity) and its ability to transmit fluid (its permeability). In the usual case, the void space is already occupied with natural water, either fresh or mineralized to some extent. Thus, injection usually involves compression or displacement of existing fluids. Since the compressibility of water is small, there must be large spaces within the strata to accept the wastes and/or the displaced water (Walker and Cox 1976, p. 2).

Deep well disposal involves the use of limited formation space, is expensive in construction and operation, and is the subject of ever-tightening regulation. Thus, the method should only be used for those wastes for which there are no other feasible management options. Intensive operational oversight and monitoring is necessary to preclude contamination of nearby aquifers. Sudden changes in operating pressure or annulus pressure are a major concern. The former may indicate hydrofracturing and break out from the confining formation. The latter usually indicates failure of the well integrity, introducing the possibility of contamination of other formations. Another major concern is the fact that Class I injection wells must penetrate drinking water aquifers to reach deep disposal zones. If the casing is damaged during installation or later by seismic activity, the penetrated aquifer may be contaminated.

* Class I injection wells are completed below the lowermost underground sources of drinking water. Class I wells are further classified for hazardous or nonhazardous wastes.

** Note that the 1993 Class I well count is down from the 245 count in 1989 (Table 7.5), a very substantial reduction.

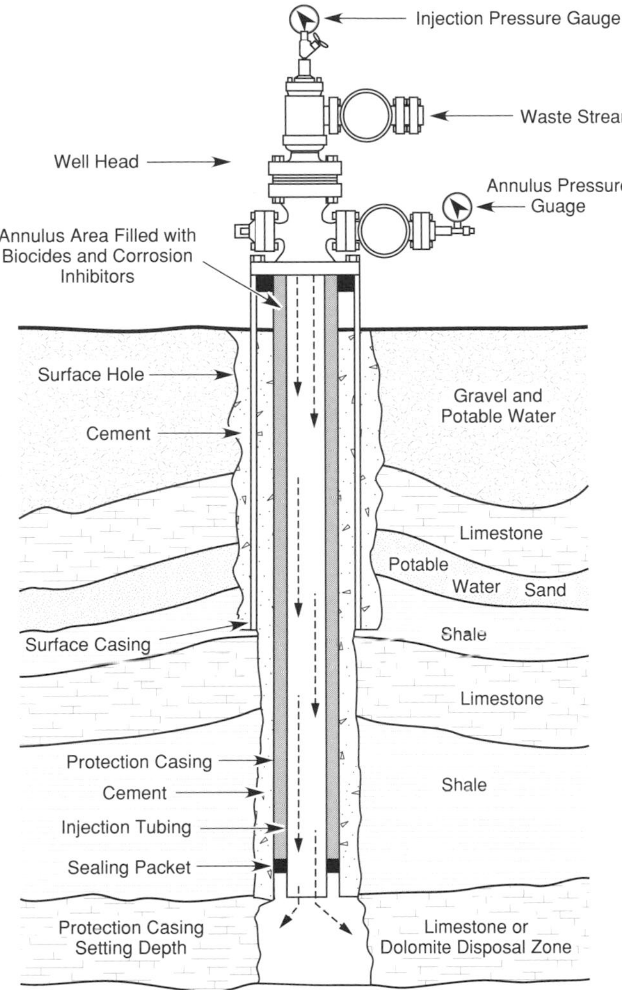

FIGURE 7.38 Schematic of a cross-section of the design of a hazardous waste injection well. (Adapted from Wentz, Charles A. 1989. *Hazardous Waste Management*. McGraw-Hill, New York.)

Subpart R — Underground Injection

Underground injection of hazardous wastes is jointly regulated by the RCRA and Safe Drinking Water Act (SDWA). The wells are permitted at the state level under SDWA and by rule under RCRA. Owners and operators of these facilities must meet the general standards outlined in Subparts A through E of 40 CFR 265 and the closure and post-closure requirements of SDWA. The SDWA regulations, including the land disposal restrictions applicable to the Underground Injection Control (UIC) Program, are found in 40 CFR 144 through 148. The EPA defines injection wells of Class I through Class V. These are briefly described in Table 7.5.

Table 7.5 EPA Classifications of Injection Wells

U.S. EPA Classification	Injection Well Description	1989 EPA Active Inventory
Class I	Wells used to inject liquid hazardous wastes beneath the lowermost USDW	245
	Wells used to inject industrial non-hazardous liquid wastes beneath the lowermost USDW	233
	Wells used to inject municipal waste waters beneath the lowermost USDW	76
Class II	Wells used to dispose of fluids associated with the production of oil and natural gas	38,152
	Wells used to inject fluids for enhanced oil recovery	121,086
	Wells used for the storage of liquid hydrocarbons	918
Class III	Wells used to inject fluids for the extraction of minerals	21,027[a]
Class IV	Wells used to dispose of hazardous or radioactive wastes into or above a USDW (the EPA has banned the use of these wells)	20
Class V	Wells not included in the other classes used to generally inject nonhazardous fluid into or above a USDW	173,159[b]

[a] Located in 192 facilities.

[b] Inventory from the EPA Class V Report to Congress (U.S. EPA 1984).

HSWA prohibits the disposal of hazardous waste by underground injection into or above a formation within 0.25 or 1/4 mile of an underground source of drinking water (USDW). The SDWA standards, paraphrased, are:

- *Construction Requirements* — New wells must be sited so that they inject into a separate formation from underground sources of drinking water, free of faults or fractures. Drilling logs and similar tests must be used to ensure that this requirement is met. Both new and existing wells must be cased and cemented to protect sources of drinking water, so that the injection well does not create a significant risk to human health.
- *Operating, Monitoring, and Reporting Requirements* — The injection pressure of the well must not be so great as to fracture the disposal formation. The owner or operator must monitor the injection well to ensure the integrity of the well bore. Pressure, flow rate, and cumulative volume of the injected material must be periodically monitored and reported to the EPA (U.S. EPA 1990, p. III-52).

The EPA has recently banned the underground injection of wastes that do not meet the applicable treatment standards of the land disposal restrictions. The owner/operator must successfully demonstrate that wastes will not migrate from the injection zone for as long as the wastes remain hazardous (40 CFR 148.1). The agency has also indicated intent to propose new regulations in 1995 for operating Class V injection wells.

Other Treatment and Disposal Methods

There are many treatment and some disposal methods, practices, or processes that have not been discussed in this chapter. There are too many of them to cover, and they are less significant in terms of numbers, popularity, or utility than those discussed. Three methods which have been frequently employed, but are in declining acceptability, require brief mention.

Ocean Dumping

The U.S., with 46 other nations, is signatory to the Convention on the Prevention of Marine Pollution by Dumping of Wastes and Other Matter, generally known as the London Dumping Convention (LDC). The convention requires the member nations to establish national systems to control the dumping at sea of wastes and other matter. The convention was negotiated in 1972 and became effective in 1975. The Marine Protection, Research, and Sanctuary Act (MPRSA) of 1972 was enacted to implement the provisions of the LDC. The MPRSA and its 1988 amendment, the Ocean Dumping Ban Act (ODBA), make ocean dumping of industrial waste and municipal sewage sludge unlawful after December 31, 1991 (U.S. EPA 1991, p 9).

Ocean dumping of all manner of wastes has been practiced by many nations, and the practice continues in some areas of the world. In American waters and from American ports, dumping was on the decline due to implementation of the MPRSA and was vigorously opposed by environmentalists and the public. MPRSA permitted some dumping of industrial wastes, and proponents of ocean dumping continued to argue, in the courts and elsewhere, that the practice of dumping in deep ocean strata is less harmful than land disposal. Amendments in 1974 and 1980 tightened dumping restrictions, and dumping of industrial waste was ended in 1988. Dumping of sewage sludge continued until the ODBA implementation date of December 31, 1991. The act permits the continued dumping of dredged material. District engineers of the U.S. Army Corps of Engineers (COE) issue permits for dumping of dredged materials after an EPA review and approval of the permit application. The COE and EPA share joint responsibility for monitoring to ensure that permit conditions are met and that the marine environment is protected.

Ocean Incineration

As noted earlier, the incineration of hazardous wastes in ocean-going ships was originated by the West Germans and was initially well received. An incinerator vessel was acquired by an American firm and began a series of test burns.

The operating permit was never issued by the EPA, and the future of the practice is in doubt.

A number of operating problems and environmental concerns have become problematical. The most serious technical problems appear to be:

1. The constraints of ocean-going vessel design do not permit an incinerator design that will provide the minimum 2-second residence time.
2. Similar constraints preclude the necessary stack-gas scrubbers or other emission control devices that are required to capture heavy metals and neutralize the HCl produced in the incineration of chlorinated hydrocarbons.

Concerns for the environmental impacts of a collision or sinking at sea were also a factor, and the enactment of the OBDA in 1988 effectively eliminated further consideration of incineration-at-sea by the EPA. (U.S. EPA 1991, p. 41).

Land Treatment

"Land treatment," "land application," and "land farming" are terms that have been used to label the practice of spreading hazardous wastes on the land surface. The practice ostensibly uses the interaction between plants and the soil surface to stabilize the waste. There have been successful applications of the practice in the treatment and disposal of hydrocarbon wastes from the petroleum industry and domestic sewage sludge. Chlorinated and other persistent compounds and wastes bearing heavy metals are not suitable for land applications for treatment or disposal. Sewage sludge containing heavy metals is similarly unsuitable. The practice requires very careful monitoring and controls to prevent contamination of surface and groundwaters.

Significant amounts of sewage sludge and petroleum industry wastes continue to be "land treated," but the practice is in disfavor among environmentalists and regulatory agencies. The EPA continues to legitimize the practice with Subpart M regulations.

Subpart M — Land Treatment

Owners or operators of land treatment facilities must basically ensure that hazardous constituents placed in or on the treatment zone are degraded, transformed, or immobilized within the treatment zone. The elements specified in the permit include:

- which wastes can be treated.
- design and maintenance of the land treatment unit to maximize treatment.
- soil monitoring.
- the hazardous waste constituents that must be degraded, transformed, or immobilized by treatment.
- size of the treatment zone.

Prior to the application of waste, a treatment demonstration must be conducted to verify that the hazardous constituents are adequately treated by the unit. Use of the facility for growing food chain crops in a treated area containing arsenic, cadmium, lead, mercury, or other hazardous constituents is prohibited.

The permitting standards for land treatment units include extensive unsaturated zone monitoring requirements. A monitoring program must be established to detect the migration of any hazardous constituents. If migration is detected, a permit modification must be submitted, outlining changes in operating practices to resolve the problem (U.S. EPA 1990, pp. III-48, 57).

Land Disposal Restrictions

The awakening to the fact that land disposal of hazardous wastes can be the cause of major groundwater contamination problems came to us in the early to mid-1970s. Prior to 1984, efforts to restrict land disposal were focused in regulatory restrictions on land disposal facilities. These restrictions are seen in the increasingly complex 40 CFR 264/265 regulations, as modified over the years.

The 1984 enactment of HSWA mandated stringent new land disposal limitations. The EPA was required to promulgate five new sets of regulations to implement these limitations.

- Since spent solvents and dioxins were of greatest concern, Congress required the EPA to issue regulations restricting the land disposal of these wastes by November 8, 1986. These regulations are found in 40 CFR 268.30 and 268.31.
- The State of California had earlier banned land disposal of a group of wastes consisting primarily of liquids containing cyanides, heavy metals, PCBs, halogenated organic compounds (HOCs), and acids having a pH ≤2.0. The EPA was directed to issue land disposal restrictions for these "California wastes" by July 8, 1987. These regulations are found in 40 CFR 268.32.
- HSWA required the EPA to assess each of the hazardous wastes listed in 40 CFR 261 (the "listed wastes" discussed in Chapter 2). The listed wastes number in excess of 800 — accordingly, the EPA was directed to divide the lists into three categories ranging from high volume/high hazard to low volume/low hazard and to stage the corresponding restrictions in three promulgations. The "first third" were to be issued by August 8, 1988; the "second third" by June 8, 1989; and the "third third" by May 8, 1990. These regulations are found in 40 CFR 268.33, 268.34, and 268.35, respectively (McCoy and Associates 1993, p. 1.1).
- HSWA section 3004(f) required that the EPA determine the conditions under which underground injection of each hazardous waste will be allowed. These waste specific prohibitions are provided in 40 CFR 148, Subpart B.

- The fifth requires that additional wastes listed after November 8, 1984 will be evaluated on a case-by-case basis. The EPA must make a determination of whether the waste may be land disposed within six months of the identification or listing.

The original and basic purpose of the land disposal restrictions was to discourage activities that involve placing untreated wastes in or upon the land when a better treatment or destruction alternative exists.* For each hazardous waste, the EPA must establish treatment standards that are protective of human health and the environment when the wastes are land disposed. Land disposal is specifically declared to include placement in a landfill, surface impoundment, waste pile, injection well, land treatment facility, salt dome or salt bed formation, underground mine or cave, or concrete vault or bunker.

The treatment standards require either the use of one or more specified treatment technologies (e.g., halogenated organic compounds must be incinerated) or that wastes be treated to meet certain concentration limits on the hazardous constituents of the waste. For each waste, the "Treatment Standards for Hazardous Waste" table in 40 CFR 268, Subpart D identifies one of three types of treatment standards:

1. All hazardous constituents in the waste or in the treatment residue must be at or below the values found in the table for that waste, i.e., "total waste standards."
2. The hazardous constituents in the extract of the waste, or in the extract of the treatment residue, must be at or below the values found in the table, i.e., "waste extract standards."
3. The waste must be treated using the technology specified in the table, i.e., "technology standard."

Concentration limits are based upon concentrations which the EPA assumes (or has data to support) are achievable when treated by the best-demonstrated available technology (BDAT). In treatment of wastes for which treatment standard concentrations apply, the EPA does not require the use of BDAT, but treatment residues must not exceed those achievable by BDAT.

In recognition of shortages of treatment capacity for some waste categories, the EPA initially provided for "National Treatment Capacity Variances." Exemptions from various aspects of the rules were also allowed in special cases. The variances have diminished as regulatory deadlines have passed, as new facilities began operation, as treatment processes have developed or improved, and as waste minimization efforts have intensified. At this writing, the only capacity variances in effect are those for debris.

As noted in Chapter 5, the McCoy and Associates guide is an excellent reference for detailed and concise explanation of the land disposal restrictions (McCoy and Associates 1994).

* Consideration of alternatives has generally ended except for debris. Land disposal has become almost entirely contingent upon meeting the land disposal restriction standards.

TOPICS FOR REVIEW OR DISCUSSION

1. Simple aeration of liquid hazardous wastes or pumped groundwater is not considered to be acceptable practice. Why not? What must be done to cause the practice to become acceptable?
2. Carbon adsorption processes are generally most effective for what kinds of hazardous wastes? The effectiveness of activated carbon in removing waste constituents from aqueous streams depends upon what characteristic of the carbon?
3. What is the usual objective of the introduction of a hydroxide ion in the neutralization and precipitation of a metal-bearing waste?
4. Air or steam stripping is frequently employed to remove __________ from wastewaters or contaminated groundwater. Early applications of this process were environmentally unsound because they ___________ .
5. Biological treatment of toxic organic components in industrial wastewaters require considerably more sophisticated controls than are required in similar domestic sewage treament processes. Why?
6. RCRA-permitted hazardous waste surface impoundments must meet three basic requirements. What are they?
7. The validity of the concept that liquid wastes can be injected into, and contained by, confined geologic strata having no other actual or potential uses of a more beneficial nature, thereby providing long-term isolation of the waste material from man's environment" depends upon two basic factors. What are they? Discuss.
8. The heavy metal constituents in a sludge can usually be destroyed in a well-designed and operated hazardous waste incinerator. True? False? Why?
9. A well-designed and operated incinerator of chlorinated hydrocarbon wastes will produce at least three residues which are environmentally harmless. Identify the three. One other residue must be managed. What is that product and how may it be managed?
10. Where in the RCRA regulations does the owner/operator of a generator facility find the applicable requirements for contingency planning for his/her facility?

REFERENCES

Barton, Robert G., W. D. Clark, and W. R. Seeker. 1992. "Fate of Metals in Waste Combustion Systems." *Incineration of Hazardous Waste: Toxic Combustion By-Products,* Wm. Randall Seeker and Catherine P. Koshland, Eds. Gordon and Breach Science Publishers, Philadelphia, PA.

Brunner, Calvin R. 1988. "Industrial Waste Incineration." *Hazardous Materials Control* July-August:26ff.

Cadmus Group, Inc. 1991. *Drinking Water Contamination By Smallow Injection Wells.* Prepared for U.S. Environmental Protection Agency, Office of Drinking Water, Washington, D.C.

Combs, George D. 1989. *Emerging Treatment Technologies for Hazardous Waste*, Section XV. Environmental Systems Company, Little Rock, AR.

Dawson, Gaynor W., and Basil W. Mercer. 1986. *Hazardous Waste Management.* John Wiley & Sons, New York.

Dempsey, Clyde R., and E. Timothy Oppelt. 1993. "Incineration of Hazardous Waste: A Critical Review Update." *Air and Waste* January:25ff.

DuPont, Andre. 1988. "Treating Liquid Waste with Lime." *Hazardous Materials Control* July-August:24ff.

Ehlers, Victor M., and Ernest W. Steel. 1958. *Municipal and Rural Sanitation.* McGraw-Hill, New York.

Johnson, Nancy P., and Michael G. Cosmos. 1989. "Thermal Treatment Technologies for Haz Waste Remediation." *Pollution Engineering* October:66ff.

McCoy and Associates. 1994. *The RCRA Land Disposal Restriction: A Guide to Compliance 1993.* Elsevier Science Publishing Company, New York.

Ozbilgin, Melih M., Jennifer L. Goodell, Joseph P. LeClaire, and Michael C. Kavanaugh. 1992. "The Use of Existing Water Supply Wells to Evaluate the Hydrogeologic and Transport Characteristics of Alluvial Aquifers." *Hazardous Waste Site Investigations,* Richard B. Gammage and Barry A Bervin, Eds. Lewis Publishers, Chelsea, MI.

Rappe, Christoffer, Gangadhar Choudhary, and Lawrence Keith. 1986. *Chlorinated Dibenzofurans and Dioxins.* Lewis Publishers, Chelsa, MI.

Smart, Glenn R., and David K. Cook. 1988. *Hazardous Materials Control* 1(3) May-June:26–33.

U.S. Environmental Protection Agency. 1981. *Guidance Document for Subpart F Air Emission Monitoring — Land Disposal Toxic Air Emissions Evaluation Guideline.* National Technical Information Service, Springfield,VA. PB87-155578.

U.S. Environmental Protection Agency. 1982. *RCRA Guidance Document: Landfill Design, Liner Systems, and Final Cover.* National Technical Information Service, Springfield, VA. PB87-157657.

U.S. Environmental Protection Agency. 1987a. *Background Document on Bottom Liner Performance in Double-Lined Landfills and Surface Impoundments.* National Technical Information Service, Springfield, VA. PB87-182291.

U.S. Environmental Protection Agency. 1987b. *Background Document on Proposed Liner and Leak Detection Rule.* National Technical Information Service, Springfield, VA. PB87-191383.

U.S. Environmental Protection Agency. 1988. *Design, Construction, and Evaluation of Clay Liners for Waste Management Facilities.* National Technical Information Service, Springfield, VA. PB89-181937.

U.S. Environmental Protection Agency. 1990. *RCRA Orientation Manual, 1990 Edition.* Superintendent of Documents, Government Printing Office, Washington, D.C.

U.S. Environmental Protection Agency. 1991. *Report to Congress on Ocean Dumping 1987 – 1990.* Office of Water, Washington, D.C. EPA 503/9-91/009.

U.S. Environmental Protection Agency. 1993a. *Report to Congress on Cement Kiln Dust.* Solid Waste and Emergency Response, Washington, D.C. EPA 530-S-94-001.

U.S. Environmental Protection Agency. 1993b. RICRIS National Oversight Database.

Voice, Thomas C. 1989. "Activated Carbon Adsorption." *Standard Handbook of Hazardous Waste Treatment and Disposal,* Harry M. Freeman, Ed. McGraw-Hill, New York.

Walker, William R., and William E. Cox. 1976. *Deep Well Injection of Industrial Wastes: Government Controls and Legal Restraints.* Virginia Resources Research Center, Blacksburg.

Wentz, Charles A. 1989. *Hazardous Waste Management.* McGraw-Hill, New York.

Wilson, R. D., and C. H. Thompson. 1988. "Activated Carbon Treatment of Groundwater: Results of a Pilot Plant Program." *Hazardous Materials Control* July-August:17ff.

8 HAZARDOUS WASTE MINIMIZATION, REUSE, AND RECYCLING

OBJECTIVES

At completion of this chapter, the student should:

- understand the basic operational approaches to waste minimization, i.e., product changes, source controls, use and reuse, and reclamation.
- be familiar with the principles, process, and practice of waste reduction assessment.
- understand the imperatives of waste minimization, reduction, reuse, and recycling.
- be familiar with the Resource Conservation and Recovery Act (RCRA) regulatory mechanisms and program incentives to achieve waste minimization, the national policy aspects, and the local impediments.
- be similarly familiar with the objectives of the Pollution Prevention Act and the implementing mechanisms.

INTRODUCTION

We now take up the most important issue in the study of hazardous waste management — the elimination or reduction in the quantity of waste generated. Throughout the previous chapters, we have emphasized the fact that much of what has passed for hazardous waste management ultimately came to little more than moving it around, transferring it from one environmental medium to another, changing its form, or hiding it.

Although great strides have been made in the sophistication of regulatory programs, treatment technology, and secure disposal, the fact remains that our approach continues to be pollution control rather than pollution prevention. The next generation of industrial managers must transcend this traditional hazardous waste treatment mindset.

The legislate-regulate-treat-dispose approach has three primary roots:

1. As hazardous wastes became a more serious aspect of industrial management, they were initially handled in a manner similar to the handling of sewage and refuse. There is little that can be done to reduce the amount of sewage generated, so we taught ourselves to treat it to make it less threatening to our health and esthetic sensibilities and to our environment. Refuse management was based upon similar thought processes, but with somewhat less validity. Politicians (and others) are fond of referring to this traditional sanitary engineering approach as the "end-of-the-pipe mentality."

   Sanitary engineers did not advocate adding hazardous wastes to our sewerage systems and had little to do with the dumping of hazardous wastes into whatever refuse management systems were in use. The sewers, the atmosphere, and the dumping grounds were there, and our use of them was dictated by the politics and the economics of the free enterprise system.

2. During and after the Vietnam War, former President Lyndon Johnson and his Secretary of Defense Robert McNamara were criticized for their failure to mobilize the nation and vigorously prosecute the war. The policy was referred to as "gradualism," meaning that the resources (men and materials) were added in small increments, to which the enemy was able to accommodate. The parallel with the nation's approach to hazardous waste management is unmistakable.

   When hazardous wastes began to require our attention, we did not mobilize to deal with them. We did not examine the sources to determine their necessity; or whether there might be alternative processes, raw materials, or end products; or even good operating practices that might *reduce* quantities or strengths of wastes. The feeble impact of the resurrected 1899 Rivers and Harbors Act and the early efforts of environmentalists led us to put in equally feeble "treatment" schemes and to hide our dumping more carefully. As regulatory pressures increased, we added new treatment units; upgraded existing ones; and created the treatment, storage, and disposal industry. With the advent of the Hazardous and Solid Waste Amendments (HSWA), we pushed innovative treatment and destruction and tried to reduce our dependence upon disposal. Only recently have we begun to seriously consider new approaches.

3. The third of these roots is, of course, economics. The economic pressures upon American industry have ranged over the ever-escalating labor–wage demands of the 1960s and 1970s, the profit greed of the 1970s and 1980s, and the overseas competition of the later 1980s. Industry representatives and lobbyists have been highly effective in softening environmental legislation and regulatory issues. Fears of job losses, recessions, stockholder

demands, and debt have been the dominant themes. Industrial decision makers tend to opt for the least-expensive option of the moment, and in hazardous waste management that frequently translates into the purchase of a *treatment* unit or a new contract with a *disposal* facility.

Until recently, there have been few, if any, economic incentives to examine major changes in products, raw materials, materials handling, or process controls to eliminate a waste stream or reduce it in volume or strength. The economic incentives of Superfund nomination, tort filings, and criminal penalties have much to do with the newly found interest in waste minimization. More pointedly, the Pollution Prevention Act of 1990 (PPA) intensifies requirements for reporting of releases and analysis of progress in achieving waste minimization goals. The new act and the U.S. Environmental Protection Agency's (EPA) implementation program stop just short of *mandated* reductions of releases. Ever-diminishing availability of space for disposal services, public resistance to siting of any kind of hazardous waste management facility, and increasingly stringent regulation add further pressures to rethink our traditional approaches.

Waste Minimization Techniques

The statutory authorities, in HSWA, for waste minimization programs and, in the PPA, for pollution prevention strategies will be overviewed later in this chapter. These authorities do not include mandatory controls or mechanisms to regulate waste minimization programs. In lieu thereof, the EPA has developed a large number of good "how-to" publications which deal with program organization and management, as well as technical approaches. The pollution prevention programs are focused upon extensive reporting requirements, goal setting, and performance evaluation. The U.S. Congress' Office of Technology Assessment has produced an informative critique of the program, entitled *Serious Reduction of Hazardous Waste*. We borrow from these publications, and others, to provide some structure to the topic. Figure 8.1 diagrams an organized way to think about waste minimization techniques. We then follow with examples of each of the diagrammed techniques.

Source Reduction

In the previous chapter we offered Dr. George Combs' version of the hierarchy of preferable waste management options and priorities. The EPA waste minimization program has, since the enactment of HSWA, advocated a similar version, which may be helpful in thinking about approaches to hazardous waste prevention, reduction, or minimization.

1. *Waste Reduction* — Reduce the amount of waste at the source through changes in industrial processes.
2. *Waste Separation and Concentration* — Isolate wastes from mixtures in which they occur.

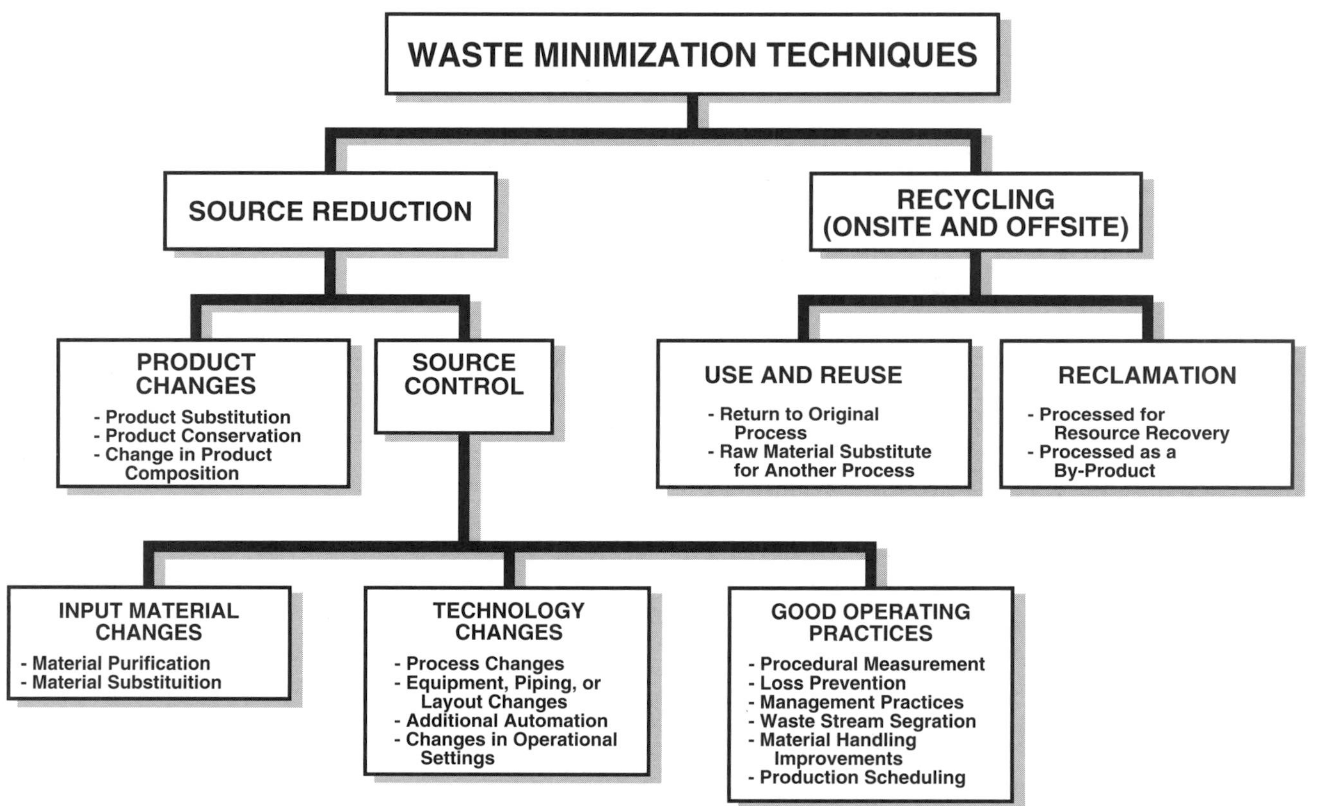

FIGURE 8.1 Waste minimization techniques (EPA).

3. *Waste Exchange* — Transfer wastes through clearinghouses so that they can be recycled in industrial processes.
4. *Energy/Material Recovery* — Reuse and recycle wastes for the original or some other purpose, such as for materials recovery or energy production.
5. *Incineration/Treatment* — Destroy, detoxify, and neutralize wastes into less harmful substances.
6. *Secure Land Disposal* — Deposit wastes on land using volume reduction, encapsulation, leachate containment, monitoring, and controlled air and surface/subsurface water releases.

Product Changes

Product Substitution. Changes in the design, composition, or specifications of end products that allow fundamental changes in the manufacturing process or in the use of raw materials can directly lead to waste reduction. Such changes are also the most difficult approach to waste reduction for several reasons, including:

- concerns on the part of the manufacturer regarding customer acceptance, cost of the conversion, cost of the new product, and quality control.
- concerns on the part of the customer regarding acceptability of the product, quality control, changes in application made necessary by the substitution, general uncertainty, and fear of the unknown.
- concerns on the part of both manufacturer and customer regarding regulatory and liability impacts.

For example, Monsanto (St. Louis, MO) reformulated a specialized industrial adhesive so that hazardous particulates remained in the product, thus eliminating the need to use and dispose of filters and particulates as waste. The company then had to convince its customers that the particulate matter formerly removed by the filters could remain in the product without affecting its adhesive qualities. From the time the idea of reformulating the product was originated, two years of effort by Monsanto's Research and Marketing Division was required before the reluctance of the purchaser to accept a different product was overcome and the change could be made (U.S. Congress, Office of Technology Assessment 1986, p. 83).

Product Conservation. One of the most fruitful areas of waste minimization through product conservation is the effective management of inventory having specific shelf-lives. Holston Army Ammunition Plant (Tennessee) reduced waste pesticide disposal from 440 to 0 kg in one year by better management of stocks (Mills 1988).

Changes in Product Composition. Dow Chemical Company (Midland, MI) changed the way it packaged a product and achieved waste reduction in doing so. A wettable powder insecticide, widely used in the landscape maintenance and horticulture business, was originally sold in 2-pound metal cans which had to be decontaminated prior to disposal, thereby creating a hazardous waste. Dow now packages the product in 4-oz, water-soluble packages which dissolve when the product is mixed with water for use (U.S. Congress, Office of Technology Assessment 1986, p. 83).

Source Control

Input Material Changes

Material Substitution. An electronic manufacturing facility of a large, diversified corporation originally cleaned printed circuit boards with solvents. The company found that by switching from a solvent-based cleaning system to an aqueous-based system that the same operating conditions and workloads could be maintained. The aqueous-based system was found to clean six times more effectively. This example of input material substitution resulted in a lower product reject rate and eliminated a hazardous waste (U.S. EPA 1988, p. 16).

Material Purification. A U.S. Air Force facility annually generated about 6500 gallons of waste 1,1,1-trichloroethane (TCA) from vapor degreasing operations. Chemical laboratory personnel discovered that the TCA was being disposed of because it did not meet an acid acceptance value of 0.10 weight %NaOH. Oil contamination levels were less than 10% at the time of disposal, far less than the expected 30% level. To restore acid acceptance levels, 1,2-butylene oxide was added to the solvent. No adverse reactions or detectable problems were observed when the butylene oxide was added to the vapor degreasers. This example of purification of input material is expected to enable reduction of disposal volumes by 4000 gallons (60%) and savings of $30,000 per year (U.S. EPA 1989, p. 19).

Technology Changes

Process Changes. An example of a classic process change, resulting in reduced waste generation, is staged use of solvent. An electronics firm switched from using three different solvents — mineral spirits for degreasing machine parts, perchloroethylene for computer housings, and a fluorocarbon-methanol blend for printed circuit boards — to a single solvent system. Fresh solvent is used for the printed circuit boards, then reused to degrease the computer housings, and reused again for machine parts. This practice not only reduced solvent consumption and waste, it eliminated potential cross-contamination of solvents, generated a single waste stream that can be recycled, simplified safety and operating procedures, and increased purchasing leverage (U.S. EPA 1989, p. 17).

Equipment, Piping, or Layout Changes. Equipment changes can be equally beneficial in waste reduction programs. Conventional paint stripping of aircraft may use 8000 gallons per aircraft of such solvents as methylene chloride or hot caustic. The U.S. Air Force has successfully employed plastic beads propelled by high pressure jets (bead blasting) to remove paint from aircraft exteriors. The bead blasting eliminated hazardous waste generation, improved personnel working conditions, was easier to perform than solvent paint stripping, and cost less and used less raw material (U.S. EPA 1989, p. 16).

Automation. Process automation assists or replaces human employees with automatic devices. Automation can include the monitoring and subsequent adjusting of process parameters by computer or mechanical handling of hazardous substances. Minimizing the probability of employee error (which can lead to spills or off-spec products) and increasing product yields through the optimum use of raw materials can reduce waste. Bar-coded labels (Figure 8.2) can link containers and materials to

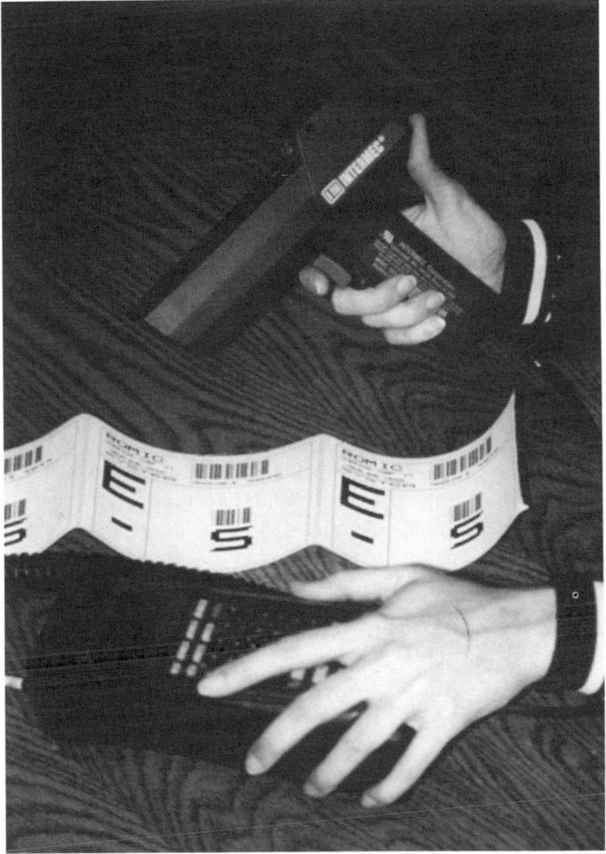

FIGURE 8.2 Bar coding as a process tracking tool (ROMIC Chemical Corporation, 2081 Bay Road, Palo Alto, CA 94303).

a computer through all stages of a container's life. This improves the accuracy of material tracking and inventory accounting. Bar codes allow material monitoring during use and can prevent materials from being lost or becoming outdated.

Good Operating Practices

Procedural Measures. The Occupational Safety and Health Administration (OSHA) requires businesses to maintain files of Material Safety Data Sheets (MSDSs) for all hazardous materials. The sheets contain the manufacturer's information regarding

- the identity of the chemical and the Chemical Abstracts Service (CAS) number.
- the physical characteristics.
- physical and health hazards.

- primary routes of entry.
- exposure limits.
- precautions.
- controls.
- emergency and first aid procedures.
- name of the manufacturer or importer.

A major industrial facility uses MSDSs to screen all material coming into their plant. Before the material is requisitioned, medical and hazardous materials experts must approve it. This approval ensures that a substance has been researched and evaluated for its hazardous characteristics prior to its use. This reduces generation of hazardous wastes by eliminating their use (University of Tennessee Center for Industrial Services 1989, pp. 8-5, 8-7).

Material Loss Prevention. Loss prevention programs are designed to reduce the chances of spilling a product. The key point is that a hazardous *material* becomes a RCRA hazardous *waste* when it is spilled, and all cleanup material and cleaned-up material must be managed as hazardous waste. A long-term, slow-release spill is often difficult to find and when found may have caused the creation of a large amount of hazardous waste. A material loss prevention program may include the following procedures (University of Tennessee Center for Industrial Services 1989, pp. 8–10):

- Use properly designed tanks and vessels only for their intended purpose
- Install overflow alarms for all tanks and vessels
- Maintain physical integrity of all tanks and vessels
- Set up written procedures for all loading, unloading, and transfer operations
- Install sufficient secondary containment areas
- Forbid operators to bypass interlocks, alarms, or significantly alter setpoints without authorization
- Isolate equipment or process lines that leak or are not in service
- Have interlock devices to stop flow to leaking sections
- Use seal-less pumps
- Use bellows-seal valves and a good valve layout
- Document all spillage
- Perform overall material balances and estimate the quantity and dollar value of all losses
- Install leak detection systems for underground storage tanks according to RCRA Subtitle I
- Use floating-roof tanks for volatile organic compound (VOC) control
- Use conservation vents on fixed-roof tanks
- Use vapor recovery systems

Management Practices. Good operating practice involving management is exemplified by a large consumer product company which adopted a corporate policy to minimize the generation of hazardous waste. The company mobilized quality circles made up of employees representing areas within the plant that generated hazardous waste. The company experienced a 75% reduction in the amount of wastes generated by instituting proper maintenance procedures suggested by the quality circle teams. Since the team members were also line supervisors and operators, they made sure the procedures were followed (U.S. EPA 1988, p. 16).

Segregating Waste Streams. Hazardous waste sent offsite to be disposed of often includes a mixture of two or more different wastes. Segregating materials and wastes can decrease the amount of wastes to be disposed. Good operating practices for successful waste segregation include the following program ingredients:

- Prevent mixing of hazardous wastes with nonhazardous wastes
- Isolate hazardous wastes by contaminant
- Isolate liquid wastes from solid waste

These measures can result in lower volumes of waste haulage and easier disposal of the hazardous waste. Recyclers and waste exchanges are more receptive to wastes not contaminated with other substances. One company altered dust collection equipment to collect waste streams from different processes separately. Each collection can now be recycled back to the process from which it originates. The firm has eliminated over $9000 per year in disposal costs and recovered useable material worth $2000 per year (University of Tennessee Center for Industrial Services 1989, pp. 8–11).

Material Handling Improvement. A major national company has reduced organics in wastewater by 93% through four separate changes in its handling of phenol and urea resins, as follows:

1. The company altered its method of cleaning the filters which remove large particles of resinous material as the resin product is loaded into tank cars. They began collecting the rinse water instead of sending it down the floor drains and into the company's onsite wastewater treatment plant. This rinse water can be reused as an input in the next batch of phenolic resin.
2. When loading urea resin, they began reversing the loading pump at the end of each load so that resin on the filters would be sucked back into the storage tank and would not be rinsed out as waste.
3. The company revised rinsing procedures for reactor vessels between batches. Previously, 11,000- to 15,000-gallon chambers had been cleaned by filling them with water, heating, stirring the water to remove resin residues, and then draining the rinse water into the plant's wastewater. The plant now has a two-step process. A small, first rinse of 100 gallons of water removes most of the residue from the containers. Then a second, full-volume rinse is used to complete cleaning. The first 100 gallons of rinse water is reused as input material for a later batch of resin. Water from the second rinse is discharged as wastewater, but has a lower phenol concentration than the previous volume of wastewater.
4. Procedures for transferring phenol from tank cars to storage tanks have been altered. Formerly, when the hose used to transfer the phenol from car to tank was disconnected, a small amount of phenol dripped down the drain — enough to cause problems given the strict regulatory limitation of

phenol. Now, the hose is flushed with a few gallons of water to rinse the last bit of phenol into the storage tank.

In addition to greatly reducing wastewater volumes, these fairly simple changes have eliminated most of the hazardous solid wastes generated by the resin manufacturing processes because the company was able to discontinue use of the onsite evaporation pond to treat these wastewaters (U.S. Congress, Office of Technology Assessment 1986, p. 81).

Production Scheduling. Management can begin good operating practices to improve production scheduling and planning. Some successful production techniques include:

- maximizing batch size.
- dedicating equipment to a single product.
- altering batch sequencing to reduce cleaning frequency.
- scheduling production to reduce cleaning frequency.

Careful examination of workload distribution may reveal opportunities for waste reduction. Dense loading may result in localized instability of the process solution. In other situations, maximizing batch size may minimize waste generated. Optimizing production schedules can greatly reduce waste in a production facility. These options offer easy implementation and immediate evidence of results (University of Tennessee Center for Industrial Services 1989, p. 8-3). (*See also* Wentz 1989, Chapter 6)

Hazardous Waste Recycling

In hazardous waste management practice and in the RCRA regulations, "recycling" refers to the effective use or reuse of a waste as a substitute for a commercial product or to the use of a waste as an ingredient or feedstock in an industrial process. It also refers to reclaiming useful constituent fractions within a waste material or removing contaminants from a waste to allow it to be reused. Recycling implies *use, reuse,* or *reclamation* of a waste, either onsite or offsite, after it is generated by a particular process (University of Tennessee Center for Industrial Services 1989, p. 1-5).

One of the most basic and frequent applications of hazardous waste recycling is the distillation of spent solvents. Large numbers of companies are engaged in the solvent reclamation business, and much of the solvent in use has been reclaimed. Figure 8.3 diagrams the distillation process. Figure 8.4 is of typical distillation columns. Figure 8.5 illustrates the "before and after" appearance of spent and reclaimed solvent.

Use and Reuse

Return of a Waste to the Original Process. A printer of newspaper advertising purchased an ink recycling unit to produce black newspaper ink from its various waste inks. The unit blends the different colors of waste ink together with fresh black

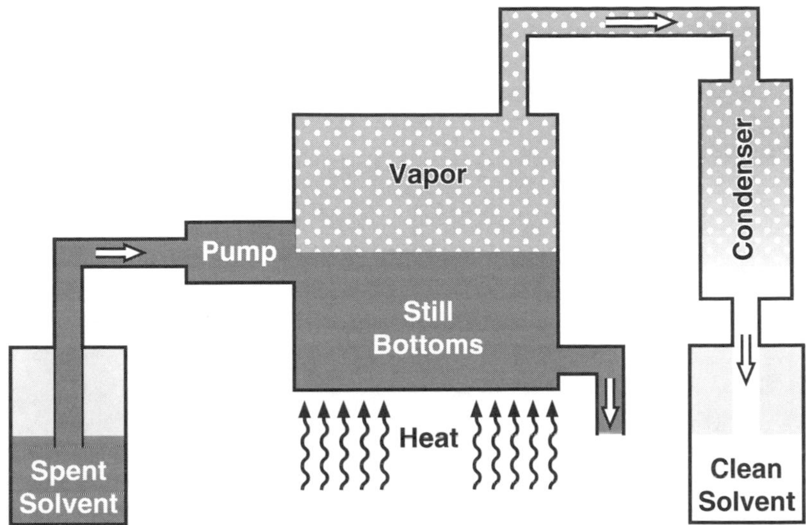

FIGURE 8.3 The distillation process (Chemical Waste Management, Inc., 107 South Motor Avenue, Azuza, CA 91707).

FIGURE 8.4 Distillation columns (ROMIC).

ink and black toner to create the black ink. This mixture is then filtered to remove flakes of dried ink and is used in lieu of fresh black ink. The need for shipment of waste ink to offsite disposal is eliminated. The price of the recycling unit was recovered in nine months, based upon savings in fresh ink purchases and costs of disposal of the waste ink (U.S. EPA 1988, p. 17).

FIGURE 8.5 Before and after — spent solvent and reclaimed solvent (ROMIC).

Prior to 1987, a metal-forging business disposed of approximately 30,000 gallons of oily wastewater each year to hazardous waste landfills. A holding tank with an oil skimmer was installed, enabling annual capture and recycling of 3000 gallons of waste oil. The remaining wastewater has been approved for discharge to the sanitary sewer (University of Tennessee Center for Industrial Services 1989, pp. 6–12).

Substitution for Raw Material in Another Process. A U.S. Air Force solvent reclaiming operation is successfully reclaiming polyurethane paint thinners. The original material contains 40% cellusolve acetate, 12% toluene, 30% methyl ethyl ketone (MEK), and 10% *n*-butyl acetate. The distillate, which contains only toluene and MEK, is used for wipedown and cleanup of painting equipment (Harris 1988).

Reclamation

Processing Hazardous Waste for Product Recovery. Sand used in the casting process at foundries contains residues of heavy metals such as copper, lead, and zinc. If these concentrations exceed Toxicity Characteristic Leaching Procedure (TCLP) standards, the sand is a hazardous waste and must be managed as such. Researchers are investigating various techniques for reclaiming the metal values from the sand. Recent experiments demonstrated that 95% of the copper could be precipitated and recovered in minutes (McCoy and Associates 1989, pp. 1–23). Sand may also be processed in smelters to recover metal values.

A photoprocessing company uses an electrolytic deposition cell to recover silver from the rinse water used in film processing equipment. By removing the silver from

Exchanging Waste, Information & Technology Internationally

IN THIS ISSUE:

National News Digest

Reports & Information

Technology, Trends And Business

Federal Register Announcements

Conference & Seminars

Waste & Materials Exchange

FIGURE 8.6 A waste exchange listing catalog (*Resource Exchange & News*, 3250 Townsend N.E., Grand Rapids, MI 49505).

the wastewater, the wastewater can be discharged to the sewer without additional pretreatment. The company also collects used film and sells it to the recycler. The recycler burns the film and collects the silver from the residual ash. By removing the silver from the ash, the ash becomes nonhazardous (U.S. EPA 1988, p. 17).

Processing Hazardous Waste as a Byproduct. Some classic uses of hazardous waste as a byproduct, raw material, or feedstock have been mentioned. The most common include wastewaters used for irrigation and oil field pressurization, sludges used as fertilizers or soil matrix, lime generated by the carbide process for acetylene production, and sulfuric acid from smelters. Lime and sulfuric acid are used for a variety of purposes. These uses have stimulated entrepreneurs to the development of the "waste exchange" (Figure 8.6).

Waste exchanges became numerous during the early and mid-1980s. One very large and successful exchange in Canada and several in the United States are continuing to operate. The basic idea is simple. The waste exchange serves as a clearinghouse for data on available wastes and raw materials needed. When the exchange identifies a match between an available waste commodity and a need, the parties are notified and allowed to consummate an arrangement suitable to both.

In practice, the exchange has enjoyed only limited acceptance. The potential participants tend toward secrecy, fearing compromise of trade secrets by their competitors. The liability implications of transferring control to other than a permitted treatment, storage, and disposal facility are also significant impediments to acceptance of exchanges. The EPA initially supported several exchanges through grant programs, but most of these operations had not gained sufficient momentum and failed when the grant support was discontinued.

Government and industry have demonstrated major successes in waste minimization/pollution prevention, but the range of options for achievable waste minimization will not be complete until ways and means of supporting waste exchanges are worked out. (*See also* Higgins 1991, Chapters 1–8; Breen and Dellarco 1992; Alexander 1992)

The RCRA Waste Minimization Program

As noted, the RCRA does not put forth a mandatory hazardous waste minimization program. EPA staff and members of Congress have expressed the belief that imposition of specific hazardous waste reductions would amount to an unacceptable intervention in business and industrial practice. Nevertheless, in Section 1003 of RCRA, the Congress stated succinctly:

> The Congress hereby declares it to be the national policy of the United States that, wherever feasible, the generation of hazardous waste is to be reduced or eliminated as expeditiously as possible. Waste that is nevertheless generated should be treated, stored, or disposed of so as to minimize the present and future threat to human health and the environment.

This national policy is implemented through three specific activities which were mandated by the 1984 RCRA amendments (HSWA). These specific requirements apply to generators who manage their wastes onsite or those who ship wastes offsite and to permitted facilities:

- *Reporting Procedures* — Generators subject to reporting requirements were to include in their annual or biennial reports "efforts undertaken during the year to reduce the volume and toxicity of waste generated; and … the changes in volume and toxicity of waste actually achieved during the year … in comparison to previous years."
- *Manifest System* — A section on waste minimization was added to require a generator's certification on the manifest for all regulated offsite shipments, to state that "the generator of the hazardous waste has a program

in place to reduce the volume or quantity and toxicity of such waste to the degree determined by the generator to be economically practicable; and … the proposed method of treatment, storage, or disposal is that practicable method currently available to the generator which minimizes the present and future threat to human health and the environment."

- *Permits* — Effective September 1, 1985, any permit issued for the treatment, storage, or disposal of hazardous waste on the premises where the waste was generated requires that the permittee certify no less often than annually that "the generator of the hazardous waste has a program in place to reduce the volume or quantity and toxicity of such waste to the degree determined by the generator to be economically practicable; and … the proposed method of treatment, storage, or disposal is that practicable method currently available to the generator which minimizes the present and future threat to human health and the environment" (U.S. Congress, Office of Technology Assessment 1986, pp. 154–156).

The biennial reports of generators who ship their wastes offsite and of permitted and interim status TSDFs are the only data collection mechanisms by which the effectiveness of the waste minimization program can be judged. Until recently, efforts to aggregate this information did not produce good results, due to absence of consistent definitions, procedures, and measurements among states. EPA staff members informally opined that waste minimization efforts were probably just about keeping up with the increases in hazardous waste generation. The quality of the reporting and aggregation has improved since 1989, and the 1991 data reflects new rigor in the process.

The EPA thus continues the waste minimization program in a nonmandatory format. Nevertheless, the agency intensified its efforts toward greater achievement in waste minimization by a series of pronouncements and initiatives.

- In May 1993, the administrator announced the Draft Hazardous Waste Minimization and Combustion Strategy and placed a "temporary capacity freeze" on new incinerators and other combustion units* as discussed in the previous chapter.
- In November 1993, the administrator sent letters to 22,000 large quantity generators that were required to certify that they had a waste minimization program in place in 1991. Letters were also sent to 12,000 chief executives of the parent corporations of those generators. The letters referenced current requirements for waste minimization programs and encouraged the companies to make response information available to the public (U.S. EPA 1994b).

* The EPA, the regional offices, and the states thereupon began an intensive inspection and enforcement campaign directed toward combustion facilities, requiring permit applicants to perform full risk assessments, including assessment of the risk of direct exposure to emissions through the food chain, as part of all new combustion facility permits. As this scenario unfolded, 27 incinerators and 22 boiler/industrial furnace facilities withdrew permit applications, abandoned interim status, or otherwise capitulated regarding their plans or efforts to incinerate hazardous wastes (U.S. EPA 1994a, 1994b).

- In May 1994, the EPA released a Draft RCRA Hazardous Waste Minimization National Plan which generally incorporated the thrust of the Hazardous Waste Minimization and Combustion Strategy (U.S. EPA 1994d).
- The final "Waste Minimization National Plan" was released by the EPA in November 1994. The goals of the plan are:

1. to reduce, as a nation, the presence of the most persistent, bioaccumulative, and toxic constituents by 25% by the year 2000 and by 50% by 2005.
2. to avoid transferring these constituents across environmental media.
3. to ensure that these constituents are reduced at their source whenever possible or, when not possible, that they are recycled in an environmentally sound manner (U.S. EPA 1994a).

The combustion strategy is translated, in the final plan, to the setting of "initial national priorities for metals contained in hazardous wastes treated by combustion facilities and metals in releases from combustion facilities" (U.S. EPA 1994a, p. ES-1). The Biennial RCRA Hazardous Waste Report (U.S. EPA 1994c) shows that "thermal treatment" accounts for 1.1% of the 306 million tons of hazardous waste generated in 1991. At the time of this writing, the rationale for this high profile focus on 1.1% of the hazardous waste generated (in 1991) had not been made clear.

The Pollution Prevention Act of 1990

The Emergency Planning and Community Right-to-Know Act (EPCRA) was enacted in 1986 as Title III of the Superfund Amendments and Reauthorization Act (SARA). Congress specifically required manufacturing facilities having Standard Industrial Codes 20 through 39 to report annually the quantities of toxic chemicals they release into the environment. In the Pollution Prevention Act of 1990 (PPA), Congress expanded the reporting requirements to include data on all aspects of source reduction and recycling program implementation by the reporting companies. The PPA was enacted to implement a national objective of preventing pollution at the source. To achieve this goal, the EPA is required by Congress to establish a source reduction program, not unlike that of the RCRA waste minimization program. Section 6607 of the PPA is intended to ensure that sufficient information is available to carry out the purposes of the act and to enable evaluation of progress toward the stated goals.

The act requires subject companies to provide detailed information on release of toxic chemicals, including the following (PPA, Section 6607):

- Amount entering the waste stream before recycling, treatment, or disposal and the percentage change from the previous year
- Amount recycled, percentage change from previous year, and the recycling process(es) in use
- Amount treated onsite or offsite and the percentage change from the previous year

- Estimates of the amounts that will be reported for the next two years
- Specific source reduction practices used by the facility
- Techniques used to identify source reduction opportunities
- Ratio of production in the reporting year to production in the preceeding year
- Amount(s) released because of accidents or other one-time events

To other than the seasoned practitioner or careful observer, the quantities of hazardous waste reported in the Biennial RCRA Hazardous Waste Report and the quantities of toxic chemical releases reported in the *Toxics Release Inventory* (*TRI*) may seem a duplication of effort.

The biennial RCRA report is based upon information submitted by states on quantities of *RCRA hazardous wastes* managed by RCRA facilities that are subject to the 40 CFR 262.41, 264.75, or 265.75 biennial reporting requirements.

The *TRI* is derived from Form R reports submitted to the EPA and state emergency planning commissions by manufacturing facilities that are subject to SARA Title III, Section 313 reporting requirements. These requirements pertain to releases to the environment of quantities, of any of more than 300 toxic chemicals, exceeding a threshold quantity. Threshold determinations are based upon the amount of the chemical that is manufactured, processed, or otherwise used at the facility, not upon quantity released.

In 1991, in concert with the PPA, the Clean Air Act Amendments of 1990, and the RCRA waste minimization program, the EPA established the "33/50 Program." The intent was to encourage companies to reduce releases and transfers of 17 toxic chemicals that together accounted for 25% of the total toxic pollutants reported to have been released in 1990. The program aims to reduce the amounts of these chemicals released by 33% from the 1988 level before the close of 1992 and by 50% by the end of 1995. Based upon *TRI* data, the EPA reported that toxic releases were reduced by about 1.7 billion pounds, or 35%, from 1988 to 1992.

The U.S. General Accounting Office (GAO), in two September 1994 reports to Congress, is critical of the fact that the program embodies no means for the EPA to verify the reported quantities or even that the reductions are attributable to the 33/50 Program. The reader wishing further detail may obtain the reports by contacting the GAO. The reports are:

GAO/RCED-94-94—*EPA Needs More Reliable Source Reduction Data and Progress Measures* (U.S. GAO 1994a)
GAO/RCED-94-207 — *Status of EPA's Efforts to Reduce Toxic Releases* (U.S. GAO 1994b)

(*See also* Bolstridge 1992, Chapter 12)

Typically, the EPA is caught between the imperatives of minimizing the reporting burden placed upon regulated industry and the demands of Congress and the public for verifiable showing of progress toward achieving statutory environmental quality goals.

RCRA Regulation of Recycling

As emphasized in Chapter 1 and elsewhere in this text, the Congress and EPA have justifiably focused upon the accumulation of hazardous waste as an activity rich with potential for mismanagement. At this late date, nearly two decades after enactment of the RCRA, unscrupulous operators attempt to convince the EPA and state inspectors that the stack of drums or the pile of waste on the back lot or in the shed are destined for recycling. Sham recycling of "hazardous waste fuel" remains a problem. The EPA continues to grope for the regulatory definitions and formulae which will finally end deceptive activity and questionable practice without imposing still heavier record keeping and reporting burdens. Significant progress has been made in this regard, but the regulatory scheme is complex, contorted, and ambiguous. Representatives of regulated industry chafe at the ambiguity of the regulations and the interpretations thereof. These regulations are at or near the top of target lists of industry focus groups, trade associations, and political office holders and candidates. The recycling regulations also incur the opposition of environmental activists who look upon the combustion of hazardous waste as a major threat to public health.

Part 266 of 40 CFR originally provided much of the EPA's regulatory program for recycling of hazardous wastes. Perusal of the contents for Part 266 will reveal that Subparts A, B, D, and E* are now "reserved" and Subparts C, F, and G deal with relatively simple issues. Subpart H houses the very complex and controversial regulations for "Hazardous Waste Burned in Boilers and Industrial Furnaces." Over time, the EPA has vacated much of the language of Part 266 and has increasingly relied upon the definitions of solid and hazardous waste, as set forth in 40 CFR 261, to regulate the recycling of wastes.

The Subpart H standards were published on February 21, 1991 (56 FR 7208). In Subpart H, the EPA attempted to deal with the issue of hazardous wastes being burned in boilers and industrial furnaces (BIFs) for fuel content vs. destruction of hazardous waste constituents. Although HSWA requires the EPA to develop technical standards for burning of hazardous wastes in BIFs for heat recovery, the agency had not, prior to this date, promulgated the regulation. "Sham recycling" had been commonplace, and Subpart H was intended to meet the HSWA requirement and gain control of the sham recycling problem. The regulation establishes standards for controlling emissions of organic compounds, metals, and HCl from BIFs that burn hazardous waste irrespective of the purpose of the burning, but a significant grouping of burners remain exempt from the standards.

* The Used Oil Management Standards, formerly found at 40 CFR 266, Subpart E, were published as 40 CFR 279 on September 10, 1992 (57 FR 41612).

The complexities of the Subpart H standards, including *thirteen appendices*, greatly exceed the scope of this text, and it must be left to the student or practitioner to examine the details of the standards according to his/her needs.

TOPICS FOR REVIEW OR DISCUSSION

1. The text refers to a classic process change — the use of a single solvent for several purposes and reusing the solvent in succeeding processes which require decreasing purity. Name at least three advantages of such a modification.
2. There are apparently several reasons why many hazardous waste exchanges have not prospered. What are three of the reasons?
3. What format could be used to make a regulatory distinction between burning of hazardous waste for the fuel value and incinerating to destroy the hazardous constituents?
4. The EPA waste minimization program embodies a hierarchy of preferable options for hazardous waste management. Proceeding from most desirable to least desirable, list those options.
5. The RCRA requires hazardous waste generators who treat onsite or transport offsite to certify that they have waste minimization programs in place. How is this certification accomplished?
6. How would you expect the EPA or a state environmental regulatory authority to state a regulatory requirement that RCRA facilities reduce the quantities of hazardous waste generated?

REFERENCES

Alexander, Henry, P.E. 1992. "Source Reduction and Waste Minimization for Hazardous Wastes." *Environmental Management*" May/June:37ff.

Bolstridge, June C. 1992. *EPCRA Data on Chemical Releases, Inventories, and Emergency Planning*. Van Nostrand Reinhold, New York.

Breen, Joseph J., and Michael J. Dellarco. 1992. *Pollution Prevention in Industrial Processes — The Role of Process Analytical Chemistry*. American Chemical Society, Washington, D.C.

Harris, Margaret. 1988. "In-House Solvent Reclamation Efforts in Air Force Maintenance Operations." *Hazardous Waste Minimization Within the Department of Defense*, Joseph A. Kaminski, Ed. Office of the Deputy Assistant Secretary of Defense (Environment), Washington, D.C.

Higgins, Thomas E. 1991. *Hazardous Waste Minimization Handbook*. Lewis Publishers, Chelsea, MI.

McCoy and Associates. 1989. *The Hazardous Waste Consultant* March/April:1–23.

Mills, Michael B. 1988. "Hazardous Waste Minimization in the Manufacture of Explosives." *Hazardous Waste Minimization Within the Department of Defense*, Joseph A. Kaminski, Ed. Office of the Deputy Assistant Secretary of Defense (Environment), Washington, D.C.

University of Tennessee Center for Industrial Services. 1989. *Waste Reduction Assessment and Technology Transfer (WRATT) Training Manual,* Cam Metcalf, Ed. University of Tennessee, Knoxville.

U.S. Congress, Office of Technology Assessment. 1986. *Serious Reduction of Hazardous Waste.* Superintendent and Documents, Government Printing Office, Washington, D.C.

U.S. Environmental Protection Agency. 1988. *Waste Minimization Opportunity Assessment Manual.* Hazardous Waste Engineering Laboratory, Cincinnati, OH. EPA 625/7-88/003.

U.S. Environmental Protection Agency. 1989. *Waste Minimization in Metal Parts Cleaning.* Office of Solid Waste and Emergency Response, Washington, D.C. EPA 530-SW-89-049.

U.S. Environmental Protection Agency. 1994a. *The Waste Minimization National Plan.* Office of Solid Waste and Emergency Response, Washington, D.C. EPA 530-R-94-045.

U.S. Environmental Protection Agency. 1994b. *Strategy for Hazardous Waste Minimization and Combustion.* Office of Solid Waste and Emergency Response, Washington, D.C. EPA 530-R-94-044.

U.S. Environmental Protection Agency. 1994c. *The Biennial RCRA Hazardous Waste Report (Based on 1991 Data) Executive Summary.* Office of Solid Waste and Emergency Response, Washington, D.C. EPA 530-S-94-039.

U.S. Environmental Protection Agency, Solid Waste and Emergency Response. 1994d. *Draft RCRA Waste Minimization National Plan Summary.* Report No. EPA530-S-94-002, Washington, D.C.

U.S. General Accounting Office. 1994a. *Toxic Substances EPA Needs More Reliable Source Reduction Data and Progress Measures.* U.S. General Accounting Office, Washington, D.C. GAO/RCED-94-93.

U.S. General Accounting Office. 1994b. *Toxic Substances Status of EPA's Efforts to Reduce Toxic Releases.* U.S. General Accounting Office, Washington, D.C. GAO/RCED-94-207.

Wentz, Charles A. 1989. *Hazardous Waste Management.* McGraw-Hill, New York.

9 RCRA PERMITS, COMPLIANCE, AND ENFORCEMENT

OBJECTIVES

At completion of this chapter, the student should:

- understand the basic outline of the Resource Conservation and Recovery Act (RCRA) permitting process.
- be familiar with the four steps of the RCRA corrective action process and the application of each of the steps.
- understand the goals of the RCRA enforcement program and the actions which may be taken to achieve these goals.
- be familiar with the administrative, civil, and criminal enforcement provisions of RCRA.

INTRODUCTION

In the previous chapters, we have attempted to first present materials on the generally accepted practice pertaining to the hazardous waste management subject at hand. We have followed the general (or "generic") material with an overview of the regulatory requirements of the RCRA, and other pertinent statutes as they apply to the subject. This chapter deals with three related aspects of RCRA which have no generic counterpart.

Similarly, we have attempted to present the highly complex subject of hazardous waste management, and the respective components of RCRA, in an orderly flow of compartmentalized subjects. We now find it necessary to present an important set of materials which do not "fit together" as nicely. Certainly, compliance is required of permit holders, and enforcement actions are taken against those not in compliance. But compliance with RCRA (and other) statutes and regulations is required of all who handle hazardous wastes (not just permit holders or applicants), and enforcement actions may be taken against those who do not comply with the regulations. We will attempt to keep these aspects clear, but the reader should approach the subject with care.

The requirement to apply for, and obtain, an operating permit to treat, store, and dispose of hazardous waste is the subject of Section 3005 of RCRA. The related authority of the U.S. Environmental Protection Agency (EPA) and/or state inspectors to enter upon the premises of any "person who generates, stores, treats, transports, disposes of, or otherwise handles or has handled hazardous waste" to inspect, obtain samples, and copy records is contained in Section 3007. Section 3008 provides authority for enforcement of RCRA provisions. Section 3013 provides the EPA with authority to require owners or operators of treatment, storage, and disposal facilities (TSDFs) to conduct monitoring, testing, analysis, and reporting and to take enforcement action against any person who fails or refuses to comply with an order issued under this section.

Permits to Treat, Store, or Dispose of Hazardous Waste

Permits identify the administrative and technical standards which must be met by TSDFs. Permits are issued by the EPA or by a state agency which has been authorized by the EPA to administer the program. The permit specifies the operating requirements for the facility based upon the general and technical standards of 40 CFR 264, as well as requirements for corrective actions.

Facilities Permitted

RCRA requires every owner or operator of a TSDF to obtain an operating permit. Congress and the EPA recognized that several years would be required to issue permits to all TSDFs and made provisions for granting "interim status" to TSDFs that were in operation on November 19, 1980 and had "notified" the EPA prior to that date. Other TSDFs that are in operation "on the effective date of statutory or regulatory amendments, under the Act, that render the facility subject to the requirement to have a RCRA permit shall have interim status and shall be treated as having been issued a permit" provided they have notified the EPA of hazardous waste activity and comply with applicable operating standards (40 CFR 270.70).

Interim status facilities are allowed to operate in that status until a final permit is issued or denied. New facilities or existing facilities that failed to qualify for interim status are ineligible for interim status and must obtain a permit before commencing operations. Only in a very limited number of circumstances can a person treat, store, or dispose of hazardous waste without interim status or a permit. Such circumstances include:

- generators storing waste onsite for less than 90 days.
- small quantity generators (SQGs) who store waste onsite for less than 180 days.
- farmers disposing of their own pesticide wastes onsite.
- owners or operators of totally enclosed treatment facilities, wastewater treatment units, and elementary neutralization units.
- transporters storing manifested wastes at a transfer facility for less than ten days.

- persons engaged in containment activities during an immediate response to an emergency.
- owners or operators of solid waste disposal facilities handling only conditionally exempt SQG waste.
- persons engaged in Superfund onsite cleanups and RCRA Section 7003 cleanups.

Permits are also issued for research, development, and demonstration projects; post-closure of land disposal facilities; emergency situations involving imminent and substantial endangerment to human health or the environment; facilities having permits under other laws which impose similar requirements (e.g., underground injection control permits, ocean dumping permits for dredge spoil and for emergency situations); for temporary permits for incinerators to conduct trial burns; and for land treatment facilities to demonstrate acceptable performance (U.S. EPA 1990, Chapter 5).

The Permitting Process

Owners and operators of TSDFs must submit a comprehensive permit application consisting of two parts. Part A of the application is a short form which calls for basic information about the facility, such as name, location, nature of business conducted, regulated activities, and topographic map of the site. Part B is much more extensive than Part A and requires the submission of substantially more detailed technical information. General requirements are provided by 40 CFR 270.14. Specific information requirements for containers, tanks, surface impoundments, incinerators, land treatment facilities, landfills, and miscellaneous units are provided by 40 CFR 270.15 through 270.23. The applicant must become familiar with the requirements of 40 CFR 264 and 270 in order to determine the nature of the data required for the particular facility.

Technically, Part A may be submitted initially, to be followed by the Part B when "called in" by the EPA. This procedure grew from the necessity for then-existing facilities to apply prior to November 19, 1980 in order to be granted interim status.* Some authorized states no longer want Part A submissions, requiring Part B as the initial submission. Others require that Parts A and B be submitted simultaneously. Except in the case of very simple or primitive facilities, the assigned permit writer will require even further submissions after reviewing Part B. The supplemental data is requested through a "notice of deficiency" (NOD) letter to the applicant.

New facilities must apply at least 180 days before construction of the facility is to begin. In any event, the applicant should carefully coordinate preparation of the required submissions with the EPA or state program manager and/or assigned permit writer. The process is time-consuming, detailed, and exacting. For large and/or

* In recent years, the EPA has granted interim status to facilities burning hazardous wastes in boilers and industrial furnaces which apply for permits.

complex facilities, the process may require from one to three years to complete (U.S. EPA 1990, Chapter 5.)

After a complete RCRA permit application is filed, the 40 CFR 124 regulations establish the procedure for processing the application and issuing the permit. The process includes:

- review of the permit application.
- preparation of a draft permit.
- public comment and/or hearing.
- issue or denial of the permit.
- maintenance and termination of the permit.

In addition to RCRA requirements, activity at the facility must not conflict with other federal laws, including the:

- Wild and Scenic Rivers Act.
- National Historic Preservation Act of 1966.
- Endangered Species Act.
- Coastal Zone Management Act.
- Fish and Wildlife Coordination Act.

Permits for land disposal facilities, storage facilities, incinerators, and other treatment facilities can be issued for a ten-year fixed term. While permits may be reviewed and modified at any time during their terms, permits for land disposal facilities must be reviewed within five years following issue. When reviewed, the permit may be modified to incorporate changes in standards or policies regarding land disposal facilities.

The Corrective Action Process

The 1984 Hazardous and Solid Waste Amendments (HSWA) expanded the authority of the EPA and authorized states to address releases of hazardous waste through corrective actions beyond those contained in 40 CFR 264, Subpart F. Corrective action requirements are imposed through a permit or an enforcement order. The TSDF owner or operator becomes responsible for complying with the corrective action requirements. Permits issued to RCRA facilities must contain schedules for achieving compliance and include requirements for financial assurance to cover the cost of implementing the corrective measures.

The EPA can require permitted facilities with releases from regulated units to:

- take corrective action only on those releases to the uppermost aquifer (under 40 CFR 264, Subpart F).
- clean up any other contaminated media [under Sections 3004(u) and (v)].

The decision regarding these alternatives is made by the EPA on a case-by-case basis, taking into account the nature and magnitude of the release.

Corrective actions proceed through one or more of four steps. The procedures are detailed and tailored to the situation at the facility in question. The steps, briefly, involve:

- RCRA Facility Assessment (RFA), a review of existing information on contaminant releases, and sampling, if needed.
- RCRA Facility Investigation (RFI), wherein the owner or operator of a facility may be required to conduct further investigations to verify and/or characterize a release or releases.
- Corrective Measure Study (CMS), in which the owner or operator is required to identify, evaluate, and recommend specific corrective measures that will correct the release.
- Corrective Measures Implementation (CMI), which may include design, construction, maintenance, and monitoring the selected corrective measures.

Interim corrective measures may be required at any point in the process where the EPA or authorized state agency believes that expedited action should be taken to protect human health or the environment.

Compliance Requirements of RCRA

The goals of the RCRA enforcement program are to ensure that the regulatory and statutory provisions of RCRA are met and to compel corrective action where necessary. Facility inspections by the EPA and/or state agency officials are the primary tool by which compliance is monitored; however, self-monitoring and reporting activities are important elements of the program.

EPA regional administrators and officials of authorized state agencies have some discretion in reaction to findings of noncompliance by a facility that is subject to RCRA regulations. When noncompliance is detected, the range of enforcement options include the use of administrative orders, civil lawsuits, or criminal indictments, depending upon the nature and severity of the offense.

Federal and state administrators must have reliable compliance data in order to make fair and equitable decisions regarding enforcement options and to assess the overall effectiveness of the RCRA program. Competent monitoring acts as a deterrent by determining the extent to which a facility is in or out of compliance, by identifying potential and actual problems, and by generating credible data for use as leverage in negotiated settlements and as evidence in judicial proceedings.

Self-Monitoring

Many regulatory agencies do not have the field or laboratory resources to conduct definitive compliance monitoring of each and every potential and actual source of release of pollutants to the environment. Most environmental laws and regulations require the regulated entity to perform self-monitoring and to report or maintain the data in files. The RCRA is no exception to that generality.

With some limited exceptions, owners and operators of permitted surface impoundments, waste piles, land treatment units, and landfills must comply with the groundwater monitoring requirements of 40 CFR 264.91 through 264.100. The requirements are prescribed by the permitting authority and are tailored to the type and configuration of the facility, the type(s) of wastes to be managed, the geological and hydrogeological conditions of the site, and other variables.

The general groundwater monitoring requirements of 40 CFR 264.97, paraphrased, are the groundwater monitoring system must consist of a sufficient number of wells, installed at appropriate locations and depths to yield groundwater samples from the uppermost aquifer that:

1. represent the quality of background water that has not been affected by leakage from a regulated unit.
2. represent the quality of groundwater passing the point of compliance.*
3. allow for the detection of contamination when hazardous waste or hazardous constituents have migrated from the waste management area to the uppermost aquifer.

Figure 9.1 illustrates placement of clusters of monitoring wells to provide data on background water and on downgradient water quality.

In general, these requirements are met by three categories of monitoring:

1. *Detection Monitoring Program* — The owner or operator must monitor for indicator parameters, waste constituents, or reaction products that provide a reliable indication of the presence of hazardous constituents in groundwater (40 CFR 264.98).
2. *Compliance Monitoring Program* — If the Detection Monitoring Program indicates contamination of the uppermost aquifer, a permit modification establishing a *compliance* monitoring program must be initiated. The owner or operator must determine whether there is statistically significant evidence of increased contamination by any chemical parameter or hazardous constituent specified in the permit (40 CFR 264.99).
3. *Corrective Action Program* — If the Compliance Monitoring Program verifies that any concentration limit specified in the permit is being exceeded, the owner or operator must notify the EPA or authorized state agency administrator within seven days and initiate a permit modification to establish a corrective action program. The program, when approved,

* The "point of compliance" is a "vertical surface located at the hydraulically downgradient limit of the waste management area that extends down into the uppermost aquifer underlying the regulated units" (40 CFR 264.95).

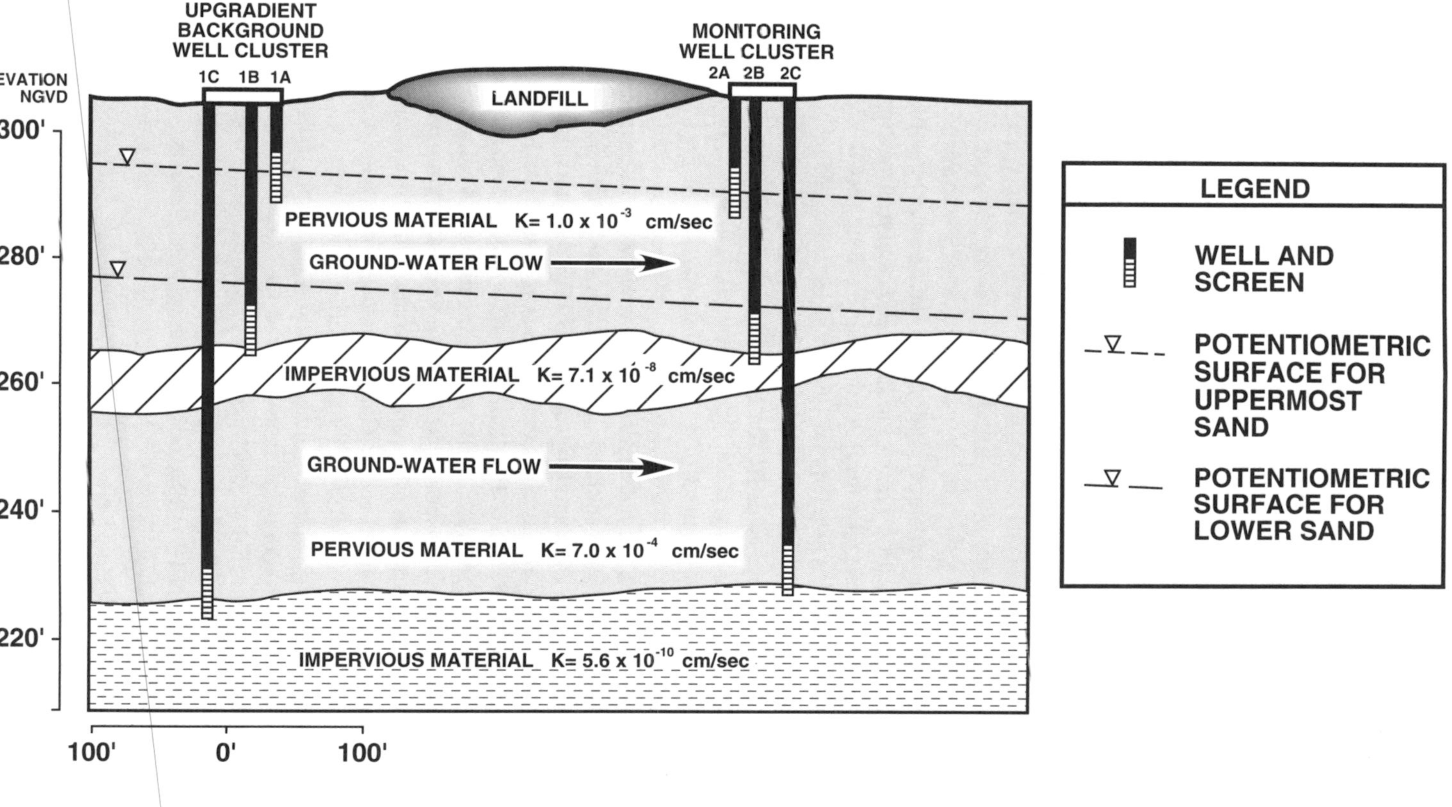

Figure 9.1 Placement of background and monitoring wells (EPA).

will require the owner or operator to take action to remove the hazardous waste constituents or treat them in place (40 CFR 264.100).

In each of the previous steps the permit and/or permit modification will detail the specific corrective measures that are to be implemented. Interim status land treatment and disposal facilities are subject to somewhat less stringent self-monitoring requirements. Regional administrators, authorized state agency officials, and permit writers have wide discretion regarding the type, extent, and frequency of monitoring that may be required. The EPA has published a number of guidance documents which inject a degree of consistency into the monitoring programs, but the system is designed to enable the regulatory authority to tailor the monitoring requirements to the individual facility. (*See also* U.S. EPA 1986, 1981, Chapter 5; Sara 1993, Chapter 10)

Inspections

The preferred method of obtaining compliance data is by the conduct of an inspection of the regulated facility. The Compliance Evaluation Inspection (CEI) is the primary enforcement mechanism for detecting and verifying RCRA violations. The CEI serves two important enforcement functions:

- Determining compliance with RCRA regulations, permit provisions, or preexisting enforcement orders
- Supporting enforcement actions

The inspection may include a formal visit to the owner or operator, a review of records, taking of samples, observation of operations, or combinations of these.

Inspections are usually conducted by state or EPA regulatory personnel. In instances where criminal activity is suspect, investigators from the EPA National Enforcement Investigations Center (NEIC), Office of Criminal Investigation at EPA headquarters, state attorney general's staff, or combinations thereof may become involved. U.S. Department of Transportation (DOT) investigators may participate in inspections involving transportation of hazardous wastes, and customs officers will play a major role in cross-border cases. Contractor personnel may be tasked to perform inspections; however, complications may arise in the use of contractor-obtained evidence, particularly where criminal penalties are sought.

HSWA requires that all federal- or state-operated facilities be inspected annually. All TSDFs must be inspected at least once every two years. Facilities may also be inspected at any time the EPA or the state agency has reason to suspect that a violation has occurred (U.S. EPA 1990, pp. III-82, 83).

Types of Inspections. Several types of inspections have been developed to meet RCRA requirements. The formats and descriptors for RCRA inspections change frequently due to changes in the statutes, regulations, and policies. Court decisions also play a major role in the processes of evidence gathering. In addition to the CEI, the currently used formats include:

- *Case Development Inspection (CDI)* — The CDI is conducted when significant RCRA violations are known, suspected, or revealed and is structured to gather data in support of a specific enforcement action.
- *Comprehensive Groundwater Monitoring Evaluation (CME)* — The CME is a detailed evaluation of the adequacy of the design and operation of groundwater monitoring systems at RCRA facilities.
- *Compliance Sampling Inspection (CSI)* — Samples are collected for laboratory analysis. A sampling inspection may be conducted in conjunction with, or in support of, other inspection formats.
- *Operation and Maintenance Inspection (O&M)* — The O&M inspection is structured to determine whether or not groundwater monitoring and other systems are functioning properly after closure of a land disposal facility.
- *Laboratory Audits* — These are inspections of laboratories performing groundwater analyses. The audit is intended to ensure that the laboratory is using proper sample handling and analysis protocols.
- *RCRA Facility Assessment (RFA)* — The RFA is performed at a TSDF to identify releases or potential releases of hazardous constituents from solid waste management units that may require corrective action. RFAs are usually conducted as part of the permitting process.

Evidence of noncompliance obtained during an inspection may result in the regulatory agency taking one of the following actions:

- Issuance of a warning letter
- Issuance of an administrative order
- Assessment of an administrative civil penalty
- Commencement of a permit action
- Institution of a civil court action
- Institution of a criminal court investigation

These actions are discussed in the following section. (*See also* U.S. EPA 1988, 1992)

Enforcement of RCRA Regulations

RCRA provides a variety of enforcement options to the EPA and authorized state agencies. The goals of these provisions, quite simply, are to compel:

- proper handling of hazardous waste.
- compliance with RCRA record keeping and reporting requirements.
- necessary corrective action.

The enforcement program is carried out through evaluation of compliance monitoring data and the various levels of inspection activity discussed earlier. Appropriate legal action may be taken pursuant to findings of noncompliance. *Administrative actions* that can be taken include informal actions and administrative orders.

Informal Actions

The EPA and authorized state agencies have a wide range of informal actions which may be taken to notify owners or operators of waste handling facilities of a problem with their compliance status. Such actions may involve no more than a telephone call or a face-to-face conversation. They include issuance of a "notice of violation," or an NOV. This type of action is appropriate where the violation is of a minor nature, such as a record keeping error or omission.

If the owner or operator does not take steps to comply within a reasonable or specified time period, a "warning letter" may be sent. The warning letter also sets forth the enforcement actions that will follow if the recipient fails to take the necessary steps to bring the operation into compliance.

Administrative Orders

More severe violations or failure to respond to an informal action can be the basis for the agency to issue an administrative order. Such an order, issued under RCRA authority, imposes enforceable legal duties. Orders can be used to force a facility to comply with specific regulations; to take corrective action; to perform monitoring, testing, and analysis; or to address a threat of harm to human health and the environment. Four types of order can be issued under RCRA.

Compliance Orders. A Section 3008(a) order may be issued to any person who is in noncompliance with an RCRA requirement. The order may require immediate compliance or may set a timetable to be followed in achieving compliance. The order may specify penalties as great as $25,000 per day for each day of noncompliance and can suspend or revoke the permit or interim status of the facility.

Corrective Action Orders. A Section 3008(h) order may be issued requiring corrective action at an interim status facility when there is evidence of a release of a hazardous waste to the environment. Such orders can be issued to require corrective action ranging from investigative activity to repairing liners or pumping and treating a plume of contaminated groundwater. The order may utilize "reach back" authorities to require cleanup of previously caused problems. These orders can also impose penalties as great as $25,000 per day for each day of noncompliance.

Section 3013 Orders. Section 3013 provides authority for the EPA to issue an administrative order to correct a "substantial hazard to human health and the environment." The order requires that the nature and extent of the problem be evaluated through monitoring, analysis, and testing. The order may be issued to the current owner of the facility or to a past owner or operator, as appropriate.

Section 7003 Orders. The 7003 order is used to order cleanup of an "imminent and substantial endangerment to health or the environment" which is or has been caused by the handling of nonhazardous or hazardous waste. The order may be issued to any contributing party, including past or present generators, transporters, owners, or operators of the site. Violation of a Section 7003 order can result in penalties of as much as $5000 per day.

Civil Actions

Formal lawsuits may be brought in civil jurisdictions to seek court-ordered compliance with RCRA provisions, cleanup following a release, or to obtain court orders to persons whom have failed to comply with administrative orders issued under Sections 3008, 3013, or 7003. Civil actions are generally employed in situations that present repeated or significant violations or where there are serious environmental concerns.

Criminal Actions

Criminal actions resulting in fines or imprisonment may be taken in seven specific instances. These are *knowingly:*

- Transporting hazardous waste to a nonpermitted facility
- Treating, storing, or disposing of waste without a permit or in violation of a material condition of a permit or an interim status standard
- Omitting important information from, or making a false statement in, a label, manifest, report, permit, or compliance document
- Generating, storing, treating, or disposing of waste without complying with the RCRA record keeping and reporting requirements
- Transporting waste without a manifest
- Exporting waste without the consent of the receiving country
- Treating, disposing of, or exporting any hazardous waste in such a way that another person is placed in imminent danger of death or serious bodily injury

Enforcement policies of the EPA and Justice Department have traditionally reserved criminal prosecution for only the most egregious violations. In the mid-1990s, however, both agencies are focusing on criminal activity by policy statements, increases in numbers of criminal investigators, and numbers of criminal prosecutions:

- "The Agency brought 2,247 enforcement actions with sanctions in fiscal year 1994, 137 more than were taken in 1993, the previous record year … The record number of enforcement actions consisted of 220 criminal cases … preliminary estimates totaled a record $165.2 million combined for civil penalties and criminal fines" (EPA news release, November 30, 1994).
- In an August 23, 1994 memorandum, the attorney general overturned a Bush administration policy that required U.S. attorneys to obtain clearance from the Department of Justice headquarters in Washington, D.C. before filing a criminal case and allows the local attorneys to file cases as they see fit (*Environment Reporter,* September 9, 1994, p. 852).

- The Director of Office of Criminal Enforcement (EPA) is quoted as stating that the "EPA had doubled its special agents since the passage of the Pollution Prevention Act in 1990 and had achieved 'a presence in nearly all federal judicial districts' " (*Environment Reporter*, January 21, 1994).

(*See also* Blattner and Bramble 1994, p. 127ff; U.S. EPA 1994)

TOPICS FOR REVIEW OR DISCUSSION

1. What was the rationale on the part of the EPA for grouping TSDFs as the third element in the "cradle-to-grave" system of hazardous waste control?
2. Why would the EPA or a state regulatory agency insist that groundwater monitoring continue for 30 years after closure of a land disposal facility?
3. Why was Congress concerned about conflicts with the National Historic Preservation Act of 1966 at a RCRA facility?
4. What rationale does the EPA have for entrusting facilities to conduct self-monitoring of critical compliance parameters?

REFERENCES

Blattner, J. Wray, and Gary M. Bramble. 1994. "Avoiding Criminal Liabilities." *Chemical Engineering* June:127ff.

Environment Reporter January 21, 1994. Bureau of National Affairs, Washington, D.C.

Environment Reporter September 9, 1994, p. 852. Bureau of National Affairs, Washington, D.C.

Sara, Martin N. 1993. *Standard Handbook for Solid and Hazardous Waste Facility Assessments.* Lewis Publishers, Chelsea, MI.

U.S. Environmental Protection Agency. 1981. *NEIC Manual for Groundwater/Subsurface Investigations of Hazardous Waste Sites.* National Enforcement Investigations Center, Denver, CO. EPA 330/9-81-002.

U.S. Environmental Protection Agency. 1986. *RCRA Ground-Water Monitoring Technical Enforcement Guidance Document.* Office of Waste Programs Enforcement, Washington, D.C. OSWER Directive Number 9950.1.

U.S. Environmental Protection Agency. 1988. *RCRA Inspection Manual.* Office of Waste Programs Enforcement, Washington, D.C. OSWER Directive Number 9938.2A.

U.S. Environmental Protection Agency. 1990. *RCRA Orientation Manual, 1990 Edition.* Superintendent of Documents, Government Printing Office, Washington, D.C.

U.S. Environmental Protection Agency. 1994. News release, November 30.

U.S. Environmental Protection Agency. 1992. *Multi-Media Inspection Manual.* National Enforcement Investigations Center, Denver, CO. EPA 330/9-89-003-R.

U.S. Environmental Protection Agency. 1994. *Enforcement Accomplishments Report FY 1993.* Office of Enforcement, Washington, D.C. EPA 300-R-94-003.

10 ASSESSMENT TECHNIQUES FOR SITE REMEDIATION

OBJECTIVES

At completion of this chapter, the student should:

- be cognizant of the necessity for an appropriate form of site environmental asssessment where individuals or organizations have "care, custody, and control" of real property or contemplate assumption of same.
- be familiar with the general format for site assessments for property transactions and for remediation by regulatory agencies.
- be familiar with the kinds of background information that are needed for establishing compliance history, assessing the need for additional or new data, designing new information/data gathering activity, ensuring safety of the investigators and public, and protecting the rights of the responsible parties.
- be familiar with site assessment factors such as information-gathering activity appropriate to the problem site, behavior of site owner/manager, severity of the health/environmental threat, health and welfare of the public, safety of workers on the site, and the applicable laws and regulations.
- understand the importance of record keeping, documentation, and chain-of-custody procedures, irrespective of the nature of the corrective action contemplated.

INTRODUCTION

Our focus in previous chapters has been upon the management of hazardous waste as it is generated, transported, stored, treated, destroyed, or disposed of. The primary objective of hazardous waste management is the handling of the waste in a manner that prevents harm to the public health and the environment. Whatever the degree or numbers of our successes in attaining this goal may be, the fact remains that large numbers of sites have been contaminated with hazardous waste(s). Contaminated sites must be remediated, whether preparatory to transfer of ownership or as a result of regulatory requirements. Similarly, prospective landowners must have reliable mechanisms for evaluating the extent or absence of contamination of potential aquisitions. Individuals and organizations having responsibility for remediating contaminated sites must have generally recognized and accepted procedures for assessment of site cleanup needs. In this and the following chapter, we will overview techniques and regulatory procedures for accomplishing these tasks.

Two sets of considerations bring about the need for definitive evaluation of site contamination:

1. The Comprehensive Environmental Response, Compensation, and Liability Act (CERCLA)* and several court findings impose strict, joint, and several liability** upon owners or operators of hazardous waste sites, i.e., sites where a release of hazardous substance(s) has occurred. These liabilities can be so severe that avoidance of such liability has become an imperative that transcends most others in commercial property transactions. The acquisition of property, particularly property previously used for industrial or commercial activity, is now made contingent upon a "clean bill of health" determination by a competent environmental investigator. Such determination, variously labeled a due diligence evaluation, an environmental audit, environmental site assessment, or property transfer site assessment, has become a major activity of consultants and attorneys. There are significant differences between and within the assessment procedures, and these will be discussed briefly. Regardless of the assessment procedure used, the stakes are exceedingly high, and the need for exactness in all aspects of the work is of the highest order. "Super lien" laws in many states (e.g., New Jersey, Massachusetts) allow the state to attach a priority lien to any property to pay for the cost of remediation should environmental contamination be discovered (Hopper 1989).
2. Sites suspected or known to be contaminated are subject to cleanup under state and federal laws. Such cleanup may be carried out voluntarily by the "responsible party(ies),"*** as a result of a negotiated agreement, in response to an administrative order, under a court-ordered settlement, or by a regulatory agency implementing a funded cleanup (i.e., Superfund) type provision of a statutory authority. Moreover, there are seemingly limitless variations upon each of these mechanisms.

* The acronym CERCLA is traditionally used to identify the statute. The nickname "Superfund" usually refers to the program which implements CERCLA. The Superfund process will be overviewed in the next unit.

** "Strict" liability means that no showing of actual fault is required in order to assign liability; joint and several liability means that multiple contributors of hazardous waste to a site may all be held equally liable unless one or more can demonstrate that its wastes can be separately identified or could not possibly have contributed to the harm (*see* CERCLA Section 107).

*** Persons having caused, permitted, or contributed to the contamination of a site that is caught up in the Superfund process are referred to as "potentially responsible parties" (PRPs). As the Superfund process continues to the stage that responsibility(ies) has (have) been established, the term becomes "responsible parties" (RPs).

As in the first instance, exacting standards of investigation and analysis are in order. The cost of cleanup of a contaminated site is nearly always measured in millions of dollars. The average Superfund site cleanup cost is now more than $10 million (Priznar 1995, p. 168). That cost inevitably falls upon property owners, responsible parties, taxpayers, or is passed along to consumers or users of products and services in the form of higher prices. The costs (and environmental impacts) of a misdirected, inadequate, or overdone cleanup, resulting from erroneous or incomplete assessment data, can be unacceptably high.

It is not possible in the time and space available to provide a detailed study of site assessment procedures. The student should become conversant in the general concepts and actions involved and understand their importance. In the next section, we provide the generic approach to identification of problem sites and some approaches to obtaining necessary background information for the conduct of site assessments. In the following section, we discuss the procedural organization of a site assessment as conducted in the private sector. In subsequent sections, we outline the corollary procedure for site assessments leading to remediation under the Resource Conservation and Recovery Act (RCRA) or CERCLA, and we outline the regulatory site evaluation process established by the U.S. Environmental Protection Agency (EPA) to carry out CERCLA mandates.

Identifying Problem Sites and Obtaining Background Information

Purpose

Given either of the two most likely situations — (1) a site is under consideration for acquisition or (2) there is concern or doubt regarding regulatory compliance — a review of background information is needed. The background report for the acquisition site will contain similarities to that done for the suspect site, but the objectives and follow-on activity may be greatly divergent. An authority and practitioner provides the following explanation:

- "In an audit, an auditor is seeking to verify expectations. More specifically, the auditor is seeking to confirm or deny a specific condition. Typically, in an environmental context, the auditor seeks to understand whether regulatory or policy requirements are being met (compliance audit). The answers to an auditor's questions are limited to 'yes', 'no', and 'do not know'."
- "Greater judgement is involved in an assessment, which is similar to an appraisal. An assessor seeks to estimate, or judge, environmentally important factors that affect value or character… . An assessment does not measure expectations of conditions documented in standards against actual conditions, whereas audits should" (Priznar 1995, p. 160).

In either event, a background data collection process is necessary. Background information is that which is available or can be obtained from existing records. Such records may contain:

- cultural history related to man's activities as differentiated from technical data.
- technical details including environmental data, natural phenomena, well logs, etc.
- regulatory history.

Cultural History

Records or histories of man's activities that may be significant with respect to hazardous waste contamination of a site include:

- land-use patterns, e.g., former agricultural use with pesticide residues in fields, container disposal, or heavily contaminated mixing areas.
- site use, e.g., type(s) of industrial or commercial activity.
- records of catastrophic events.
- interviews with former or present residents, employees, owners, labor unions, local officials, or historical societies regarding past activities on the site.

Technical Information

Technical information may be nonexistent, primitive, or otherwise questionable. The investigator should seek out corroborating or coincident data to strengthen existing technical data if possible. Useful data may include:

- geological studies, soil tests, groundwater pump tests, or ground or surface water quality data.
- ground and/or surface water hydrological data.
- irrigation history.
- utility and right-of-way maps.

Regulatory History

Files of regulatory agencies may contain highly pertinent data, including:

- zoning and ordinance changes.
- tax assessments and business licenses.
- building permits.
- fire code, sanitation, or health violations.

In some areas, the U.S. Department of Agriculture has extensive aerial photography coverage. It is possible (again, in some areas) to view five- or ten-year sequences of the property under consideration. Other governmental agencies also maintain remote sensing and aerial imagery files which can be very helpful in constructing historical use patterns.

If past or present hazardous waste activity is known or acknowledged, the state or local regulatory agencies should have records indicating:

- types and volumes of wastes on the site.
- sources and processes associated with the waste.
- chronology and location of waste disposal activity.
- records of violations, spills and other releases, cleanup activity, monitoring activity, and disposition of cleanup or treatment residues.

The historical review of an acknowledged hazardous waste site should include records of inspections, site investigations, and regulatory activity on adjacent and nearby sites.

Background Report

All data must be carefully reviewed, conflicts in data must be reconciled, and questionable data must be set aside and so noted. The background report is the basis for decisions regarding follow-on activity and should focus on the findings, the additional data needed, and recommended strategies for dealing with the site.

Consulting firms with extensive historical involvement in the area of the site may be able to confidently advise their client based upon a simple background report. At the opposite extreme, a background report for a site being brought into the federal Superfund process is highly structured and voluminous. In the Superfund lexicon the background report is called a preliminary assessment (PA) and is but the first step in a protracted process that can lead to remedial action and cost recovery. Although the sophistication of the background report may vary according to the needs of the client and the history of the site, the importance of thoroughness and accuracy cannot be overemphasized.

Site Assessment Procedures in the Private Sector

Site assessments for property transactions are usually less ponderous than those for regulatory purposes. As will be seen, a site investigation leading to a remedial action under CERCLA or RCRA may consist of many more steps or "phases" than is normally the case in a property transaction site assessment (PTSA). Most practitioners of the PTSA structure the activity in, at the most, three phases. The following, adapted from Burby (1989), is an example. References for other examples are provided. These structures are for guidance and are flexed to meet the client's needs.

Pre-Phase I

Variously called a "scoping step," the Pre-Phase I is intended to provide a preliminary environmental survey. This activity might involve a one-day site visit to make a PA of the hazardous materials situation. The site visit includes observing general physical conditions; collecting readily available materials such as copies of permits and records; and interviewing present and past employees, managers, and/or owners. The Pre-Phase I may culminate in a letter report to the client that summarizes site observations and findings and includes a scope of recommended additional work.

Phase I

Phase I is a thorough qualitative review of the site based on field observations and reasonably available existing information. A typical Phase I investigation includes:

- review of appropriate files (e.g., title search, property records, regulatory permits, and databases) to investigate past or current activities at the site or adjacent properties with respect to wastewater; site drainage; air emissions; and toxic substance and hazardous material/waste handling, storage, treatment, disposal, and spills.
- review of reasonably available historic aerial photographs of the site and adjacent properties to identify the timing of past activities in the area and associated significant topographic changes.
- reconnaissance visit(s) to the site and adjacent properties, including the interiors of any onsite buildings, to inspect the general condition of the property and surrounding area for evidence or suspicion of contaminant releases to the soil, surface, and/or groundwater from spills, dumping, or burial of hazardous materials.
- interviews of available personnel and past or present site owners and operators.

The Phase I assessment concludes with a written report that summarizes the observations and findings made and includes recommendations for sampling or other investigative work if needed.

Phase II

Phase II may consist of air, soil surface, and/or groundwater sampling on and near the property and analyses, as needed, to characterize the site. A sampling plan is developed which includes quality assurance and quality control (QA/QC) criteria. Upon completion of the sampling and chemical characterization and the related data, a Phase II report is prepared detailing the procedures and protocols followed and the findings. Depending upon the findings, the report may include recommendations for additional investigative activity, a scope of recommended remedial actions (Phase III), or other recommendations (Burby 1989).

Standardized Environmental Site Assessments

Various entities, public and private, have sought to achieve some standardization of the environmental site assessment (ESA) procedure. The motive(s) for standardization generally centers upon assurances of acceptance, by any/all parties and courts of review, of the findings produced by an ESA. A very thorough and structured format has been developed by the American Society for Testing and Materials (ASTM) for the conduct of an *environmental site assessment*.* The E 1527-93 Standard Practice for Environmental Site Assessments: Phase I Environmental Site Assessment Process has filled the described need and has become widely accepted as the standard for Phase I assessments. The ASTM standard cannot be reproduced herein, but the overall structure can be seen from the contents and report format, which is provided as Appendix A to this chapter. The full text of the standard may be obtained by writing to:

> The American Society for Testing and Materials
> 1916 Race Street
> Philadelphia, PA 19103.

(*See also* Consulting Engineers Council 1989; Von Oppenfeld 1990; Turim 1991; Sara 1994; Priznar 1995)

Environmental Audits

The concept of the environmental audit has, at this writing, at least a 15-year history characterized by uncertainty. The uncertainty is seen in the current ASTM definition of an environmental audit:

> the investigative process to determine if the operations of an existing facility are in compliance with applicable environmental laws and regulations. This term should not be used to describe Practice E 1528 or this practice, although an environmental audit may include an *environmental site assessment* or, if prior audits are available, may be part of an environmental site assessment. (ASTM E 1527-93, par. 3.3.10)

The concept, whether carried out in a management format or in a regulatory/enforcement context, is regarded by regulatory and enforcement program directors as a means of extending limited staff resources and by corporate officials and industry managers with suspicion and hesitance. The EPA began proposing environmental audits as elements of enforcement case settlements in the mid-1970s, and such settlements have now become routine (U.S. EPA 1994).

Early discussions and proposals contained language similar to that now seen in descriptions of site assessments. A current definition reads:

> A process that seeks to verify documented expectations, typically regulations and policies, by conducting interviews, reviewing records, and making first-hand observations… . (Priznar 1995, p. 160)

* The italics are used by the ASTM to indicate any terms that are specifically defined in the standard. The ESA is defined by the ASTM as "the process by which a person or entity seeks to determine if a particular parcel of real *property* (including improvements) is subject to *recognized environmental conditions*. At the option of the user, an environmental site assessment may include more inquiry than that constituting *appropriate inquiry* or, if the user is not concerned about qualifying for the *innocent landowner defense*, less inquiry than that constituting *appropriate inquiry* … An environmental site assessment is both different from and less rigorous than an *environmental audit*."

The EPA now defines environmental audits as:

> a systematic, documented, periodic and objective review by regulated entities of facility operations and practices related to meeting environmental requirements. Audits can be designed to accomplish any or all of the following: verify compliance with environmental requirements; evaluate the effectiveness of environmental management systems already in place; or assess risks from regulated and unregulated materials and practices. (59 FR 38455)

Thoughtful industry managers and executives turned to internal audits as state and federal enforcement programs became active. The practice was seen as a "heads-up" management technique which would detect noncompliance, enable timely correction, and generally avoid problems. Priznar states the reasoning succinctly:

> typically, requestors want assurance that their organization will not be surprised by fines, negative publicity, and related distractions if they are caught in noncompliance by regulatory agencies. Audits also serve to demonstrate to internal staff and external entities the organization's good faith with regard to environmental management. (Priznar 1995, p. 160)

With time, however, executives and managers have become wary of the process. Concerns center upon revelation of sensitive information, compromise of business confidential/trade secret information, discovery by regulatory agencies, and personal risks of executives and managers. The EPA continues to advocate and propose auditing and has attempted to assuage doubts, but a recent restatement of policy does little to achieve that end:

> Corporate culpability may be indicated when a company performs an environmental compliance or management audit, and then knowingly fails to promptly remedy the non-compliance and correct any harm done. On the other hand, EPA policy strongly encourages self-monitoring, self-disclosure, and self-correction. When self-auditing has been conducted (followed up by prompt remediation of the non-compliance and any resulting harm) and full, complete disclosure has occurred, the companys constructive activities should be considered as mitigating factors in EPAs exercise of investigative discretion. Therefore a violation that is voluntarily revealed and fully and promptly remediated as part of a corporations systematic and comprehensive self-evaluation program generally will not be a candidate for the expenditure of scarce criminal resources. (59 FR 38455)

Practices which have been employed, by practitioners, to offset some or all of the concerns include use of internal auditors to improve protection from "leaks"; use of attorneys to perform the audits, thus enabling the protection of the attorney-client priviledges; and elimination of written audit reports (Priznar 1995, p. 166ff).

Compliance Inspections/Investigations by Regulatory Agencies

Purpose

CERCLA Section 104(e) contains authority enabling the EPA to conduct inspections at sites and facilities where hazardous substances are or may have been generated, stored, treated, disposed of, or transported to or from. As overviewed in previous chapters, RCRA Sections 3007 and 3008 authorize entry, inspections, data collection, sampling, file review, etc. These authorities are the basis for compliance inspections and/or investigations conducted in the implementation of the CERCLA and RCRA regulations.

In practice, the CERCLA authorities are used to request information, inspect, obtain samples, investigate, monitor, survey, test, and study actual or suspected releases on or from a site. These actions are taken pursuant to a finding in a PA that a release may have occurred and are performed as a site inspection (SI). The SI provides portions of the input data to a hazard ranking procedure which is overviewed later in this chapter.

The RCRA authorities are generally directed toward more immediate enforcement actions, such as the assessment of an administrative penalty, commencement of a permit action, or institution of civil or criminal proceedings. They may also be used in a closure or post-closure investigation.

Although each investigation must be tailored to specific objectives, many of the technical procedures are similar, whether conducted under CERCLA or RCRA. Figure 10.12 diagrams a comparison of RCRA and CERCLA remedial processes.

The Inspection Plan

Site inspections may be carried out by consultants having appropriate expertise or by federal, state, or local regulatory agency personnel. The inspector is trained and drilled in the necessity (1) for a detailed plan for the conduct of the inspection and (2/b) for careful adherence to the plan. The inspector must always anticipate that the plan may be subjected to intense review in a court of law and that seemingly minor deviance from the plan may sharply affect the credibility of evidence developed in the inspection. Courts and defense attorneys take a dim view of vaguely planned and/or executed inspections which appear to be "fishing expeditions."

Items which the plan should address include:

- scope of the inspection which depends upon the purpose and objectives. The scope is expressed in terms of issues to be addressed, areas to be inspected, depth of detail required, time allocated to conduct the inspection, etc. For example, inspections performed in response to information received concerning alleged violations will generally be comprehensive in scope and entail a detailed evaluation of all RCRA regulated activities at the site.
- coordination required with other offices, agencies, or services.
- procedure regarding prior notification, denial of entry, denial of access to records, areas, units, etc.
- entering the facility, i.e., is there to be an opening conference? Items to be covered? Proceed with a visual inspection immediately to preclude hasty adjustments or concealment?
- summarized findings from the background report.
- applicable regulations, policies, and guidance documents.
- procedure regarding records review, i.e., review onsite, copy for later review, or other arrangement.

- personnel assigned and their duties.
- sampling plan, including list of equipment.
- protective clothing and safety equipment requirements.
- site safety plan, as appropriate.
- contingency plan for emergencies that may arise during the inspection.
- checklists (if any) to be used.

In general, the plan should lay out the activities and sequences which are to be followed and the resources which are to be required and should highlight any particular issues which may pertain at the site.

Conduct of the Inspection/Investigation

In some cases, the inspector will have limited information on the facility or may be inspecting an uncontrolled site. The inspector should be prepared to encounter the worst conditions in such cases. *Inspectors should never proceed with inspections involving site conditions for which they are not prepared or do not have the proper safety equipment* (U.S. EPA 1988, pp. 2:17–20).

Entry. The RCRA regulations have been interpreted to allow either announced or unannounced inspections. If an inspection is to be announced, the facility is contacted and advised of the forthcoming inspection. The time and date of arrival is usually provided, but is not required. In an unannounced inspection, no notice is provided before the inspector's arrival on site.

The regulations require that the inspector:

- enter the premises at a reasonable time and complete the inspection as promptly as is possible.
- issue receipts for samples collected.
- provide duplicate samples.
- furnish the owner, operator, or agent a copy of any sample analysis conducted.

Upon arrival the inspector should:

- locate the owner, operator, or agent as soon as possible and determine that this official has the proper authority to speak and act for the facility.
- present identification to the owner, operator, or agent, even if it is not requested.
- document entry activity in a logbook or field notebook, noting date, time, and the names and titles of facility personnel encountered.

Inspectors may be requested to sign a log- or passbook and may do so. Such documents are useful in the event of fire or other emergency. The EPA instructs inspectors *not* to sign waivers or other legal documents that limit the facility's liabilities in the event of an accident. Inspectors are also instructed not to sign documents that may limit the inspector's rights or the owner's responsibilities.

The owner or agent in charge at the time of the inspection either gives or denies consent to inspect the premises. Consent may be withdrawn at some point during the inspection. Such action is considered denial of access. Other actions which amount to denial include not allowing the inspector to bring in necessary equipment (e.g., a camera) or not allowing the inspector access to documents.

When an inspector is denied access, the EPA specifies that step-by-step procedures be followed. The procedures begin with a request for the reason for denial and may culminate in a return to the facility with a search warrant, or company officials may be issued a subpoena (U.S. EPA 1992, pp. 29–30).

Opening discussions with the owner, operator, or agent are usually held to:

- outline the objectives of the inspection or investigation.
- brief facility management on the applicable elements of RCRA or other regulations, as appropriate.
- establish the sequence of the operations to be inspected.
- establish schedules for meetings and other events.
- arrange for facility personnel to accompany the inspector.
- arrange to provide duplicate samples and sample receipts.
- determine whether the owner or operator intends to make confidential business information claims.

Owners, operators, or agents should expect the inspector to be highly inquisitive. The EPA instructs inspectors to "question, question, and question some more ... Inconsistencies must be pursued until they are resolved" (U.S. EPA 1988, Chapter 4).

Operations, Waste Handling, and Records Review. Early in the inspection/investigation process, the inspector will ask the facility representative to describe operations and waste management practices in detail. The purpose of this discussion will be to:

- gain a detailed understanding of the operations.
- answer any questions the inspector may have regarding waste generation, waste flow, and waste management activities.
- identify changes in operating and/or waste management practices from those indicated in the permit and/or facility files.
- identify and reconcile any discrepancies between the operations described by the facility representative and those described in the files.

The EPA does not attempt to prescribe a format for the records review; however, Appendix H of the Multi-Media Investigation Manual provides a suggested record/documents request (U.S. EPA 1992). The general thrust of inquiry can be expected to follow the record keeping requirements of 40 CFR 262, 263, 265 (or 264), and 270. They include personnel and training records, agreements with local authorities, contingency plans, manifests, biennial reports, exception reports, waste analysis plans, waste analyses and test results, inspection schedules and results, operating records, groundwater monitoring plans, groundwater monitoring records, closure plans, post-closure plans, annual assessment for tanks, certification of major repairs, contingent post-closure plans, land treatment operating record and closure plans, landfill operating record, and contents and organization of land disposal cells.

The records review frequently leads to large numbers of what facility managers disparage as "paperwork" violations. EPA officials consider the records review to be the primary option available to ensure that the "cradle-to-grave" management system is being implemented and have successfully defended that view before congressional and other inquiries.

Visual Inspection. EPA inspectors attempt to organize the visual inspection in such a way that the flow of waste materials and the related processes can be understood and that the compliance status of each process or unit can be determined. The EPA provides the example of inspection of a plant which generates hazardous waste, stores waste for offsite disposal, and treats some waste onsite. The visual inspection could proceed as follows, in brief:

- Inspect points of waste generation and accumulation. Determine if the owner/operator has identified all hazardous wastes based on generating operations, and determine if accumulation points meet satellite storage area requirements.
- Evaluate in-plant waste transport from generation and accumulation points to storage and treatment units. Determine if there is potential for mislabeling, misplacing, or mishandling wastes and if wastes are adequately tracked to enable proper identification at storage and treatment units.
- Evaluate storage and treatment units for compliance with applicable standards. Determine if waste in units correspond to those whose points of generation have been inspected, and identify where any other wastes in the units originate. Determine if any hazardous wastes are generated in the unit (e.g., treatment sludge), and evaluate the management of such waste for compliance.

The sequence of this procedure enables the inspector to understand the movement and control of waste within the facility and thereby identify:

- hazardous wastes which may not currently be considered hazardous by the owner/operator.
- non-complying procedures or management practices which are part of the facility's routine operations.
- steps in the management process during which wastes may be mishandled or misidentified and in which there are opportunities for spills or releases.
- unusual situations which may be encountered during the inspection, varying from the facility's stated normal operating procedures and indicating potential violations (U.S. EPA 1988, Chapter 4).

The EPA has developed a number of general and industry-specific checklists which can help the inspector approach the inspection in an organized way. In addition, a large number of guidance documents, pertaining to Subtitle C requirements, are available to the inspector and to the regulated community. The availability can be ascertained by contacting an EPA regional office or by obtaining a catalog of the documents (U.S. EPA 1994) by calling the RCRA Hotline (800-424-9346).

Sampling and Monitoring. If the site is permitted or if sampling has been accomplished in accord with interim status requirements, sufficient data may be available in the files to meet the needs of a Superfund SI or a RCRA compliance investigation. EPA guidance deemphasizes drum sampling at these stages, if the data on hand is believed sufficient for the immediate activity. This policy reflects the fact that (1) drum sampling is resource intensive, and (2) if the investigation proceeds to a removal action, it may be necessary to sample all drums on the site. This requires "staging" of the drums and a highly efficient sampling and analysis scheme.

Similarly, if groundwater monitoring has been performed and the data are available, the inspection or investigation may require only minimal confirming sampling and analysis. If groundwater data are needed and monitoring wells are not in place, various options may suffice.

- Seeps and springs obviously reflect the near-surface groundwater quality and may reflect the effects of local contamination
- Nearby water supply wells may similarly reflect local contamination
- In the absence of other options and where depth to groundwater permits, driven well points may provide sampling access to leachate plumes or near-surface groundwater

Comprehensive groundwater monitoring networks are rarely installed specifically for SIs. They may be installed to support a large-scale RCRA compliance investigation or may come into the Superfund process at the Remedial Investigation/Feasibility Study sequence of activity. The procedures, techniques, and standards for groundwater monitoring network systems are extensive and dependent upon many factors. The technologies are the subject of entire training courses, manuals, and textbooks and cannot be covered here. References are provided at the end of this chapter.

Surface water, including streams and impoundments, may receive contaminated groundwater flow or runoff. Surface water sampling can supplement groundwater monitoring or, in the absence of other monitoring points, be the most practical way of identifying offsite pollutant movement. Downgradient surface water suspected of receiving groundwater inflow should be sampled.

Ambient concentrations of pollutants may be very low, yet their presence in any measurable concentration may be significant. Procedures used or materials contacting the sample should not cause pollutants to be gained or lost. Sampling equipment and sample containers must be fabricated from inert materials and must be thoroughly cleaned before use.

Sampling Equipment and Procedures. Samples must be secured in a manner which will ensure the safety of the sampler, all others working in the area, and the surroundings. Stored, abandoned, or suspect waste will often be containerized in drums or tanks. Such containers pose special safety problems. Care must be exercised in opening drums or tanks to prevent sudden releases of pressurized materials, fire,

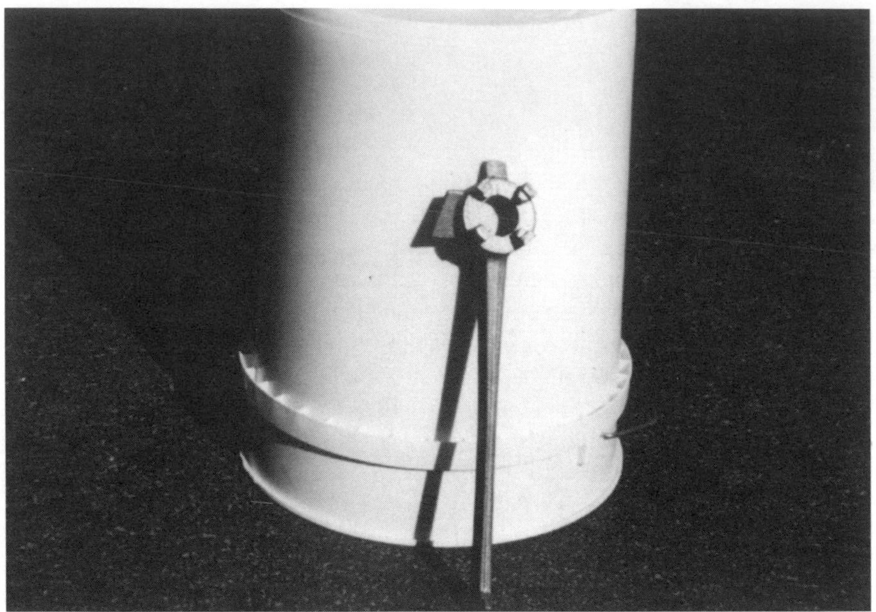

FIGURE 10.1 Spark-proof, brass bung wrench.

explosion, or spillage. The guidance manual SW 846 (U.S. EPA 1986) should be consulted regarding sampling procedures, materials, and containers.

Drums should be opened using the spark-proof brass bung wrench shown in Figure 10.1. Drums with bulged heads are particularly dangerous (Figure 10.2). The bulge indicates that the contents are or have been under extreme pressure. If it is deemed necessary to sample a bulged drum, a remotely operated drum opening device such as that shown in Figure 10.3 enables the sampler to open suspect drums from a safe distance (Figure 10.4). This device can be fabricated using an ordinary pneumatic impact wrench and a brass bung attachment (Figure 10.5). Such operations should only be carried out by fully trained technicians in full-protective gear.

Liquid waste in tanks must be sampled in a manner which assures that the sample is representative of the contents of the tank. The EPA continues to specify that such sampling be done with the "colawassa" sampler. The colawassa consists of a long tube with a stopper at the bottom end. The stopper is opened and closed by use of the handle at the top of the tube. The device is intended to enable the sampler to retrieve representative material from throughout the depth of the tank. The colawassa has many shortcomings, the most troublesome of which is the need to completely clean it and remove all residues between each sampling. This is not only difficult to accomplish, but it also creates another batch of hazardous waste that must then be managed. The colawassa shown in use, in Figure 10.6, is a single-use item which can be disposed of as hazardous waste after use.

A glass colawassa (Figure 10.7), which eliminates the possibility of sample contamination by metals and stopper materials, is available through the technical and

FIGURE 10.2 Drum with a bulged head [Arizona Department of Environmental Quality (DEQ)].

FIGURE 10.3 Remotely controlled pneumatic wrench and positioning device for bung removal (EPA).

FIGURE 10.4 Remote operation of the bung removal apparatus (EPA).

scientific supply houses. In situations involving depths of no more than 36 inches, ordinary glass tubing (Figure 10.8) can be used to obtain a representative sample and can be discarded after use.

"Bomb samplers" (Figure 10.9), which can be lowered into a liquid waste container and then opened at a selected depth, are also useful in special situations.

Long-handled dippers can be used to sample ponds, impoundments, large open tanks, or sumps. An obvious shortcoming is the fact that the device cannot cope with stratified materials. Makeshift devices using tape or other porous or organic material (Figure 10.10) introduce the likelihood of contamination of the sample by the extraneous material.

Dry solid samples may be obtained using a thief or trier (Figure 10.11) or an auger or dipper. Sampling of process units, liquid discharges, and atmospheric emissions all require specialized equipment and training that greatly exceed time and space in this chapter.

FIGURE 10.5 Brass bung fitting used with pneumatic wrench (EPA).

FIGURE 10.6 Single-use colawassa sampler in use (Laidlaw Environmental Services, Inc., 2500 Lokern Road, Buttonwillow, CA 93206).

FIGURE 10.7 Glass colawassa sampler.

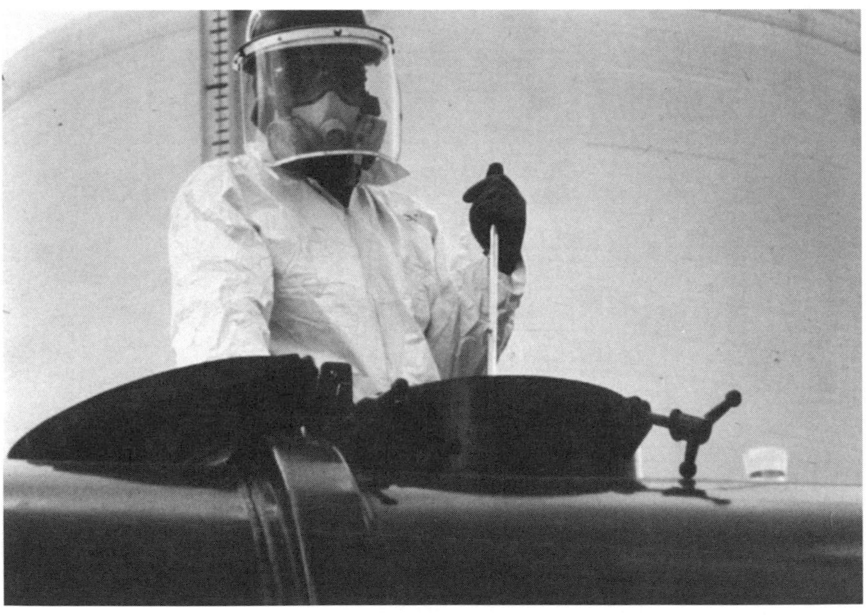

FIGURE 10.8 Sampling liquid waste with standard laboratory glass tubing (Laidlaw Environmental Services, Inc.).

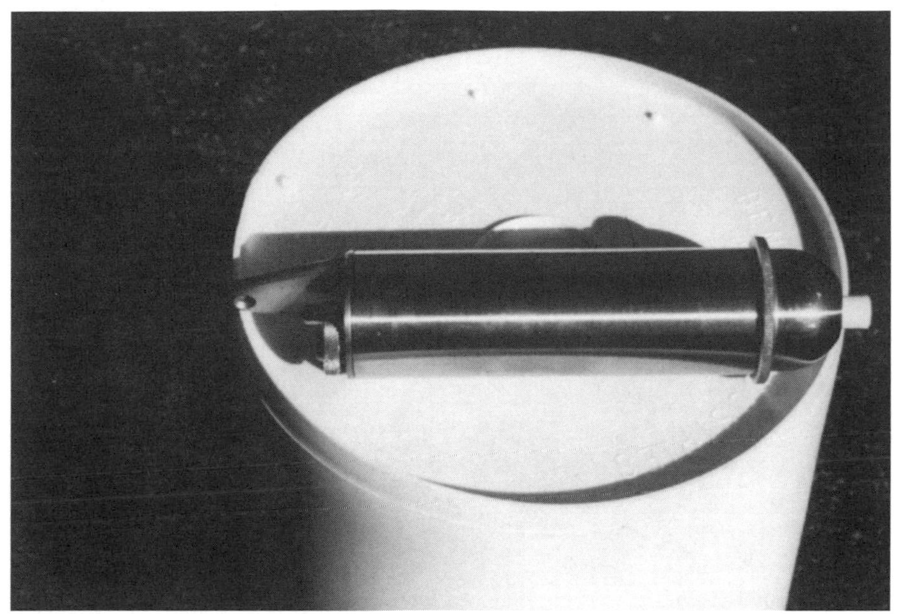

FIGURE 10.9 "Bomb" sampler (Arizona DEQ).

FIGURE 10.10 Makeshift dipper using improper materials (Arizona DEQ).

FIGURE 10.11 Two types of "thief" samplers for solid waste sampling (EPA).

The EPA has published several guidance documents which deal with the details of hazardous waste, soil, surface and groundwater, and waste stream sampling (U.S. EPA 1981, 1985, 1986). (*See also* De Vera et al. 1980; Evans and Schweitzer 1984; Corbitt 1990, Table 9.7; Gammage and Berven 1992)

Site Evaluation

CERCLA Section 105 requires the EPA to issue a revised National Oil and Hazardous Substances Pollution Contingency Plan [commonly referred to as the National Contingency Plan (NCP)] to provide guidance to on-scene coordinators (OSC) and others responsible for removal and remedial action following a release of hazardous substances. The NCP (40 CFR 300) is structured in eight subparts, but we will overview only Subpart F, entitled "Hazardous Substances Response."

National Priorities List

Section 105(a)(8) requires the EPA to establish a National Priorities List (NPL),* prioritizing sites for possible removal and remedial action. "Removal" as used in CERCLA means the physical removal of a hazardous substance, pollutant, or contaminant from the location of release. Remedial action means those additional

* The NPL is found at 40 CFR 300, Appendix B. The NPL is revised frequently.

measures which may be necessary to protect the public health or to protect or prevent harm to the environment.

Hazard Ranking System

The EPA implemented this requirement by the development of a "Hazard Ranking System" (HRS).* This mathematical model enables the EPA and state agencies to assign "scores" to sites based upon basic environmental data. The scores, in turn, are ranked to ostensibly assign highest priority to the sites representing the greatest threat to human health and the environment.

The EPA uses preliminary investigations such as the PA and the SI, outlined earlier, and data from generators, transporters, and/or others to estimate quantities and kinds of wastes that may have been placed upon the site. The site is then scored using the HRS model, and, if the site is scored above a cut-off point, it is nominated for listing on the NPL.

Remedial Investigation/Feasibility Study

Once listed, this initial investigation is followed up by a more formal Remedial Investigation/Feasibility Study (RI/FS). These separate studies, usually performed by contractors, involve major technical investigations, including ground and surface water monitoring, atmospheric emissions, hazards of human contact, or explosion threat (Hall and Bryson 1985, pp. 115–123).

Record of Decision

Following listing and evaluation of the site, the EPA makes a determination of the extent of the threatened or actual damage to human health or the environment and of the most feasible and cost-effective remedial action to mitigate the threat or damage. This determination is formally issued as a Record of Decision (ROD). The ROD identifies the remedy that the EPA will require and establishes the framework for remedial negotiations between the EPA and PRPs.

Negotiations, Enforcement

In the course of the negotiations, many complex issues must be settled, for example:

- Release from liability
- Resolution of disputes
- Timing of cleanup
- Stipulated penalties
- *De minimis* settlements
- Liabilities of municipalities

* The HRS may be found at 40 CFR 300, Appendix A.

Factors that may affect settlement outcomes include:

- volume and nature of wastes contributed.
- strength of the evidence tracing the wastes.
- ability to pay.
- litigative risks of proceeding to trial.
- public interest considerations.
- precedential value.
- present value of money.

Any of the criteria listed can affect the timing of the settlement, the value of the remedy achieved, and the amount of costs recovered.

Where negotiations fail, administrative actions that can be taken pursuant to CERCLA Section 106 include administrative orders requiring PRPs to undertake specific cleanup measures. The EPA may collect daily penalties for noncompliance. Noncompliance also sets the stage for seeking treble damages if the case proceeds to cost recovery.

The EPA initiates judicial action where negotiations are unsuccessful or where an administrative order is disregarded. If these actions are unsuccessful or the responsible party(ies) is(are) bankrupt or if responsible parties cannot be identified, funded cleanup proceeds. All CERCLA cleanup actions are carried out under EPA and/or state agency oversight.

Although there are distinctions of detail, the RCRA and CERCLA corrective action processes follow a similar pattern, as shown in Figure 10.12. RCRA Subtitle D (solid waste) corrective actions now involve similar investigative patterns.

APPENDIX A — ASTM STANDARD PRACTICE FOR ENVIRONMENTAL SITE ASSESSMENTS: PHASE I ENVIRONMENTAL SITE ASSESSMENT PROCESS — APPENDIX X2

X2. RECOMMENDED TABLE OF CONTENTS AND REPORT FORMAT

X2.1 Summary
X2.2 Introduction
  X2.2.1 Purpose
  X2.2.2 Special Terms and Conditions
  X2.2.3 Limitations and Exceptions of Assessment
  X2.2.4 Limiting Conditions and Methodology Used
X2.3 Site Description
  X2.3.1 Location and Legal Description
  X2.3.2 Site and Vicinity Characteristics
  X2.3.3 Descriptions of Structures, Roads, Other Improvements on the Site (including heating/cooling system, sewage disposal, source of potable water)

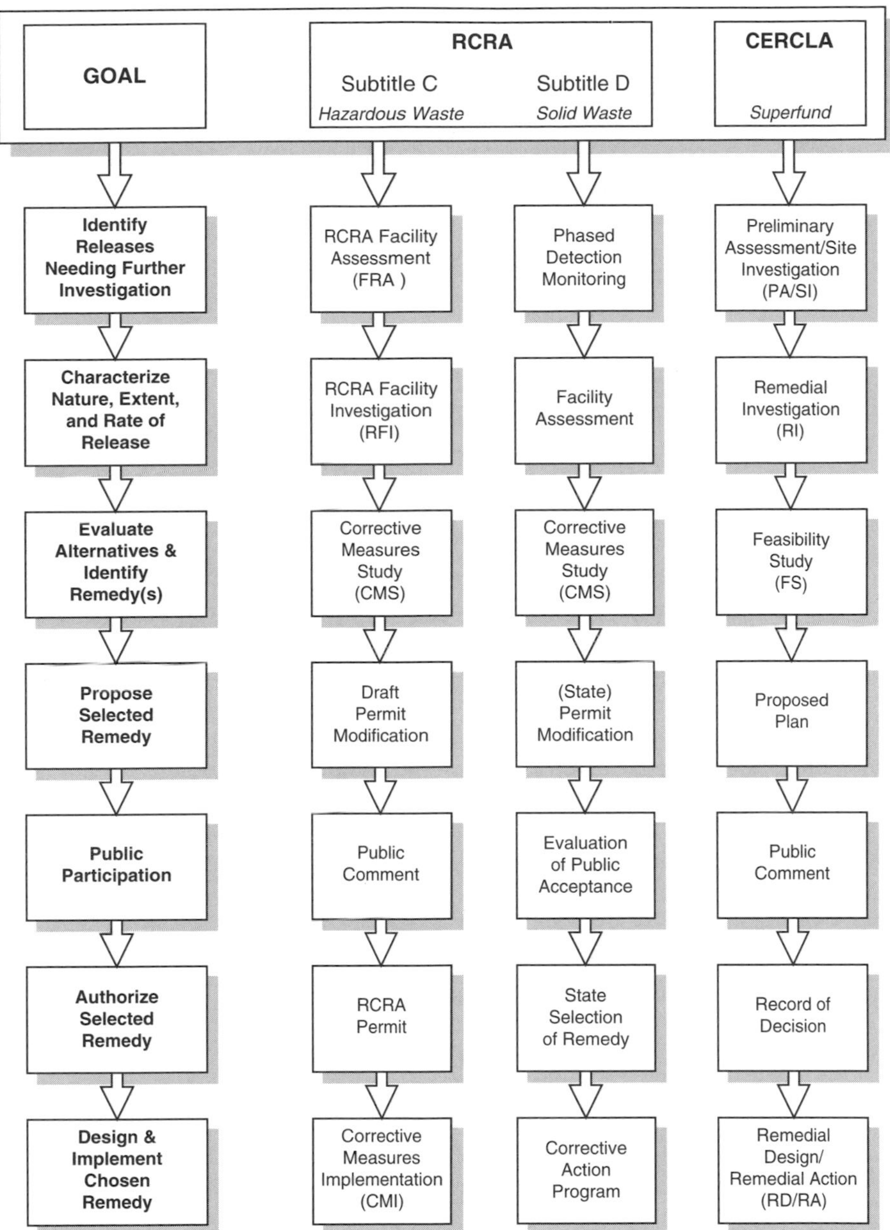

FIGURE 10.12 Comparison of RCRA corrective action and CERCLA Superfund processes. *Source:* SARA 1994.

X2.3.4 Information (if any) Reported by User Regarding Environmental Liens or Specialized Knowledge or Experience (pursuant to Section 5.)
X2.3.5 Current Uses of the Property (to the extent identified)
X2.3.6 Past Uses of the Property (to the extent identified)
X2.3.7 Current and Past Uses of Adjoining Properties (to the extent identified)
X2.3.8 Site Rendering, Map, or Site Plan

X2.4 Records Review
X2.4.1 Standard Environmental Record Sources, Federal and State
X2.4.2 Physical Setting Source(s)
X2.4.3 Historical Use Information
X2.4.4 Additional Record Sources (if any)

X2.5 Information from Site Reconnaissance and Interviews
X2.5.1 Hazardous Substances in Connection with Identified Uses (including storage, handling, disposal)
X2.5.2 Hazardous Substance Containers and Unidentified Substance Containers (including storage, handling, disposal)
X2.5.3 Storage Tanks (including contents and assessment of leakage or potential for leakage)
X2.5.4 Indications of PCBs (including how contained and assessment of leakage or potential for leakage)
X2.5.5 Indications of Solid Waste Disposal
X2.5.6 Physical Setting Analysis (if migrating Hazardous Substances are an issue)
X2.5.7 Any Other Conditions of Concern
X2.5.8 Site Plan (if available)

X2.6 Findings and Conclusions
X2.7 Signatures of Environmental Professionals
X2.8 Qualifications of Environmental Professionals Participating in Phase I Environmental Site Assessment
X2.9 Optional Appendices (for example)
X2.9.1 Other Maps, Figures, and Photographs
X2.9.2 Ownership/Historical Documentation
X2.9.3 Regulatory Documentation
X2.9.4 Interview Documentation
X2.9.5 Contract Between User and Environmental Professional

TOPICS FOR REVIEW OR DISCUSSION

1 Identify two sets of circumstances that might bring about the necessity for a background report on a former site.
2. A "Phase I" review of a site would not normally include extensive groundwater sampling. True? False?
3. Review the meanings of "strict" liability, "joint and several" liability, and their implications for present or potential property owners, "responsible parties," contractors performing site cleanups, others.

4. Why would facility owners be reluctant to have environmental audits preformed on their facility — even if performed by a private contractor/consultant?
5. How might a facility owner maintain confidentiality of the contractor's findings?
6. Why are inspection policies, sampling procedures, and records review procedures of regulatory agencies of concern to the facility owner/operator?

REFERENCES

American Society for Testing and Materials (ASTM). 1993. *Standard Practice for Environmental Site Assessments: Phase I Environmental Site Assessment Process.* E 1527-93, Philadelphia, PA.

Burby, Brian G. 1989. "An Overview of Methods for Conducting Property Transaction Site Assessments." *Environment Reporter* December 29, Bureau of National Affairs, Washington, D.C.

Consulting Engineers Council of Metropolitan Washington. 1989. *Guidelines for Environmental Site Assessments.* Consulting Engineers Council of Metropolitan Washington, Washington, D.C.

Corbitt, Robert A. 1990. *Standard Handbook of Environmental Engineering.* McGraw-Hill, New York.

De Vera, E. R., B. P. Simmons, R. D. Stephens, and D. L. Storm. 1980. *Samplers and Sampling Procedures for Hazardous Waste Streams.* Environmental Protection Agency, Cincinnati, OH. EPA 600/2-80-018.

Evans, Roy B., and Glenn E. Schweitzer. 1984. "Assessing Hazardous Waste Problems." *Environmental Science and Technology* 18(11).

Gammage, Richard B., and Barry A. Berven, Eds. 1992. *Hazardous Waste Site Investigations.* Lewis Publishers, Chelsea, MI.

Hall, Ridgeway M., Jr., and Nancy S. Bryson. 1985. "Comprehensive Environmental Response, Compensation and Liability Act (Superfund)." *Environmental Law Handbook*, Eighth Edition. Government Institutes, Inc., Rockville, MD. Chapter 3.

Hopper, David R. 1989. "Cleaning Up Contaminated Waste Sites." *Chemical Engineering* August:95ff.

Priznar, Frank J. 1995. "Environmental Audits and Site Assessments." *Accident Prevention Manual for Business and Industry Environmental Management,* Gary R. Krieger, Ed. National Safety Council, Itasca, IL.

Sara, Martin N. 1994. *Standard Handbook for Solid and Hazardous Waste Facility Assessments.* Lewis Publishers, Chelsea, MI.

Turim, Jay. 1991. "Environmental Assessments for Property Transfers." *Environmental Claims Journal* 3(2) Winter 1990/91.

U.S. Environmental Protection Agency. 1981. *NEIC Manual for Groundwater/Subsurface Investigations at Hazardous Waste Sites.* National Enforcement Investigations Center, Denver, CO.

U.S. Environmental Protection Agency. 1985. *Characterization of Hazardous Waste Sites — A Methods Manual, Volume II, Available Sampling Methods.* U.S. EPA, Washington, D.C. EPA 600/4-84/075.

U.S. Environmental Protection Agency. 1986. *Test Methods for Evaluating Solid Waste. Physical/Chemical Methods. Third Edition.* Superintendent of Documents, Government Printing Office, Washington, D.C. EPA SW 846.

U.S. Environmental Protection Agency. 1988. *RCRA Inspection Manual*. Office of Waste Programs Enforcement, Washington, D.C. OSWER Directive Number 9938.2A.

U.S. Environmental Protection Agency. 1992. *Multi-Media Investigation Manual*. National Enforcement Investigations Center, Denver, CO. EPA 330/9-89-003-R.

U.S. Environmental Protection Agency. 1994. *Catalog of Hazardous and Solid Waste Publications*. Solid Waste and Emergency Response, Washington, D.C. EPA 530-B-93-002.

Von Oppenfeld, Rolf. 1990. "Environmental Due-Diligence: Risk Assessment and Management." *Arizona Attorney* April.

11 SITE REMEDIAL TECHNOLOGIES, PRACTICES, AND REGULATIONS

OBJECTIVES

At completion of this chapter, the student should:

- be familiar with the technologies which may be employed in site remediation, e.g., onsite encapsulation, treatment, and destruction; "pump-and-treat" regimes; containment; offsite treatment and disposal; and related Resource Conservation and Recovery Act (RCRA) and Comprehensive Environmental Response, Compensation, and Liability Act (CERCLA) requirements and policies.
- understand the respective roles of RCRA and CERCLA in site remediation.
- be familiar with "How Clean is Clean" issues, the basis for them, and some resolutions thereof.
- be familiar with the National Contingency Plan (NCP), the "blueprint" role of the NCP in site remediation, how to find the NCP, and how to maintain or ensure currency with it.

INTRODUCTION

In Chapter 10, we introduced and briefly overviewed the technologies and processes involved in the evaluation of contaminated or suspect sites. The generic and Superfund approaches to site evaluation are the necessary precursors to site cleanup. We now continue with the overview of site cleanup procedures. To the extent possible, we will continue the pattern of introduction of technologies and processes in the "generic" or established practice format. We will then overview the options and/or requirements as applied to RCRA and Superfund site remediation.

The technologies for site remediation have been developed over a relatively short period of time. Some of the technologies were introduced in the 1970s or earlier, and some sites were remediated in the latter part of the decade. But it is arguable that *actual cleanup* of Superfund sites did not begin making significant progress until the mid-1980s. Thus, some of the technologies are clearly to be regarded as developmental or evolving, while a few have become proven and standardized.

Development of treatment technologies has been given support by the U.S. Environmental Protection Agency (EPA) Superfund Innovative Technology Evaluation (SITE) program. The Superfund Amendments and Reauthorization Act (SARA) of 1986 authorized $20 million per year, through 1991, to support development of new treatment technologies and to provide sound engineering and cost data on selected technologies. Approximately ten new project awards are made each year to test and/or demonstrate innovative or improved hazardous waste management technologies in laboratory and full-scale operations. The program was extended with the Superfund reauthorization in 1991, but SITE reauthorization died with Superfund reauthorization in 1994. (*See also* U.S. EPA 1989b)

The national programs for cleanup of uncontrolled hazardous waste sites (e.g., RCRA corrective actions, Superfund removal, and/or remedial actions) have been the focus of great controversy. Both programs were fought tenaciously by lobbyists, in the courts, and by policy makers of the Reagan Administration. To many in Congress and elsewhere, the Superfund program has progressed too slowly and at excessive costs. To others, it has been overly aggressive, unyielding, and utopian in cleanup objectives. It has been bedeviled by the "how-clean-is-clean" issue, by charges that it merely moves the contaminants and creates future Superfund sites, and by the ponderousness of the Superfund process. (*See also* RAND 1989; GAO 1993, 1994a, 1994b)

Nevertheless, the program is beginning to make significant progress and is having some notable successes. Superfund, imperfections notwithstanding, is here to stay and will be a major factor in the nation's hazardous waste cleanup.* The National Priorities List (NPL) now includes approximately 1232 sites (59 FR 27989), and more are added each year. These sites must be cleaned up, and no preferable program format has been suggested, although the 1994 reauthorization bill contained significant changes to the earlier statute.

Remedial Objectives

Programmatic Objectives

In the most general sense, hazardous waste site remedial activity is pursued to correct the results of mismanagement and accidental releases. Remedies usually involve removal of contaminated materials and safe disposition thereof; treatment, destruction, and/or containment in place; or some variation of these.

Remedial actions may be taken by individuals or corporations without the involvement of federal and/or state regulatory agencies. Indeed, privately funded and/or executed cleanup activity preceded the advent of RCRA and Superfund, and both statutes are structured to encourage (leverage) private cleanups.

* The 1994 Superfund reauthorization bill failed in the final days of the 103rd Congress, the victim of executive and legislative preoccupations with health care reform, adjournment imperatives, and other political issues. Backers vowed to resume the effort in the new Congress.

RCRA corrective actions are an essential element of the national policy objective, i.e., the minimization "of the present and future threat to human health and the environment." These authorities enable the EPA to address releases to the groundwater and other environmental media at RCRA-regulated sites. The RCRA authorities do not extend to abandoned sites nor those for which responsible parties cannot be identified.

Superfund was originally intended to enable timely response to emergency cleanup needs and to provide resources and authorities for cleanup of abandoned sites and those for which responsible parties (1) cannot be identified or (2) refuse or are unable to conduct the necessary cleanup. Over time, government-owned and/or -operated facilities have been made subject to the law, and the "innocent landowner" provision has been added in an effort to limit the reach of the strict joint and several liability provisions. Provision has been made for *de minimis* settlements for small contributors to Superfund sites (King and Amidaneau 1995, pp. 68–69). (*See also* U.S. GAO 1993, 1994a)

Technical Objectives

Whether privately funded and/or executed, or carried out under statutory mandates, remedial actions must have the protection of human health and the environment as their overall objective.* The more applicable objectives are the prevention of further migration of releases that have occurred, amelioration of exposures and impacts caused by those releases, and prevention of further releases. These objectives are pursued by one of two basic operations:

1. Removal of hazardous wastes and contaminated materials, followed by treatment, destruction, or safe disposal
2. Treatment, destruction, or containment onsite

While there are many variations and combinations of these two basic techniques, it is useful to categorize remedial actions as "removal"** or "onsite" activities. Figure 11.1 diagrams this categorization and the related techniques.

On another level, the technical objectives must be stated in terms of the degree of cleanup to be achieved (i.e., how much residual contamination at the site is acceptable?). This question is the crux of the how-clean-is-clean issue. The answer to the immediate question and the eventual resolution of the issue both have far-reaching implications for managers of public health risks and for responsible parties.

There is no single, safe level of hazardous chemical concentrations applicable to all chemicals and all sites that, if achieved, would justify a declaration of "clean."

* Studies have shown that higher than expected cancer rates may be associated with proximity to Superfund sites, e.g., the Baird and McGuire site (*Environment Reporter* November 16, 1990, p.1359).

** The term "removal" is used as stated in this general or generic overview. In the Superfund context, removal has a somewhat different connotation, as explained in the section on "RCRA and Superfund Remedial Actions."

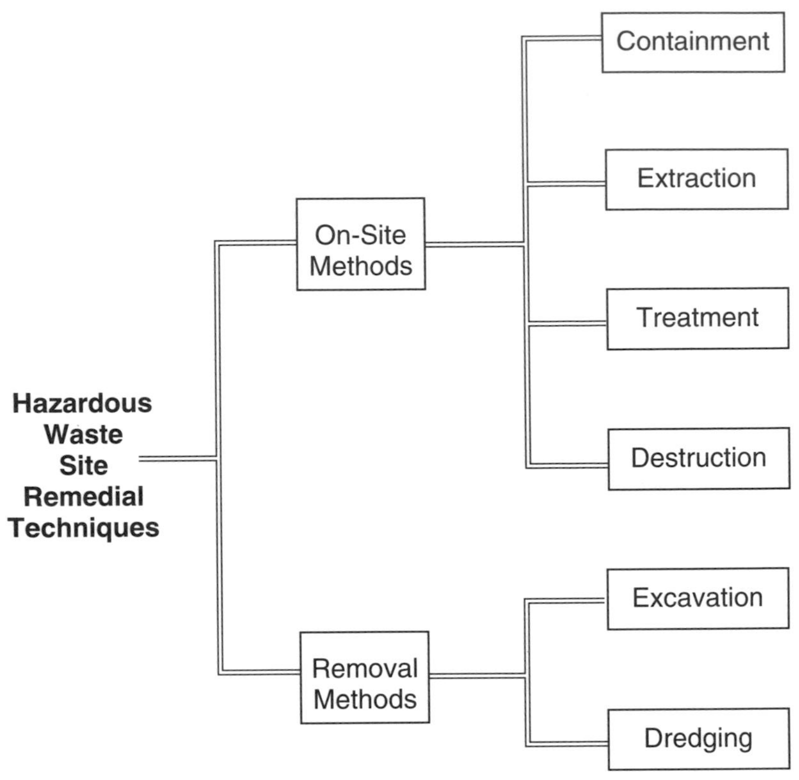

FIGURE 11.1 Categories of hazardous waste site remedial actions.

Epidemiologists, risk managers, and policy makers have found it necessary to rely upon exposure criteria such as drinking water and air quality standards which were never intended for use as hazardous waste site cleanup standards. Moreover, these standards deal with only a few simple inorganic and organic pollutants, whereas the hazardous waste site cleanup criteria must consider a wide variety of inorganic and complex organic compounds.

To compound the problem, there is no generally accepted methodology for determining appropriate levels of cleanup. RCRA and CERCLA require use of risk assessment techniques based upon site-specific data and the circumstances of the site. Some states simply impose a blanket requirement that all cleanups achieve background concentrations of waste constituents.

Some rationalization of standards has gradually emerged with respect to known carcinogens. Where laboratory or other exposure data exist to support a risk assessment process (*see* Chapter 4), EPA policy is that the level of *total* individual carcinogen risk from exposures attributable to a Superfund site may be in the range of 1 excess occurrence in 10,000 (10^{-4}) to 1 in 10 million (10^{-7}). The most frequently proposed criteria is 10^{-6}.

The administration's 1994 Superfund reauthorization bill contained language calling for a "numeric national cleanup goal" and a "national risk protocol." The protocol would have contained standardized exposure scenarios for a range of unrestricted and restricted land uses and standardized formulas for evaluating exposure pathways and developing chemical concentration levels for the 100 contaminants that occur most frequently at Superfund sites. (*Environment Reporter* April 29, 1994, P. 2219). This format, of course, does little to solve the how-clean-is-clean question. Viable exposure criteria continue to be absent or unproven for many of the most commonly discarded chemicals and chemical compounds. Without exposure criteria, any health risk assessment format is a hollow one. Failure of the 1994 Superfund reauthorization was regarded by many as a major disappointment, but the how-clean-is-clean issue was certain to continue with us, regardless of the 1994 reauthorization outcome.

The EPA also requires that remedies meet "applicable or relevant and appropriate federal and state requirements" (ARARs), such as state mine drainage limits for heavy metals or federal limits for polychlorinated biphenyls (PCBs) established under the Toxic Substances Control Act (TSCA) authorities. (*See also* Staples and Kimerle 1986; U.S. EPA 1989a; Travis and Doty 1992; Burke 1992)

Onsite Remedial Techniques

Containment Methods

As the name implies, containment methods are directed toward prevention of migration of liquid hazardous wastes or leachates containing hazardous constituents. Containment usually involves the construction of impermeable barriers to retain liquids within the site or to divert ground and surface waters away from the site. Successful application of these methods is usually contingent upon the presence of an impervious layer beneath the material to be contained and the achievement of a good seal at the vertical and horizontal interfaces. Some examples follow.

Slurry Walls. The slurry trench is excavated down to and, if practicable, into an impervious layer. The trench is typically 2 to 5 ft in width. Early applications used a 4 to 7% bentonite clay suspension in water to make up the slurry. The slurry may be mixed with the excavated soil or with other suitable soils to form a very low permeability wall. More recent applications have made use of additives such as polymers to improve the permeability or to protect the slurry from the deleterious effects of leachate. Figure 11.2 shows a trench and soil–bentonite slurry wall under construction. The soil removed from the trench is mixed with bentonite clay and replaced in the trench. Figure 11.3 shows a cement–bentonite wall being installed. In this case, the excavated soil is not used. Cement is mixed with the bentonite slurry, which "sets" as a solid wall.

Grout Curtains. In a somewhat similar fashion, suspension grouts composed of bentonite, or Portland cement, or both may be injected under pressure to form a barrier. The method is most effective when the receiving formation is unconsolidated and porous deposits can be filled by the injection. In other situations, single, double, or triple lines of holes are drilled in staggered positions. Ideally, the grout injected in adjacent holes should penetrate to merge and form a continuous barrier. Chemical

FIGURE 11.2 Soil–bentonite slurry wall construction (Geo-Con, Inc., P.O. Box 17380, Pittsburgh, PA 125235).

grouts are a more recent development and have the advantage of a range of viscosities. Some have viscosities approaching that of water and can be used to seal very fine rock and soil voids.

Sheet Piling Cut-Off Walls. Pilings of wood, concrete, or steel can be used to form a cut-off wall. Sheet piling of steel is the most effective and has the advantage that it can be driven to depths as great as 100 ft. It has the disadvantages that it cannot be used effectively in rocky soil and may fail if the contained liquids are corrosive.

Other containment methods make use of surface diversions to route runoff away from the waste deposit and of impervious caps to carry rainfall and snowmelt beyond the perimeter of the deposit.

Extraction Methods

Two basic approaches to onsite extraction have gained general acceptance and are effective when properly designed and operated. The methods are pumping of

FIGURE 11.3 Cement-bentonite cut-off wall (Geo-Con, Inc.).

contaminated groundwater to the surface for treatment and discharge or reinjection and active or passive extraction and treatment of soil gases produced in a waste deposit. Uncontaminated groundwater may also be pumped to deny it contact with a waste deposit. These methods are briefly overviewed, as follows.

Groundwater Pumping. At least three different applications of groundwater pumping are used to control contaminated water beneath a disposal site. These applications are:

- pumping to lower a water table.
- pumping to contain a plume.
- groundwater treatment systems.

The effect of lowering a water table may be to prevent contaminated water from reaching a surface stream as base flow; to prevent contact with a contamination source; or to prevent migration to another aquifer, as shown schematically in Figures 11.4 through 11.7.

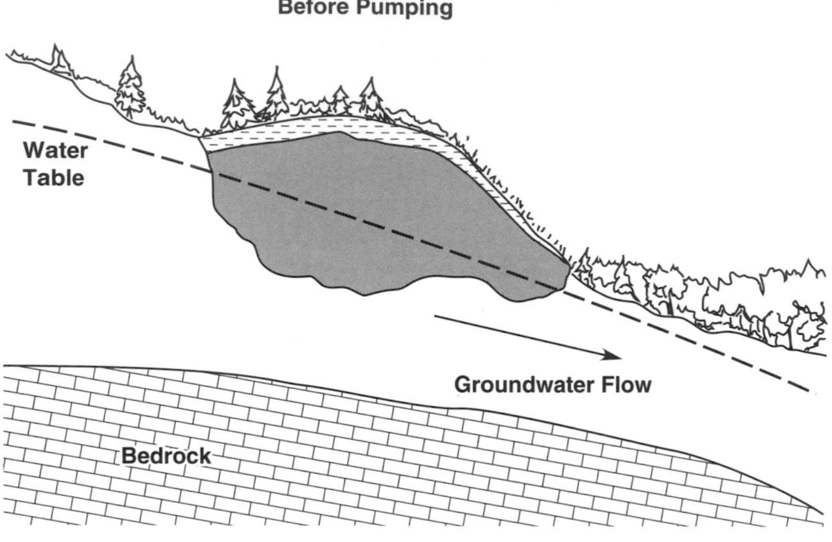

FIGURE 11.4 Schematic of lowering a water table to eliminate contact with a disposal site (before pumping) (EPA).

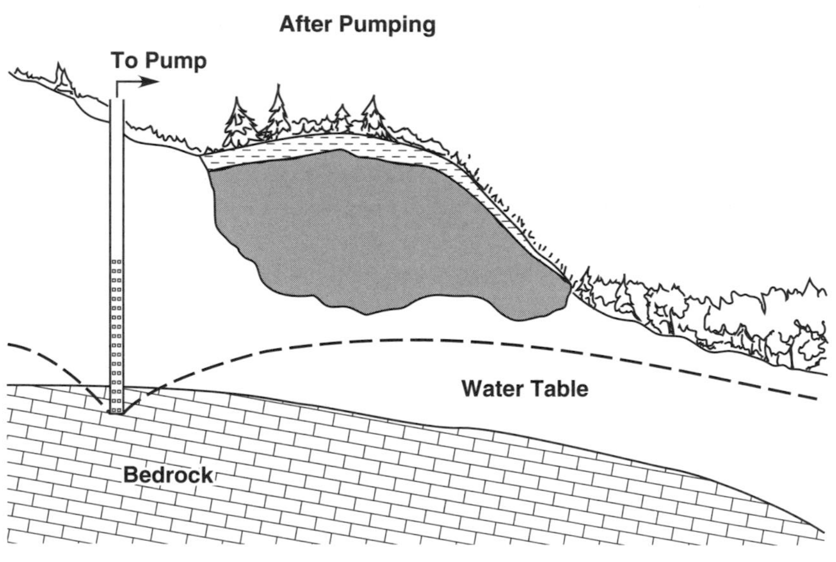

FIGURE 11.5 Schematic of lowering a water table to eliminate contact with a disposal site (after pumping) (EPA).

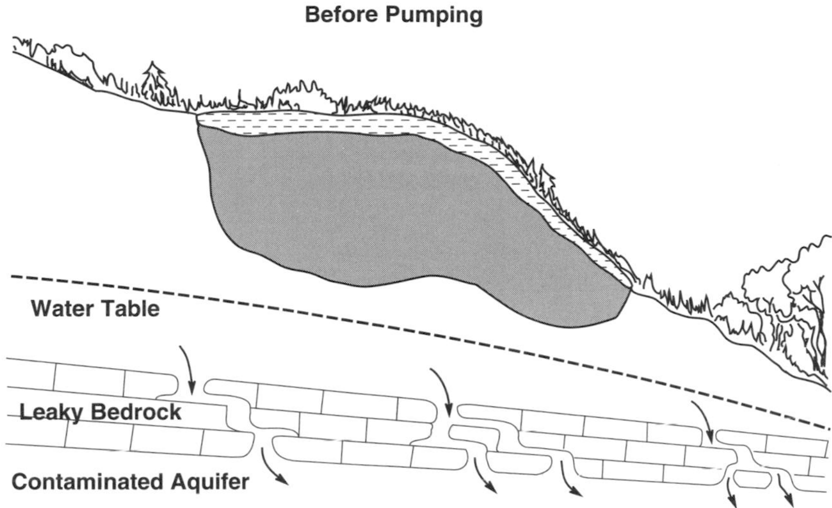

FIGURE 11.6 Schematic of lowering a water table to prevent contamination of an underlying aquifer (before pumping) (EPA).

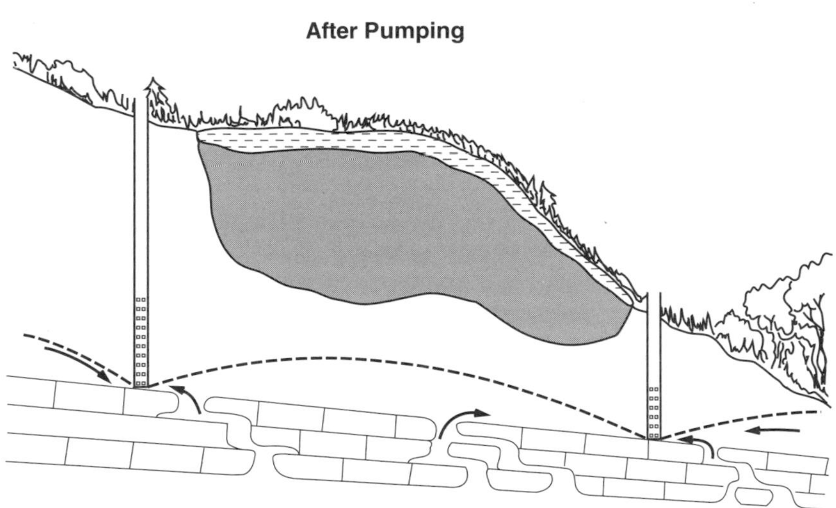

FIGURE 11.7 Schematic of lowering a water table to prevent contamination of an underlying aquifer (after pumping) (EPA).

Extraction wells or combinations of extraction and injection wells may be used to contain a plume and/or alter plume movement to force contaminated groundwater toward collection wells, as illustrated in the schematic Figures 11.8 and 11.9.

One of the most frequently employed remediation procedures for large plumes of contaminated groundwater is the pump and treat (P & T) approach, wherein extraction wells are placed to draw from the plume and prevent or reverse downgradient movement of the plume. The extracted water is treated to remove the pollutant(s) and is then discharged or used on the surface. The extracted water may be reinjected at the perimeter of the contaminant plume to create an artificial groundwater mound, thereby assisting in moving the contaminants toward the extraction well. The system illustrated schematically in Figure 11.10 employs the ion exchange process for removal of chromium, air stripping of chlorinated solvents, and carbon adsorption to remove stripped organics from the exhaust stream.

Recent evaluations of P & T projects at 28 groundwater contamination sites reveal that the technique does not always attain expectations, with respect to cost and/or cleanup times. Eighty percent cost increases over original estimates were typical. Cleanup times are projected to be as much as three times longer than originally estimated. The studies determined that P & T systems effectively contained the dissolved phase contaminant plume at most sites. Contaminant concentrations dropped rapidly as treatment progressed, but leveled off at concetrations greater than the maximum concentration limits (MCLs) The concentrations slowly decreased once they reached this plateau, resulting in long cleanup times. The observed phenomena are attributed to preferential flow in areas of high permeability, low or differential desorption rates, immobile water zones within soil grains, and/or continuing sources of groundwater contamination. Practitioners are using other aquifer restoration techniques in tandem with P & T technology, or as alternatives, in attempts to achieve more timely cleanup goals (Olsen and Kavanaugh 1993, p. 42ff).

Soil Gas Extraction. Anaerobic decomposition of organics produces methane gas, which is flammable, can accumulate to explosive concentrations, and is toxic. Deposits of hazardous waste may generate other toxic, flammable, or malodorous gases. Prevention of dangerous buildups of such gases is an important aspect of hazardous waste management, in general, and site remediation, in particular. In earlier times, mere venting of such gases to the atmosphere was acceptable practice. These primitive practices are now prohibited by most jurisdictions and are generally unacceptable. Elaborate soil gas collection and treatment systems have been developed to meet site-specific needs, but are not always necessary.

The objective of soil gas collection and treatment systems is, of course, to prevent hazardous buildups of the gases and to render the collected gases harmless to human health and the environment. Gases may be vented by passive collection systems, but forced ventilation systems are necessary to maintain steady flow to treatment systems. The gases are collected in pipe wells or trenches by 4- or 6-in. PVC perforated pipe. If a trench or more than one well is necessary, a manifold joins the individual collectors and conveys the gases to a blower. The blower discharges to a treatment system. The schematic of Figure 11.11 illustrates some basic configurations.

Onsite treatment is usually accomplished by granular activated carbon (GAC) adsorption of the organics contained in the gases. The GAC system has the advan-

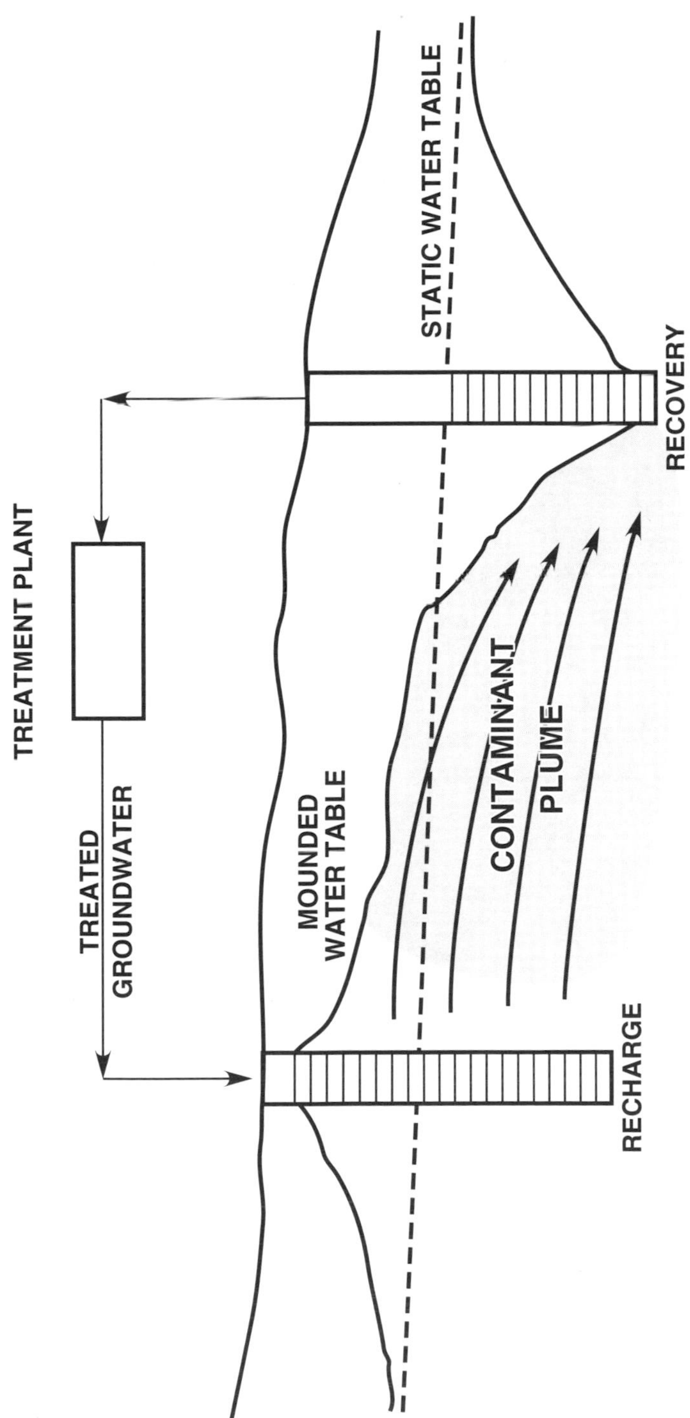

FIGURE 11.8 Schematic of reinjection of treated groundwater to contain a contaminant plume.

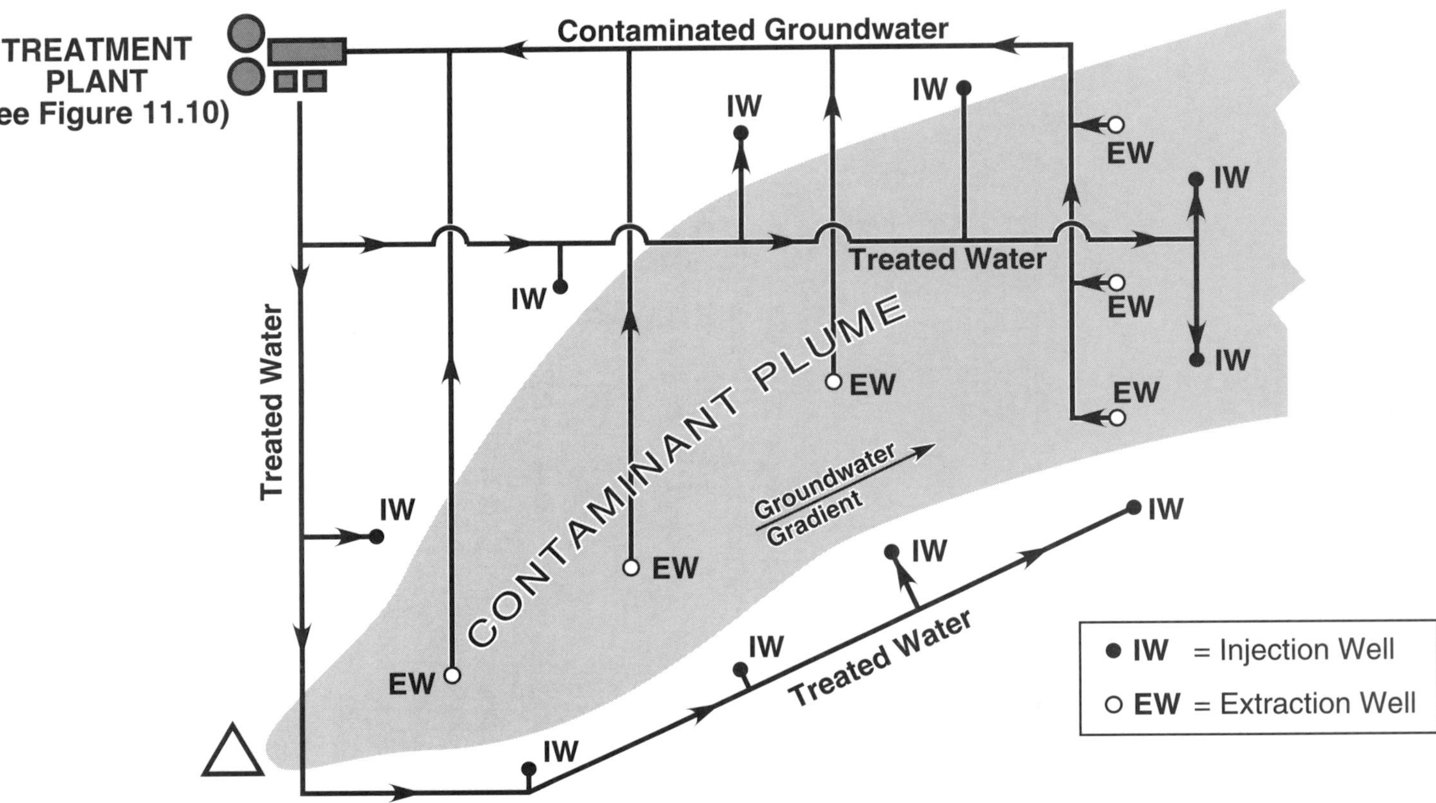

FIGURE 11.9 Schematic of combinations of extraction and injection wells to contain a contaminant plume.

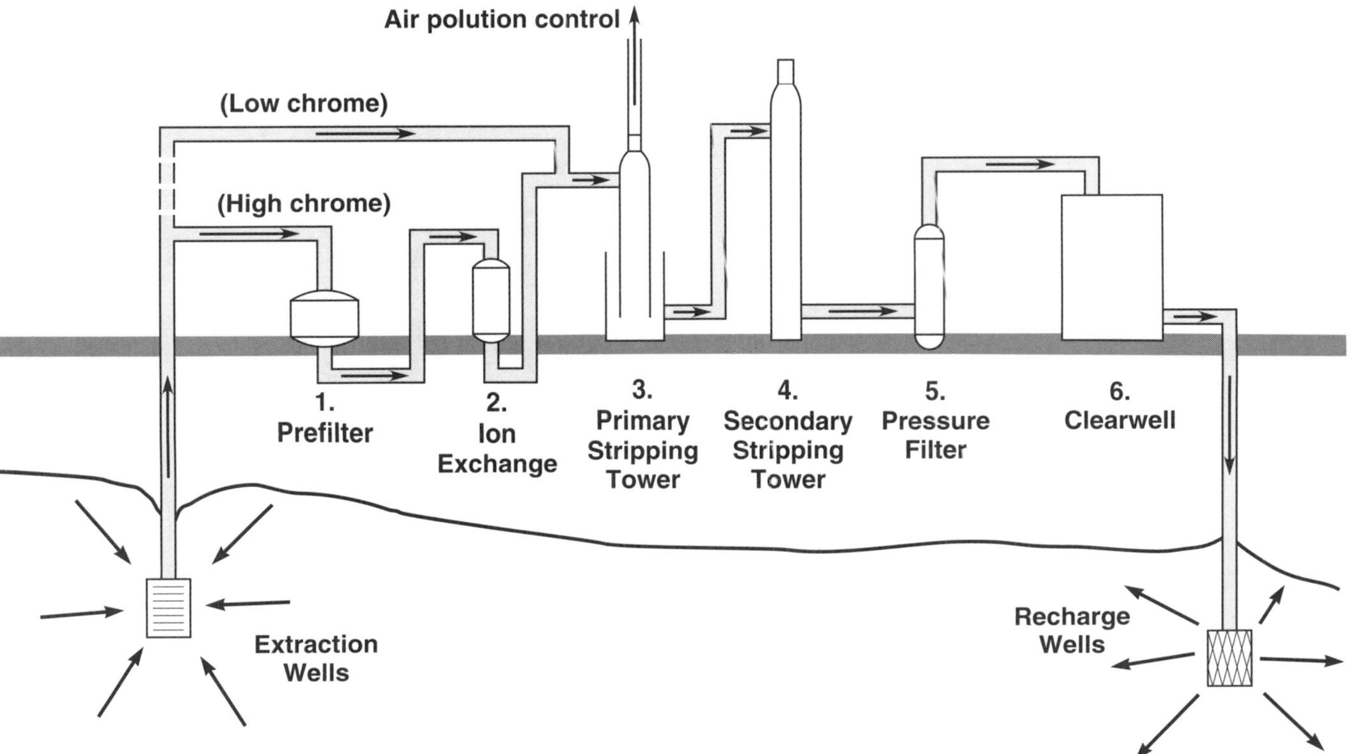

FIGURE 11.10 Schematic of a groundwater treatment plant layout (U.S. Air Force).

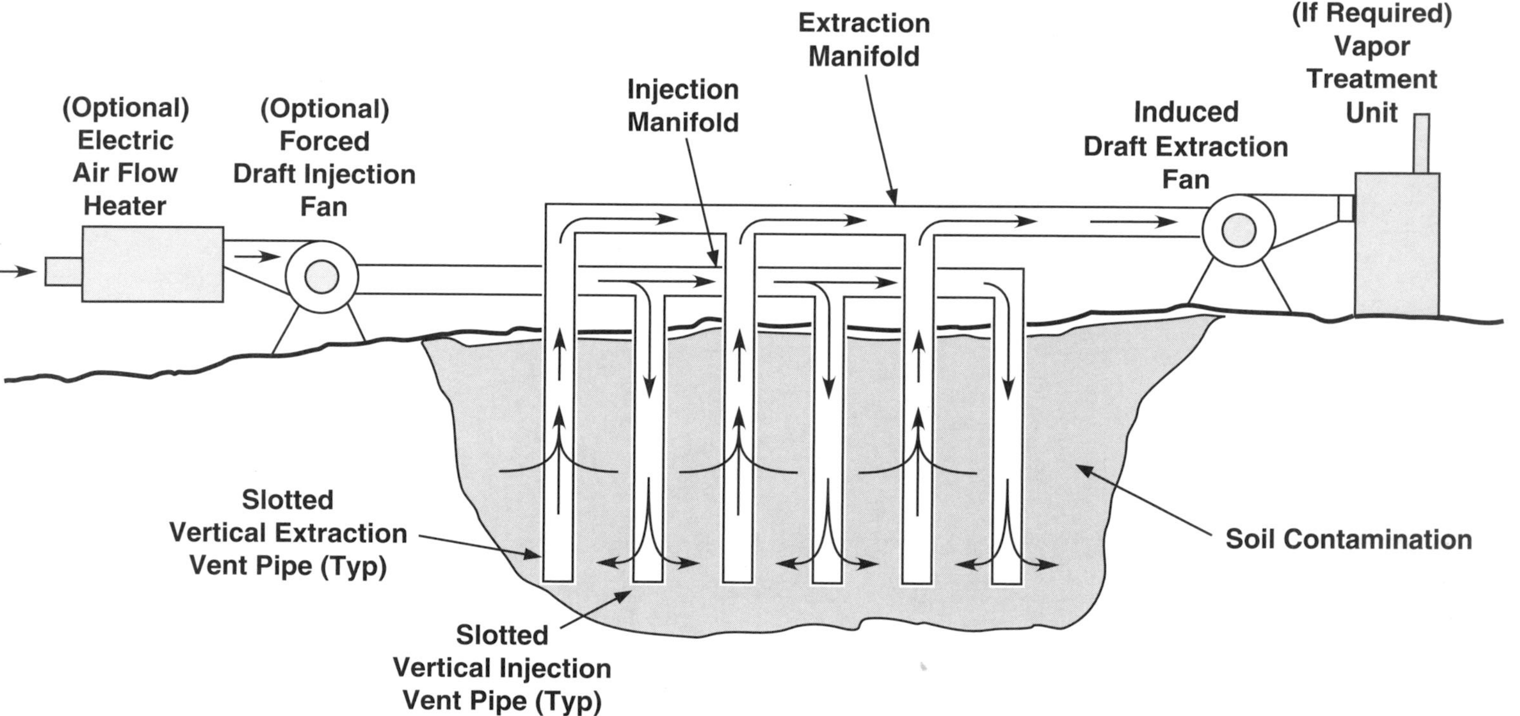

FIGURE 11.11 Schematic of a soil vapor extraction system (EPA).

tages and disadvantages discussed in earlier chapters. The most serious disadvantage is the declining efficiency of carbon adsorption as the adsorptive capacity is approached. Frequent or continuous regeneration or replacement of carbon is necessary to ensure consistent high efficiency.

Onsite destruction of some gases can be accomplished by flares or afterburners. Supplemental fuel may be neceessary to achieve the desired combustion efficiency and/or to sustain combustion (Corbitt 1990, p. 4.66ff).

Treatment Methods

Onsite treatment of hazardous wastes may be accomplished *in situ* or by excavation, treatment, and replacement. *In situ* methods include the following.

Low-Temperature Thermal Desorption. The process uses ambient air, heat, or mechanical agitation to increase the rate of mass transfer of contaminants to the gas phase. Once in the gas phase, the contaminants can be further treated by thermal or physical methods. The process can effectively remove halogenated aromatic and aliphatic compounds, volatile nonhalogenated compounds, and semivolatile nonhalogenated organics (to a limited extent) from the soil matrix (Grasso 1993). Removal efficiencies for this treatment method range from 55 to 99% and primarily depend on the volatility of the contaminant (McCoy and Associates 1989, pp. 1–19). *In situ* heating and desorption of organics may be accomplished by passing AC or DC current between electrodes placed in the waste deposit. The volatilized organics must then be collected and treated or released (Oma and Buelt 1989).

Neutralization/Detoxification. Substances that immobilize or destroy a waste constituent may be applied to, or injected into, a hazardous waste deposit. The technique is effective only for contaminants that can be degraded, have nontoxic breakdown products, and/or are convertible to insoluble precipitates. The technique has the disadvantage that if any leachate is created, it must be collected and managed. It has the further disadvantage that it is difficult to determine the degree of effectiveness achieved (U.S. EPA 1982, p. 328). Methods for *in situ* treatment of organics include soil flushing, oxidation, hydrolysis, and polymerization; methods for inorganics include precipitation, soil flushing, oxidation, and reduction (Corbitt 1990, pp. 9.27, 9.28). (*See also* Rastegar et al. 1988; Grasso 1993)

Bioremediation. Organic waste deposits may be seeded with soil microorganisms to alter or destroy the wastes. Alternatively, nutrients may be added to an organic waste to enhance naturally occurring (or extant) microorganisms and cause them to more actively consume or break down the pollutants. Bioremediation has been widely acclaimed as the hazardous waste treatment technology of the future. There continue to be limitations to the feasibility of bioremediation, and its successful use requires a thorough understanding of the onsite hydrology, microbiology, and chemical characteristics.

Aerobic biodegradation processes take place in the presence of oxygen and result in the formation of carbon dioxide, water, and cell protein. Anaerobic biodegradation processes take place in the absence of oxygen and result in the formation of methane, carbon dioxide, and cell protein. The literature reports that aerobic biodegradation has been successfully used to degrade gasoline, nonhalogenated hydrocarbons, and aromatics. Aerobic treatment schemes for contaminated soils are diagrammed in Figures 11.12 and 11.13. Other reports state that halogenated aliphatics such as trichloroethylene (TCE) and tetrachloroethylene (PCE) are not significantly degraded aerobically. Presently, anaerobic degradation of halogenated aliphatics has been conducted in treatment systems only under laboratory conditions without full-scale application (Towers et al. 1989). As was pointed out in Chapter 3, chemical transformations of PCE, TCE, and other aliphatics have been shown to occur in groundwater where anaerobic bacteria are present. (*See also* Bourquin 1989; Grasso 1993)

Immobilization. Some types of waste materials may be stabilized or solidified in a matrix by mixing with Portland cement or other pozzolanic material. The hazardous waste constituents are not destroyed, but are immobilized, thereby minimizing leaching to ground or surface waters. Small amounts of waste and solidifying material can be effectively mixed in 55-gallon drums which are then landfilled. Larger quantities may be exhumed, mixed in a pugmill or mobile mixing plant, and redeposited in the original or other site. Waste deposits may be mixed *in situ* using a backhoe, or other heavy equipment, as illustrated in Figure 11.14. The technology is reported to be most effective for treatment of metal-contaminated soils (McCoy and Associates 1989, pp. 1–19). Wastes containing oils, chlorinated hydrocarbons, calcium chloride, and organic wastes containing hydroxyl or carboxylic acid functional groups may delay or completely inhibit the solidification of pozzolanic or Portland cement (Wiles 1989, p. 7.93).

Innovative techniques for *in situ* stabilization are being introduced. Figure 11.15 shows "deep soil mixing" (DSM) equipment capable of mixing chemical reagents with contaminated soil to depths of 150 ft without excavation. The reagents are pumped through the hollow shafts of each auger. Figure 11.16 is a close-up view of the auger-mixing paddle configuration used on the DSM. (*See also* Cartledge et al. 1990; Jones 1990)

Destruction Methods

Methods for destruction of hazardous wastes have been adapted to both *in situ* and excavation applications. Examples of these applications follow.

Incineration. High-temperature incineration is a favored and highly effective means of destruction of as-generated and exhumed hazardous wastes. The wastes are exhumed and incinerated onsite by mobile incinerators, with residues redeposited in a secure landfill. Correctly designed and operated high-temperature incinerators are capable of very high destruction and removal efficiencies (see Chapter 7), but do not destroy inorganic components such as heavy metals. These residues must be captured by the emission control system in the incinerator and managed in a secure disposal site (Combs 1989, p. 2ff).

***In Situ* Vitrification.** *In situ* vitrification is a process whereby in-place soils are converted, by extreme heat, to a durable glassy material. The conversion is achieved by passing an electrical current through the subject soils to produce temperatures of 1600 to 2000°C (2912 to 3632°F), well above the initial soil-melting temperatures of 1100 to 1400°C (2012 to 2552°F). Current is applied by four electrodes driven into the soil in a square configuration. The organic constituents are pyrolized in the melt

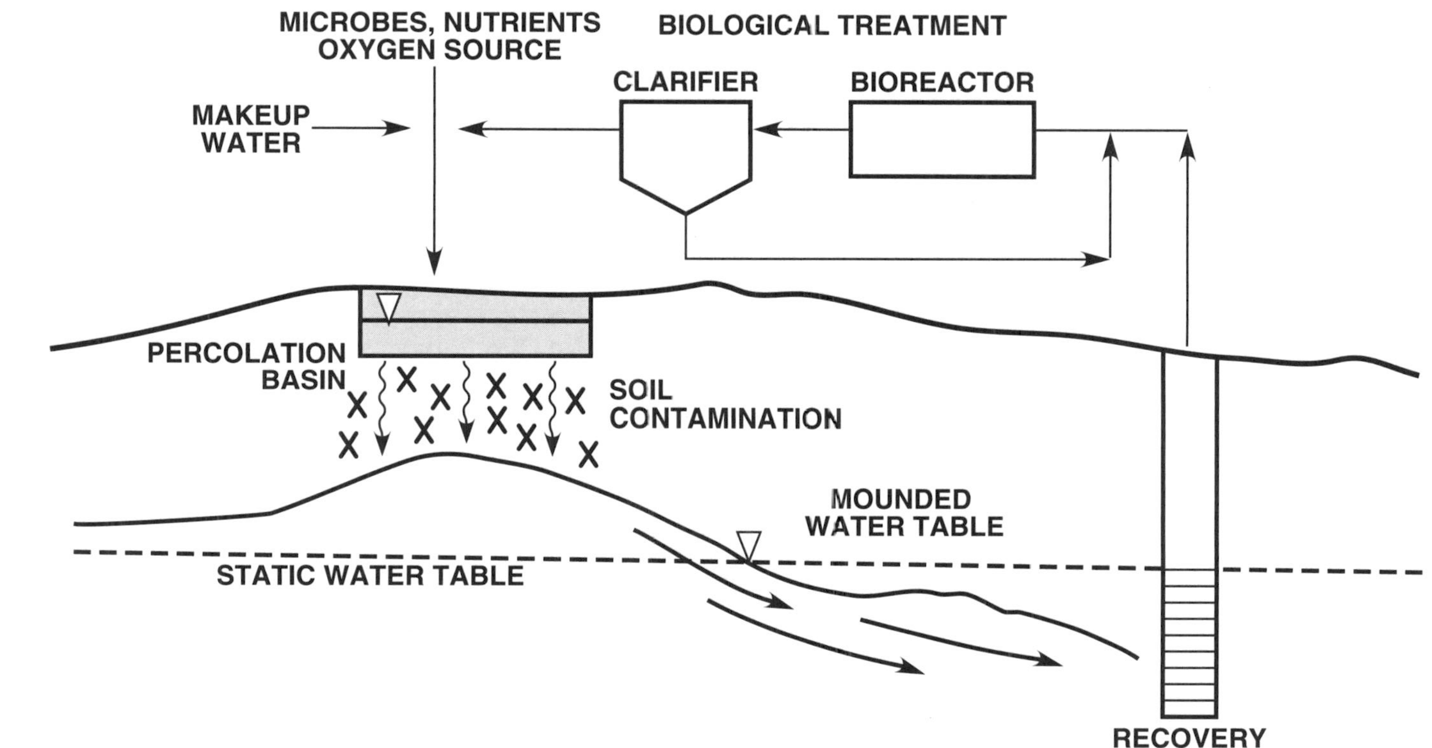

FIGURE 11.12 Schematic of *in situ* bioreclamation using infiltration. (Adapted from Bourquin, Al W. 1989. *Hazardous Materials Control* 2(5) September-October:16ff. With permission.)

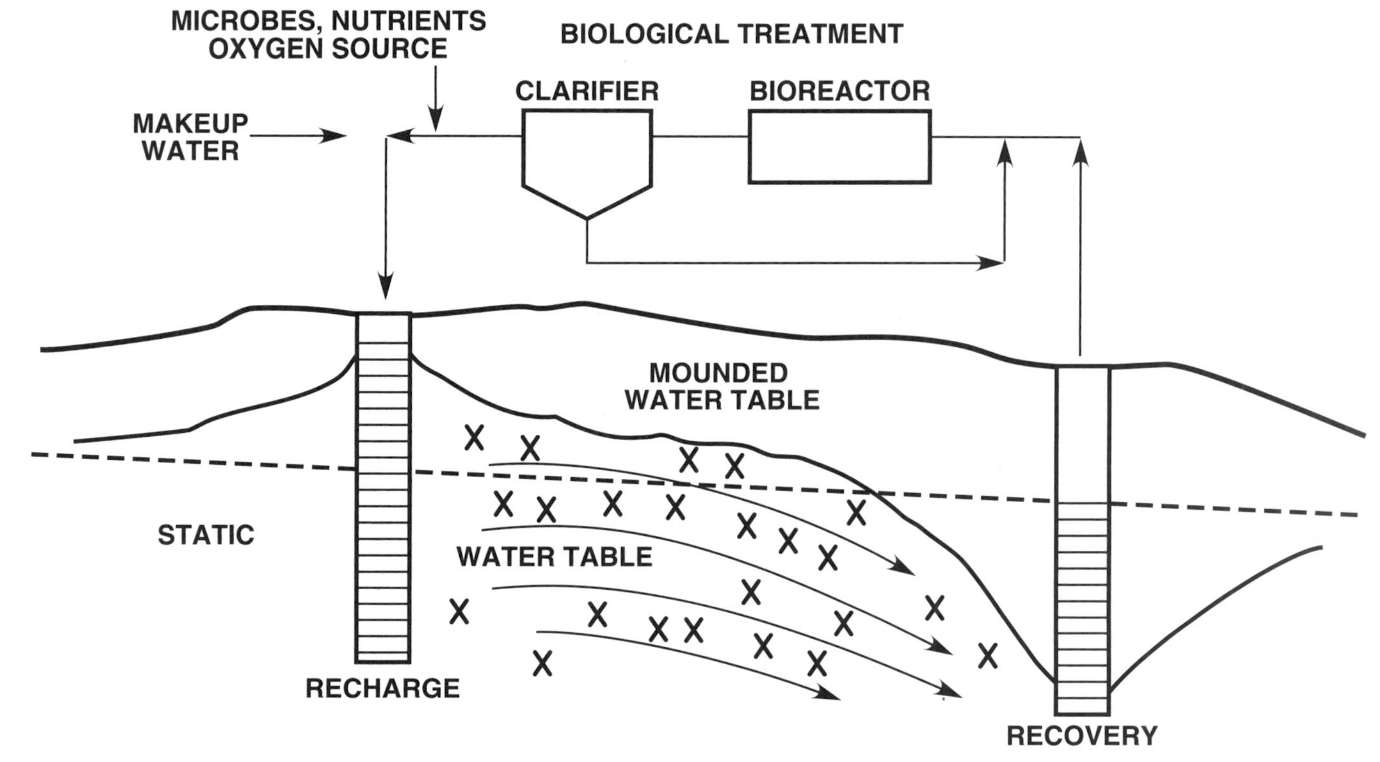

FIGURE 11.13 Schematic of *in situ* bioreclamation using recharge wells or trenches. (Adapted from Bourquin, Al W. 1989. *Hazardous Materials Control* 2(5) September-October:16ff. With permission.)

FIGURE 11.14 Solidification by *in situ* mixing using backhoes (Geo-Con, Inc.).

or migrate to the surface where they combust in the presence of oxygen. Off-gases must be captured and treated. Inorganics in the soil are effectively bound in the solidified glass (Vajda et al. 1995, p. 294ff). (*See also* Shah et al. 1989; Johnson and Cosmos 1989)

Removal Technologies and Practices

Although there are similarities between some of the technologies and practices employed in the conduct of onsite and removal remedies, it is important (1) to consider the technologies in each context, (2) to understand some of the differences that prevail, and (3) to know why the differences prevail. The following is an overview of some technologies and practices associated with removal remedies.

Excavation

Excavation of solid wastes, in site remediation, may simply be the expedient approach or may be necessary when *in situ* methods are not capable of achieving the cleanup objective and the waste to be moved is solid or semisolid.

Excavation is accomplished using standard or modified earth-moving equipment; however, specialized equipment is required for sites containing buried drums or other containers. Extraordinary care must be exercised to minimize releases from deteriorating containers during movement operations. Tedious, one-by-one exposure and recovery of drums is not an unusual necessity in removal actions. Figure 11.17 illustrates the "how-not-to-do-it" problem of damage to the drum and release of its contents. Such operations are most successful when a cable sling can be placed on

FIGURE 11.15 Deep soil mixing equipment used in *in situ* solidification (Geo-Con, Inc.).

the drum such that it can be lifted or pulled from the pile. Leaking drums should always be overpacked before movement.

In the general case, waste deposits that are exhumed by excavation are not containerized and are in the solid or semisolid phase. The exhumed wastes may be treated and redeposited onsite; transported to a treatment, storage, and disposal facility (TSDF); or used for fill material after treatment. Treatment systems that are effective for treatment of solid and/or semisolid hazardous wastes are those which remove (cleanse, desorb, detoxify, or extract) the waste constituents from the soil or other particulate matter or encapsulate or solidify the waste with the soils. Some examples follow.

Thermal Processes. Some form of incineration has been the favored approach to management of exhumed organic waste material. As discussed earlier herein, very high destruction and removal efficiencies (DRE) may be achieved by properly designed and operated thermal destruction units. As before, incineration does not destroy inorganic materials such as heavy metals. The captured solids from the

FIGURE 11.16 Close-up view of injection-mixing equipment used for deep soil mixing (Geo-Con, Inc.).

emission control equipment generally require management as a hazardous waste. Incineration is effective with solid, semisolid, or liquid hazardous wastes, but is not *cost*-effective for dilute or aqueous wastes. Liquids are usually added, if not present in the waste, to act as a catalyst in the reactions of thermal destruction.

Thermal desorption is gaining in popularity and application, primarily due to lower fuel and operating costs. The mass of the excavated waste is heated to 150 to 650°C (302 to 1202°F) to achieve desorption. The desorbed gases are then raised to destruction temperatures or otherwise managed. The method has the added advantage that metal compounds are not volatilized. A transportable low-temperature desorption unit is shown in Figure 11.18 (Vajda et al. 1995, p. 282ff). Other applicable thermal processes include pyrolysis, wherein the waste may be transformed into an inert solid by thermal decomposition in the absence of oxygen. (*See also* Brunner 1988; Grasso 1993)

Physical Treatment. Component separation techniques are effective in waste-specific situations. These techniques include solvent extraction and soil washing. The

FIGURE 11.17 Exposure and recovery of buried drums — "How Not-To-Do-It" (Arizona DEQ).

EPA has defined soil washing as a separation process that uses water as the solvent, and chemical extraction as a process that uses additives such as surfactants or chelating agents (Grasso 1993). In each case, bench-scale testing must precede full-scale operations in order to identify optimum solvents or cleansing media. The end products of these techniques, by definition, include lesser volumes of hazardous wastes which must then be managed.

Chemical Transformation. Although most of the chemical transformation processes are suitable for liquid hazardous wastes and wastewaters having hazardous constituents, they are not widely used on remediation sites. Examples include the use of reagents to remove the chlorine from chlorinated compounds such as PCBs. Examples of chemical treatment applications to solid hazardous wastes include chlorination of cyanide wastes and reduction of hexavalent chromium wastes.

Biological Degradation. *Biological treatment* processes have been used most successfully to treat dilute wastes, contaminated groundwater, and wastewaters having hazardous constituents. These processses are generally used in flow-through applications at fixed facilities. *Bioremediation* is frequently used to treat excavated soils and remediation debris in static or recirculating units. On remediation sites, soils are often excavated, and debris is removed to a bioreactor site where wastes may be layered with manure or other stimulants to enhance indigenous microbial populations. Alternatively, the waste mass may be innoculated with proprietary populations. The unit then circulates the liquid component through the mass, or the mass may be mixed and turned to stimulate the natural biodegration processes (Vajda et al. 1995, p. 289).

FIGURE 11.18 Transportable low-temperature thermal desorption unit. (From Dames and Moore, Executive Offices, 911 Wilshire Boulevard, Los Angeles, CA 90017. With permission.)

Immobilization/Solidification. Solidification and stabilization techniques employed onsite are adaptable to removal projects. A wide variety of treatment processes use Portland cement as a binding agent. Pozzolanic materials are frequently added to the cement to react with any free calcium hydroxide and thus improve the strength and chemical resistance of the concrete-like product. Waste/concrete composites can be formed that have exceptional strength and excellent durability and that retain wastes very effectively (Cullinane and Jones 1989). Certain wastes (e.g., oil, grease, chlorinated solvents) interfere with the setting process or facilitate deterioration after setting and are therefore unsuitable for solidification with Portland cement. (*See also* Soundararajan et al. 1990)

Macroencapsulation. Macroencapsulation systems contain waste constituents by bonding an inert coating or jacket around a mass of cemented waste or by sealing them in polyethylene-lined drums or containers. The method has shown encouraging results in bench testing, but has not become generally accepted for full-scale operations.

Microencapsulation. Thermoplastic microencapsulation has been successfully used in nuclear waste disposal and can be adapted to special industrial wastes. The waste is dried and then dispersed through a heated plastic matrix such as asphalt. The mixture is cooled in a fiber or metal drum to give it shape for transport and/or disposal. Other materials such as polyethylene, polypropylene, wax, or elemental sulfur can be used for specific wastes where cost is not a factor. The major advantage of asphalt encapsulation, over cement and pozzolan systems, is the ability to solidify very soluble toxic materials. The operation is complex, requiring specialized equipment and a highly trained operating staff (Cullinane and Jones 1989). (*See also* Wiles 1989)

Mechanical and Hydraulic Dredging

Many of the nation's remedial sites are (or include) impoundments, streams, or estuaries, where contaminated sediments must be removed. These deposits, until removed, may severely disrupt aquatic ecosystems or may threaten public water supplies. Their removal and management pose particular challenges. The sediments may be highly contaminated, or the contaminant may be highly toxic (or both). In such cases, special precautions may be necessary to prevent dispersal in the surrounding water or exposure of workers.

Mechanical dredging of contaminated sediments may be appropriate under conditions of low, shallow flow. If the sediments are well consolidated, they may be successfully removed by clamshell, dragline, or backhoe. Stream diversion or diking may be necessary to isolate the area of sediment removal. The physical layout may permit dewatering of the isolated area, followed by mechanical excavation of the sediments to be removed.

Hydraulic dredging is the preferred technique if the sediments have a high liquid content or are unconsolidated or if the contamination is in deep, flowing, or open water where resuspension is a problem. The dredged material may be pumped or barged to shore facilities for further management (U.S. EPA 1982, Chapter 7).

Dredged hazardous wastes are usually in the liquid or slurry form and may have sufficient solids content to justify dewatering. The liquid phase may be suitable for treatment by any of several conventional water treatment processes. The dewatered solids may be managed by the techniques listed earlier (*see* "Excavation"). (*See also* Dawson and Mercer 1986, Chapters 9 and 10; Wentz 1989, pp. 406–415)

RCRA and Superfund Remedial Actions

RCRA Corrective Actions

As overviewed in previous chapters, RCRA Sections 3008 and 7003 provide authorities for the EPA to require corrective action whenever there is, or has been, a release of hazardous waste or hazardous waste constituents from a permitted or interim status facility. Moreover, RCRA authorizes the EPA to require corrective action beyond the facility boundary. The EPA interprets the term "corrective action" to cover the full range of possible actions including full cleanups.

The RCRA and Superfund programs follow similar procedures in responding to releases. In both, the first step after discovery of a release is an examination of available data to determine whether or not an emergency action is warranted. In both, short-term measures are authorized to abate the immediate adverse effects of a release. Once an emergency has been addressed, both programs provide for an investigation and formal study of long-term cleanup options. When these analyses are completed, both provide for formal selection of a remedy.

The major procedural difference between the two programs is the ranking of Superfund sites using the Hazard Ranking System (HRS) and the remedial action funding of sites listed on the NPL. RCRA has neither of these provisions (U.S. EPA 1990, pp. VI-12, 13).

The facility owner or operator implements RCRA corrective action. A Superfund remedial action may be implemented by the responsible parties, if identified, or by state or EPA contractors. If cleanup is funded by Superfund, the government may seek cost recovery in federal court.

Perhaps the greatest area of similarity between the programs is found in procedures and requirements for removal actions initiated under RCRA to achieve "clean closure" [40 CFR 270.1(c)(5)] and an excavated removal as a Superfund remedy. In both cases, soil is excavated and treated (either on or offsite) until testing shows no contamination greater than specified. RCRA owners and operators strive to achieve clean closure in order to avoid the procedural burdens of obtaining a post-closure permit and the 30-year groundwater monitoring requirements. Figure 11.19 shows the extent and magnitude of the excavation which may be necessary to achieve clean closure of a former liquid waste impoundment. The exhumed material must be managed by treatment, incineration, or disposal in a secure landfill.

Superfund Remedial Actions

In Chapter 10, we overviewed Subpart F of the NCP and the highly structured progression of the Superfund process, beginning with the preliminary assessment (PA), followed by the site inspection (SI), Hazard Ranking Score (HRS), listing on the NPL, remedial investigation (RI), feasibility study (FS), and the record of decision (ROD). The student desiring greater detail regarding the NCP should consult 40 CFR 300. Practitioners working in Superfund cleanup operations should maintain currency with the NCP by regular reading of one or more of the EPA/Superfund-oriented newsletters and periodicals.

As we noted in Chapter 10, the ROD identifies the remedy that the EPA will require and establishes the framework for remedial negotiations between the EPA and responsible parties. The next step in the Superfund process is the remedial design (RD), wherein the selected remedy is translated into an action plan. The RD considers the objectives and technologies overviewed in this chapter, as well as new and emerging technologies, to structure a cost-effective design.

In the Superfund lexicon, removal implies a short-term cleanup action that usually addresses cleanup needs only at the surface of a site. They are conducted in response to an emergency situation (e.g., to avert an explosion, to clean up a spill of hazardous materials, or to stabilize a site until a permanent remedy can be found).

FIGURE 11.19 Extent and magnitude of excavation necessary to clean close a former hazardous waste impoundment (Laidlaw Environmental Services, Inc., 5295 South Garvey Road, Westmoreland, CA 92281).

Removal actions are limited to 12 months duration or $2 million in expenditures, although these limits may be extended.

Again, in the language of Superfund, "remedial action" (RA) refers to the final remedy for a site and may include a removal. The RA is generally more expensive and of longer duration than a removal. The EPA provides an estimate of the average cost of some current treatment remedies at $16 million. Completion of some projects may require up to ten years, and follow-up monitoring may continue for decades.

If the responsible parties have been identified and have not paid the cost of the cleanup, the EPA initiates cost recovery in the courts. In fact, cost recovery may be initiated at any phase of the process. The costs, as noted, can be exceedingly high and are a very persuasive incentive for property owners, plant managers, hazardous waste facility operators, small businesses, and corporations to manage hazardous materials and wastes properly.

Upon completion of the RA, the project enters an operation and maintenance (O&M) phase which is designed to ensure that the remedy is operational. O&M costs can be quite high in some cases and are cost-shared by the EPA and the state wherein the site is located. This little-known provision of CERCLA embodies the possibility of wreaking havoc on the budgets of "smaller" states and has been a factor in persuading state legislatures to enact state Superfund legislation. The state programs enable funding of the state portion of O&M costs. (*See also* Hopper 1989)

TOPICS FOR REVIEW OR DISCUSSION

1. What are the distinctions between "biological treatment" and "bioremediation" of hazardous wastes?
2. The text briefly discusses two methods of *in situ* remediation methods which involve heating of the contaminated soil. One is termed ______ and is an example of a __________ method. The other method is referred to as __________ and is an example of a ________ method.
3. Macroencapsulation and microencapsulation are remediation techniques that appear to hold promise. How do they differ?
4. Critics have recently complained of disappointing effectiveness and greater than anticipated time and cost of pump-and-treat groundwater remediation technology. Discuss possible alternatives for a generalized groundwater contamination cleanup project.
5. Discuss how a "numeric national cleanup goal" might be formulated. How might it be applied?
6. Discuss developments, changes, and impacts of Superfund legislation that may have occured since preparation of this edition (mid-1995).

REFERENCES

Bourquin, Al W. 1989. "Bioremediation of Hazardous Waste." *Hazardous Materials Control* 2(5) September/October:16ff.

Brunner, Calvin R. 1988. "Industrial Waste Incineration." *Hazardous Materials Control* July/August:26ff.

Burke, Thomas A. 1992. "Overview: Refining Hazardous Waste Site Policies Through Research." *Hazardous Waste Site Investigations Toward Better Decisions,* Richard B. Gammage and Barry A. Berven, Eds. Lewis Publishers, Chelsea, MI.

Cartledge, F. K., H. C. Eaton, and M. E. Tittlebaum. 1990. *The Morphology and Microchemistry of Solidified/Stabilized Hazardous Waste Systems.* U.S. Environmental Protection Agency, Risk Reduction Engineering Laboratory, Cincinnati, OH. EPA 600/S2-89/056.

Combs, George D. 1989. *Emerging Treatment Technologies for Hazardous Waste,* Section XV. Environmental Systems Company, Little Rock, AR.

Corbitt, Robert A. 1989. "Hazardous Waste." *Standard Handbook of Environmental Engineering*, Robert A. Corbitt, Ed. McGraw-Hill, New York.

Cullinane, M. John, Jr., and Larry W. Jones. 1989. "Solidification and Stabilization of Hazardous Wastes." *Hazardous Materials Control* January/February:9ff.

Dawson, Gaynor W., and Basil W. Mercer. 1986. *Hazardous Waste Management.* John Wiley & Sons, New York.

Environment Reporter November 16, 1990. p. 1359.

Environment Reporter April 29, 1994. p. 2219.

Grasso, Domenic. 1993. *Hazardous Waste Site Remediation Source Control.* Lewis Publishers, Chelsea, MI.

Hopper, David. R. 1989. "Cleaning Up Contaminated Waste Sites." *Chemical Engineering* August.

Johnson, Nancy P., and Michael G. Cosmos. 1989. "Thermal Treatment Technologies for Haz Waste Remediation." *Pollution Engineering* October:79.

Jones, Larry W. 1990. *Interference Mechanisms in Waste Stabilization/Solidification Systems.* U.S. Environmental Protection Agency, Risk Reduction Engineering Laboratory, Cincinnati, OH. EPA 600/S2-89/067.

King, Brian J., and Deborah Anne Amidaneau. 1995. "United States Legal and Legislative Framework." *Accident Prevention Manual for Business and Industry — Environmental Management*, Gary R. Krieger, Ed. National Safety Council, Itasca, IL.

McCoy and Associates. 1989. *The Hazardous Waste Consultant* March/April:1–19.

Olsen, Roger L., and Michael C. Kavanaugh. 1993. "Can Groundwater Restoration Be Achieved?" *Water Environment and Technology* March:42ff.

Oma, K. H., and J. L. Buelt. 1989. "Part 2: In Situ Heating to Detoxify Organic-Contaminate Soils." *Hazardous Materials Control* March/April:14ff.

RAND. 1989. "Rating Superfund's Progress: In a Word, 'Super-Slow'." *RAND Research Review,* Vol. XIII, No. 3, Fall. The RAND Corporation, Santa Monica, CA.

Rastegar, Hamid, James Lu, and Chris Conroy. 1988. "Chemical Treatment Technologies." *Hazardous Materials Control* July/August:8ff.

Shah, J. K., T. J. Schultz, and V. R. Daiga. 1989. "Pyrolysis Process." *Standard Handbook of Hazardous Waste Treatment and Disposal,* Harry M. Freeman, Ed. McGraw-Hill, New York.

Soundararajan, R., Edwin F. Barth, and J. J. Gibbons. 1990. "Using an Organophilic Clay to Chemically Stabilize Waste Containing Organic Compounds." *Hazardous Materials Control* January/February:42ff.

Staples, Charles A., and Richard A. Kimerle. 1986. "How Clean is Clean? Site Specific Answers." *Hazardous Substances* October:10–12.

Towers, David, Marc J. Dent, and David G. Van Arnam. 1989. "Part 1: Choosing a Treatment for VHO-Contaminated Soil." *Hazardous Materials Control* March/April:8ff.

Travis, Curtis C., and Carolyn B. Doty. 1992. "Remedial Action Decision Process." *Hazardous Waste Site Investigations — Toward Better Decisions,* Richard B. Gammage and Barry A. Berven, Eds. Lewis Publishers, Chelsea, MI.

U.S. Environmental Protection Agency. 1982. *Handbook for Remedial Action at Hazardous Waste Sites.* Office of Research and Development, Cincinnati, OH.

U.S. Environmental Protection Agency. 1989a. *Risk Assessment Guidance for Superfund Volume I Human Health Evaluation Manual.* Office of Emergency and Remedial Response, Washington, D.C. EPA 540/1-89/002.

U.S. Environmental Protection Agency. 1989b. *The Superfund Innovative Technology Evaluation Program: Technology Profiles.* Risk Reduction Engineering Laboratory, Cincinnati, OH. EPA 540/5-89/013.

U.S. Environmental Protection Agency. 1990. *RCRA Orientation Manual, 1990 Edition.* Superintendent of Documents, Government Printing Office, Washington, D.C.

U.S. General Accounting Office (GAO). 1993. *Superfund — Progress, Problems, and Reauthorization Issues.* U.S. General Accounting Office, Washington, D.C. GAO/T-RCED-93-27.

U.S. General Accounting Office (GAO). 1994a. *Superfund — Status, Cost, and Timeliness of Hazardous Waste Site Cleanups.* U.S. General Accounting Office, Washington, D.C. GAO/RCED-94-256.

U.S. General Accounting Office (GAO). 1994b. *Superfund — EPA Has Opportunities to Increase Recovery of Costs.* U.S. General Accounting Office, Washington, D.C. GAO/RCED-94-196.

Vajda, Gary F., William L. Hall, and Gary R. Krieger. 1995. "Pollution Prevention Approaches and Technologies." *Accident Prevention Manual for Business & Industry — Environmental Management,* Gary R. Krieger, Ed. National Safety Council, Itasca, IL.

Wentz, Charles A. 1989. *Hazardous Waste Management.* McGraw-Hill, New York.

Wiles, Carlton C. 1989. "Solidification and Stabilization Technology." *Standard Handbook of Hazardous Waste Treatment and Disposal*, Harry M. Freeman, Ed. McGraw-Hill, New York.

12 MEDICAL/BIOMEDICAL/ INFECTIOUS WASTE MANAGEMENT

OBJECTIVES

At completion of this chapter, the student should:

- be familiar with the hazards associated with the traditional "red bag wastes," methods to minimize the hazards, and current abuse patterns which are taxing destruction capacity and driving costs to unacceptable levels.
- be familiar with the traditional sanitarian approach to biomedical waste management and the impacts of the AIDS epidemic and the 1988 beach washups on the Atlantic seaboard.
- understand the regulatory approach of the Subtitle J regulations (40 CFR 259) and the use of the tracking form.
- be familiar with regulatory conflicts and overlaps which may be associated with onsite incineration of biomedical wastes.

INTRODUCTION

For many years, health care workers, hospital administrators, military sanitarians, and other health-related professionals have understood the necessity to protect themselves and the public from exposure to wastes that might be reservoirs of disease-transmitting organisms. Local ordinances, state and military regulations, and guidelines issued by federal agencies and professional organizations developed around a few simple practices, and vice versa. These practices generally included "red-bagging" the solid wastes,* isolating them in cool storage, followed by incineration or sterilization and landfilling.

The 1976 enactment of the Resource Conservation and Recovery Act (RCRA) included a definition of hazardous waste which continues as a basis for federal regulation of infectious waste management:

* Red bagging is the practice of disposing of medical wastes in bright red plastic bags, which distinguish the contents as distinct from other wastes.

> The term "hazardous waste" means a solid waste or combination of solid wastes, which because of its quantity, concentration, or physical, chemical or *infectious* characteristics may (1) cause, or significantly contribute to, an increase in mortality or an increase in serious irreversible, or incapacitating reversible, illness or (2) pose a substantial present or potential hazard to human health or the environment when improperly treated, stored, transported, disposed of, or otherwise managed (42 USC 6903)

In 1978, the U.S. Environmental Protection Agency (EPA) published proposed regulations for hazardous waste management which included several classifications of infectious waste. However, the agency did not make a convincing case for the supposed health hazards posed by these wastes and did not include them in the final hazardous waste regulations.

By 1982, the EPA had not promulgated regulations specific to the management of infectious wastes, state and local regulations ranged from nonexistent to overly complex and conflicting, and the agency was under pressure to provide guidance. The agency published the *Draft Manual for Infectious Waste Management* and in 1986 published the final version, *EPA Guide to Infectious Waste Management* (EPA 1986). We will borrow heavily from the 1986 guide in this chapter.

This quiet evolution ended with the nation's growing alarm toward the Acquired Immunodeficiency Syndrome (AIDS) epidemic. Truths, half-truths, and blatant untruths regarding modes of transmission of the Human Immunodeficiency Virus (HIV) caused near panic among some health care workers, in particular, and among the public, in general. Suddenly, landfills began refusing hospital wastes, health care workers began red bagging *everything*, small medical waste incinerators were overwhelmed, and management of infectious waste became a major problem.

In May 1988, a garbage slick nearly one mile long surfaced along the Ocean County shore of New Jersey. Needles, syringes, and empty prescription bottles with New York addresses washed up on the shore. Six weeks later, ten miles of Long Island beaches closed when medical wastes washed ashore. Throughout the summer of 1988, beaches — from Maine to the Gulf of Mexico, along the Great Lakes, and elsewhere — experienced washups of medical wastes (U.S. Congress, Office of Technology Assessment 1988, p. 1).

Public outrage over the closure of beaches and perceived health threats brought about enactment, in November 1988, of RCRA Subtitle J, the hastily conceived Medical Waste Tracking Act (MWTA). The EPA rushed the implementing regulations into place in March 1989, reflecting Congress' hope that their impact would prevent beach washups during the summer of 1989 (Jenkins 1990, p. 55).

The EPA promulgated Subtitle J regulations which were patterned after the RCRA Subtitle C regulations and were codified at 40 CFR 259. The regulations included the following elements:

- *Definition of "Medical Waste"* — Defined as any solid waste which is generated in the diagnosis, treatment, or immunization of human beings or animals in related research, biologicals production, or testing.

- *Medical Waste Generator Requirements* — Generators were defined as producers of more than 50 pounds of regulated medical waste monthly, managed by shipping offsite. Generators were required to separate, package, label, mark, and track waste according to the regulation.
- *Medical Waste Transporter Requirements* — Transporters submitted a one-time notification to EPA headquarters which then issued a medical waste identification number. The ID number was to be used on all tracking forms and reports. Transporters were also required to follow rules regarding transport vehicles; ensure that wastes were properly packaged, labeled, and marked; and comply with rules for tracking, record keeping, and reporting of waste shipments.
- *Medical Waste Treatment, Destruction, and Disposal Facility Requirements* — These facilities included incinerators, landfills, and treatment operations that grind, steam sterilize, or treat wastes with disinfectants, heat, or radiation. These practices were prescribed, defined, and implemented in similarity to the EPA's 1986 guide.

Subtitle J instructed the EPA to develop a two-year demonstration program to track medical waste in the participating states and to report back to Congress upon completion of the program. Connecticut, New Jersey, New York, and Rhode Island, as well as Puerto Rico, opted to participate. The EPA rendered interim reports in May and December 1990. The latter, EPA 530-SW-90-087B, offers no conclusions regarding effectiveness of the program, and the EPA has published no further evaluation (U.S. EPA 1990a). The program was completed in 1991, and Congress has shown little enthusiasm for an expanded or continued program. The focus for medical waste management regulatory programs has thus reverted to state and local governments. Available guidance includes the 1986 EPA guide and the more recent "white paper" published by the *Journal of the Air and Waste Management Association* (Drum and Bulley 1994), which will also be quoted herein.

MWTA and the 40 CFR 259 regulations were widely recognized as having minimal effect on the beach washup of medical waste. It was an effort to "do something" about the burgeoning problem of medical waste management and to gather data on the effectiveness of a tracking system patterned somewhat after the "cradle-to-grave" system for hazardous wastes.

Definition and Characterization of Medical Waste

Disagreement exists between governments, agencies, and practitioners regarding the meanings of the terms "infectious waste" and "medical waste." To avoid unproductively dwelling upon this confusion, we briefly point out the terms used and some indication of their usage. We then adopt a convention for use in this text.

Infectious Waste

In the 1986 guidance document, the EPA defines infectious waste as waste capable of producing an infectious disease. This definition requires a consideration of certain factors necessary for induction of disease. These factors include:

- Presence of a pathogen of sufficient virulence
- Dose
- Portal of entry
- Resistance of host

Thus, for a waste to be infectious, it must contain pathogens with sufficient virulence and quantity so that exposure to the waste by a susceptible host could result in an infectious disease. The EPA further recommends categories of waste to be designated as infectious waste, as summarized in Table 12.1.

In addition, the EPA has identified an optional infectious waste category which consists of miscellaneous contaminated wastes. The suggestion is that a qualified person or committee should decide whether or not to handle these wastes as "infectious" in specific situations. The optional categories and examples are listed in Table 12.2.

The terminology problem is further complicated by the fact that the terms infectious, pathological, biomedical, biohazardous, toxic, and medically hazardous have all been used to describe infectious waste.

Medical Waste

Medical wastes include all infectious waste, hazardous (including low-level radioactive wastes) wastes, and any other wastes that are generated from all types of health care institutions, including hospitals, clinics, doctor (including dental and veterinary) offices, and medical laboratories (U.S. Congress, Office of Technology Assessment 1988, p. 3).

The terminology confusion is worsened by the EPA's definition of medical waste in 40 CFR 259.10 as any solid waste which is generated in the diagnosis, treatment, or immunization of human beings or animals in related research, biologicals production, or testing.

In the Subpart J regulations, the EPA also defined "regulated medical wastes" as a subset of all medical wastes and included seven distinct categories:

- Cultures and stocks of infectious agents
- Human pathological wastes (e.g., tissues, body parts)
- Human blood and blood products
- Sharps (e.g., hypodermic needles and syringes used in animal or patient care)
- Certain animal wastes
- Certain isolation wastes (e.g., wastes from patients with highly communicable diseases)
- Unused sharps (e.g., suture needles, scalpel blades, hypodermic needles)

Table 12.1 Categories of Infectious Wastes

Waste Category	Examples[a]
Isolation wastes	Wastes generated by hospitalized patients who are isolated to protect others from communicable diseases
Cultures and stocks of infectious agents and associated biologicals	Specimens from medical and pathology laboratories
	Cultures and stocks of infectious agents from clinical, research, and industrial laboratories; disposable culture dishes and devices used to transfer, inoculate, and mix cultures
	Waste from production of biologicals
	Discarded live and attenuated vaccines
Human blood and blood products	Waste blood, serum, plasma, and blood products
Pathological waste	Tissues, organs, body parts, blood, and body fluids removed during surgery, autopsy, and biopsy
Contaminated sharps[b]	Contaminated hypodermic needles, syringes, scalpel blades, Pasteur pipettes, and broken glass
Contaminated animal carcasses, body parts, and bedding	Contaminated animal carcasses, body parts, or bedding of animals that were intentionally exposed to pathogens

[a] These materials are examples of wastes covered by each category. The categories are not limited to these materials.

[b] Unused sharps (*Note:* Unused sharps that have been improperly managed or discarded should be managed as if contaminated. Both used and unused sharps present the same potential for puncture injuries; testing of improperly disposed sharps to determine the presence of infectious agents is impractical; unused sharps present the same aesthetic degradation of the environment as do used sharps). (*See* Reinhardt and Gordon 1991, pp. 37–38)

Source: U.S. EPA 1986.

The similarities between infectious wastes as listed in the 1986 EPA guide and regulated medical wastes as listed in 40 CFR 259.10 are obvious. The relevance of the regulated medical waste definition is doubtful, unless the Subpart J program is resurrected. In hope of some consistency, we will confine the discussion in this chapter to infectious wastes, except where referenced material makes use of an alternate. (*See also* U.S. Congress, Office of Technology Assessment 1988, Chapter 1; U. S. EPA 1990b, Section 2)

Table 12.2 Miscellaneous Contaminated Wastes

Miscellaneous Contaminated Wastes	Examples
Wastes from surgery and autopsy	Soiled dressings, sponges, drapes, lavage tubes, drainage sets, underpads, and surgical gloves
Miscellaneous laboratory wastes	Specimen containers, slides and cover slips, disposable gloves, lab coats, and aprons
Dialysis unit wastes	Tubing, filters, disposable sheets, towels, gloves, aprons, and lab coats
Contaminated equipment	Equipment used in patient care, medical laboratories, research, and in the production and testing of certain pharmaceuticals.

Source: U.S. EPA 1986.

Infectious Waste Management

The objectives of an effective infectious waste management program should be to provide protection to human health and the environment from hazards posed by the waste. Proper management ensures that infectious waste is handled in accordance with established procedures from the time of generation through treatment of the waste (to render it noninfectious) and its ultimate disposal.

An infectious waste management system should be documented in a plan and should include the following elements:

- Designation/identification of infectious waste
- Segregation
- Packaging
- Storage
- Transport and handling
- Treatment techniques
- Disposal of treated waste
- Contingency planning
- Staff training

(*See also* Reinhardt and Gordon 1991, p.13ff)

Designation of Infectious Waste

The infectious waste plan should specify which wastes are to be managed as infectious waste. The six categories of Table 12.1 should be included if applicable. A responsible official or committee should determine which, if any, of the optional categories of Table 12.2 are to be included.

FIGURE 12.1 The universal biohazard symbol.

Segregation of Infectious Waste

The 1986 EPA guide recommends:

- segregation of infectious waste at the point of origin.
- segregation of infectious waste with multiple hazards as necessary for management and treatment.
- use of distinctive, clearly marked containers or plastic bags for infectious wastes.
- use of the universal biological hazard symbol on infectious waste containers, as appropriate (Figure 12.1).

Also, segregation of infectious wastes assures that the added costs of special handling will not be applied to noninfectious waste.

Packaging of Infectious Waste

Infectious waste should be packaged in order to protect waste handlers and the public from possible injury and disease that may result from exposure to the waste. Accordingly, the 1986 EPA guide recommends:

- selection of packaging materials that are appropriate for the type of waste handled:
    - Plastic bags for many types of solid or semisolid infectious waste.
    - Puncture-resistant containers for sharps.
    - Bottles, flasks, or tanks for liquids.
- use of packaging that maintains its integrity during storage and transport.

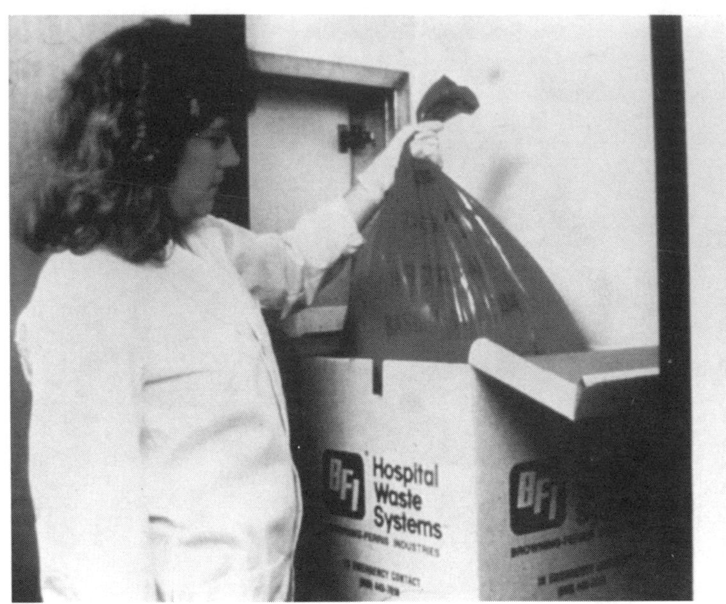

FIGURE 12.2 Red-bagged waste being placed in a rigid container for shipment [Browning Ferris Industries (BFI), 215 North Morengo Avenue, Suite 185, Pasadena, CA].

- closing the top of each bag by folding or tying as appropriate for the treatment or transport.
- placement of liquid wastes in capped or tightly stoppered bottles or flasks.
- no compaction of infectious waste or packaged infectious waste before treatment.

Shippers of infectious waste are also subject to U.S. Department of Transportation (DOT) regulations for packaging, marking, and labeling of "infectious substances" and regulated medical waste if shipped by commercial carriers.*

Figure 12.2 shows a red bag, containing infectious waste, being placed uncompacted in a rigid container for shipment. Figure 12.3 illustrates an infectious waste receptacle in a clinic. Figure 12.4 shows a sharps receptacle receiving a syringe and needle. Figure 12.5 illustrates transfer of sharps for transport. Figure 12.6 demonstrates handling of red-bagged wastes in rigid containers.

Storage of Infectious Waste

Storage temperature and duration are important considerations. Warmer temperatures cause higher rates of microbial growth and putrefaction, resulting in odor problems. The 1986 EPA guide recommends:

* *See* 49 CFR 172.101 Hazardous Materials Table entries "Infectious Substances" and "Regulated Medical Wastes"; 172.203 for proper shipping name; 172.432 and Appendix G to Part 173 for labels; 172.134 for definitions; and 173.196 and 173.197 for packaging.

FIGURE 12.3 An infectious waste receptacle in a clinic (BFI).

- locating the storage area near the treatment site.
- minimizing storage time.
- proper packing that ensures containment of infectious waste and the exclusion of rodents and vermin.
- limited access to storage area.
- posting of universal biological hazard symbol on storage area door, waste containers, freezers, or refrigerators.

Transport of Infectious Waste

The 1986 EPA guide recommends:

- avoidance of mechanical loading devices which may rupture packaged wastes.
- frequent disinfection of carts used to transfer wastes within the facility.
- placement of all infectious waste into rigid or semirigid containers before transport offsite.
- transport of infectious waste in closed leak-proof trucks or dumpsters.
- use of appropriate hazard symbols in accord with local, state, and federal regulations.

Figure 12.7 illustrates a stainless steel conveyor for movement of packaged infectious wastes within a facility. The stainless steel construction provides a smooth surface which minimizes damage to packages and is easily disinfected in the event of a spill. Figure 12.8 illustrates a refrigerated truck with a spill containment unit for transporting infectious wastes.

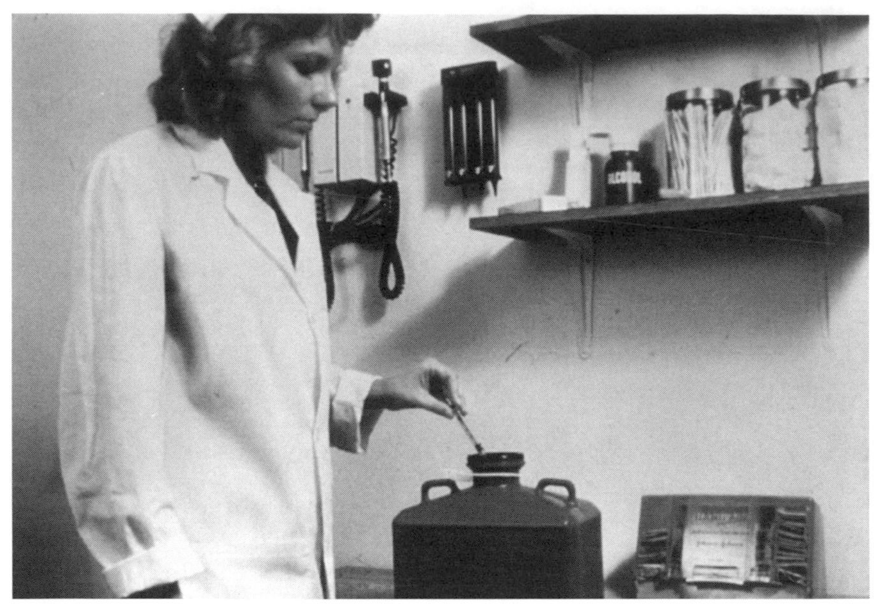

FIGURE 12.4 Sharps receptacle receiving a syringe (BFI).

FIGURE 12.5 Transfer of sharps for transport (BFI).

FIGURE 12.6 Handling of red-bagged wastes in rigid containers (BFI).

FIGURE 12.7 Stainless steel conveyor for movement of packaged infectious waste within a facility [Waste Management of North America, Inc. (WMI), 3003 Butterfield Road, Oak Brook, IL].

FIGURE 12.8 Refrigerated truck with spill containment unit (WMI).

Note: The EPA does not consider the truck as a rigid containment system; rather, it serves only as a transport mechanism. Therefore, all infectious waste should be placed in rigid or semirigid, leak-proof containers before being loaded on a truck.

Commercial shipments of infectious wastes are subject to the DOT regulations for a Class 6, Division 6.2 material. As noted earlier, the shipper is subject to requirements for assigning the correct shipping name, marking, and labeling.

Treatment of Infectious Waste

The EPA defines treatment as any method, technique, or process designed to change the biological character or composition of waste. Since landfill operations may cause loss of containment integrity and dispersal of infectious waste, the EPA recommends that all infectious waste be treated prior to disposal. The 1986 EPA guide further recommends:

- establishing standard operating procedures for each process used for treating infectious waste.
- monitoring of all treatment processes to assure efficient and effective treatment.
- use of biological indicators to monitor treatment (other indicators may be used provided that their effectiveness has been successively demonstrated).
- treatment for each of the six infectious waste categories per Table 12.3.

Table 12.3 Recommended Techniques for Treatment of Infectious Waste

Category of Infectious Waste	Recommended Treatment Technique
Isolation wastes	Steam sterilization Incineration
Cultures and stocks of infectious agents and associated biologicals	Steam sterilization Incineration Thermal inactivation Chemical disinfection
Human blood and blood products	Steam sterilization Incineration Chemical disinfection Discharge to sanitary sewer[a]
Pathological wastes	Steam sterilization[b] Incineration Handling by mortician
Contaminated animal carcasses, body parts, and bedding	
Carcasses and body parts	Steam sterilization[b] Incineration
Bedding	Incineration

[a] Provided secondary treatment is online and operating authorities have been notified.

[b] For aesthetic reasons, steam sterilization should be followed by incineration or by grinding with subsequent flushing to sewer system in accord with state and local regulations.

Source: U.S. EPA 1986.

- the following treatment methods for miscellaneous contaminated wastes (when a decision is made to manage these wastes as infectious):
  - Wastes from surgery and autopsy — incineration or steam sterilization
  - Miscellaneous laboratory wastes — incineration or steam sterilization
  - Dialysis unit wastes — incineration or steam sterilization
  - Contaminated equipment — incineration, steam sterilization, or gas/vapor sterilization

Steam Sterilization

Treatment by steam sterilization is accomplished in either an autoclave or a retort. Both have a chamber in which the waste can be subjected to sterilization by saturated steam at pressures of 15 to 30 psi. The autoclave is the most commonly used steam sterilizer. A variety of designs and capacities are available. The operating and design principle is to subject the waste to the saturated steam, in the absence of air, at a prescribed temperature and pressure for a sufficient time to ensure sterilization. Figure 12.9 illustrates a commercial autoclave for sterilization of infectious wastes (Reinhardt and Gordon 1991, Chapter 6). (*See also* U.S. EPA 1991, p. 249ff)

FIGURE 12.9 Commercial autoclave for sterilization of infectious waste (WMI).

Incineration

Incineration is, at the time of this writing, the most popular treatment process for infectious waste management. Drum and Bulley (1994, p. 1177) place the numbers of medical waste incinerators operating in the United States at 6700, but the EPA consistently reports on "more than 5,000." At hospitals, where most medical waste is generated, 60% of the waste classified as infectious is managed by onsite incineration. The onsite option provides many advantages, including sterilization of pathogenic wastes and volume reductions of 90 to 95% prior to ultimate disposal. Most modern medical waste incinerators operate on "controlled air" using two chambers. The primary chamber, into which the waste is fed, operates with restricted air flow (i.e., "starved air") at 1600 to 1800°F (871 to 982°C).* The waste is pyrolized, and the volatiles move to a secondary chamber where they are combusted at 1800°F (982°C) or a higher temperature. Excess air is provided, in the secondary chamber, to ensure complete combustion. Ash is moved through and exits the primary chamber by the use of hydraulic rams or other feed devices (Reinhardt and Gordon 1991, Chapter 7). Air pollution control equipment collects particulate matter, captures trace metals and organics, and neutralizes acid gases produced in the combustion process (Drum and Bulley 1994, p. 1178).

Figure 12.10 provides a cross-sectional view of an incinerator for infectious wastes. The stack (Figure 12.11), shown producing only faintly visible vapor,

* Green (1992, p. 110) advocates primary chamber temperatures of 1400 to 1600°F to minimize volatilization of metals in order to minimize the quantities of metals carried out by the fly ash.

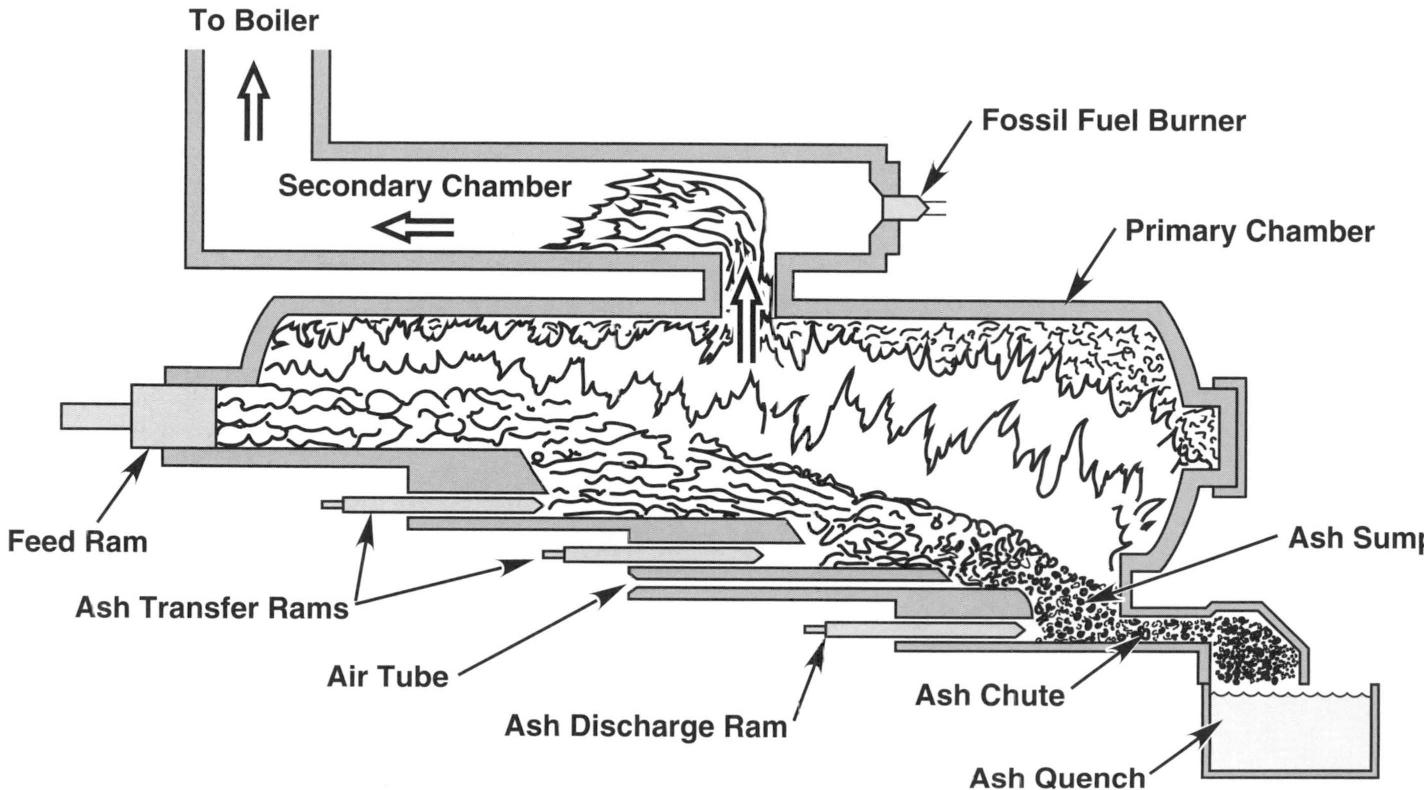

FIGURE 12.10 Cross-section of an incinerator for infectious waste (WMI).

FIGURE 12.11 Infectious waste incinerator stack showing no visible smoke and a faintly visible vapor (WMI).

should not emit visible smoke. Precision control of incinerator operation is essential (Figure 12.12).

Properly designed and operated infectious waste incinerators, with adequate emission control equipment, can achieve excellent results in terms of destruction of pathogens and organic chemicals, capture and containment of heavy metals, and reduction of volume. However, concern persists regarding atmospheric emissions of highly toxic dioxins and furans by combustion of these wastes at other than optional feed rates, temperatures, and dwell times. (U.S. EPA 1991, Chapter 2; Reinhardt and Gordon 1991, Chapter 7; Green 1992, Chapters 3–6; Drum and Bulley 1994, p. 1177ff). The EPA has developed estimates to the effect that even though dioxin emissions from individual medical waste incinerators are quite small, the collective emissions from more than 5000 facilities are the largest source of known air emissions of dioxin in the nation. The EPA was expected to propose Maximum Achievable Control Technology (MACT) Clean Air Act standards for medical waste incinerators by early 1995 (U.S. EPA news release, September 13, 1994). The new standards may have a major impact upon infectious waste management options at individual sites.

Environmental Science and Technology predicts that "The proposed medical waste incinerator standards are expected to shut down many small, on-site operations, a boon for commercial incinerator companies that hope to step into the void." (Johnson 1995, p. 34)

FIGURE 12.12 Combustion controls for an infectious waste incinerator (WMI).

Emerging Treatment Technologies

New or alternative technologies, primarily for sterilization of infectious waste, are emerging. These include units having microwave or ultraviolet heating systems, ionizing radiation source material, or chemical treatment. Self-contained microwave treatment units have recently become available commercially. The units shred and grind the waste to small, unrecognizable bits; are moistened with high temperature steam; and then pass via screw conveyor tube beneath sequential microwave generators. Temperature is maintained at 200°F (93°C) during the 30-min passage. The treated material can then be landfilled. Figure 12.13 illustrates the configuration of the microwave unit.

Ionizing radiation is considered by the EPA to be a potentially available method for treating medical waste. The process uses a source such as cobalt 60 to destroy infectious agents. The technique has the advantages of minimal use of electrical energy and is suitable for materials that cannot be thermally treated. Disadvantages include complex technology requiring highly trained operating personnel, potential for human exposure, and difficulties associated with disposal of the decayed source material. (U.S. EPA 1991, pp. 116–117). The technique is seldom used in the United States (Reinhardt and Gordon 1991, p. 120).

Disposal of Treated Waste

Infectious waste which has been effectively treated is no longer biologically hazardous and may be mixed with and disposed of as ordinary solid waste, provided the waste does not pose other hazards that are subject to federal or state regulations.

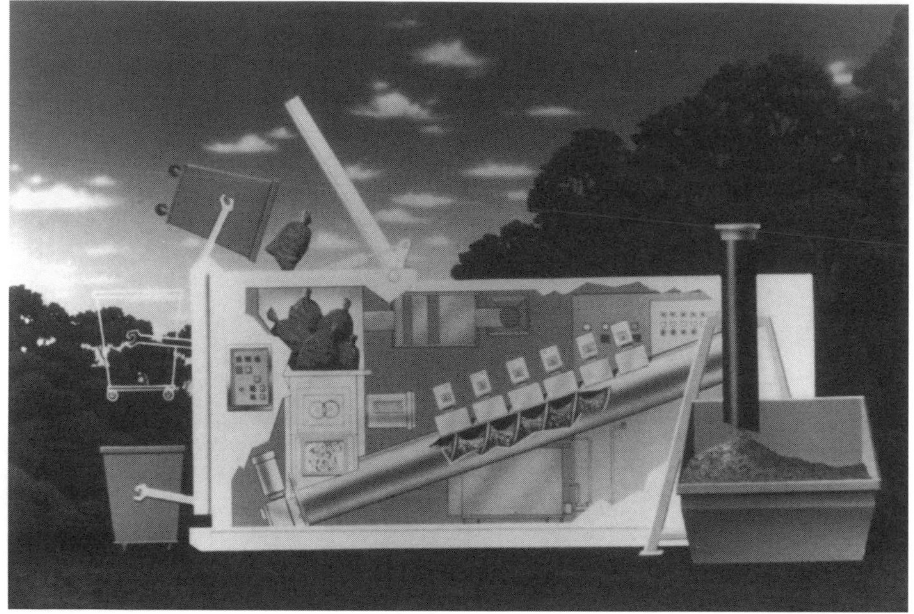

FIGURE 12.13 Microwave disinfection unit [Sanitec, Inc., 26 Fairfield Place, West Caldwell, NJ].

The 1986 EPA guide recommends:

- contacting state and local governments to identify approved disposal options.
- discharge of treated liquids and pathological wastes (after grinding) to the sewer system; approval of the local sewer authority must be obtained.
- land disposal of treated solids and incinerator ash.
- rendering body parts unrecognizable before land disposal.

Some states require that needles and syringes be rendered nonusable before disposal.

Contingency Planning

The infectious waste management plan should include a contingency plan to provide for emergency situations. The plan should include, but not be limited to, procedures to be used under the following circumstances:

- Spills of liquid infectious waste — cleanup procedures, protection of personnel, and disposal of spill residue
- Rupture of plastic bags (or other loss of containment) — cleanup procedures, protection of personnel, and repackaging of waste
- Equipment failure — alternative arrangements for waste storage and treatment (e.g., offsite treatment)

Staff Training

Facilities that generate infectious waste should provide employees with infectious waste management training. This training should include an explanation of the infectious waste management plan and assignment of roles and responsibilities for implementation of the plan. Such education is important for all employees who generate or handle infectious wastes regardless of the employee's role or type of work.

Training programs should be implemented:

- when the infectious waste management plans are first developed and instituted.
- when new employees are hired.
- whenever infectious waste management practices are changed.

Continuing education is also an important part of staff training. Refresher training aids in maintaining awareness of the potential hazards posed by infectious waste. Training also serves to reinforce waste management policies and procedures that are detailed in the infectious waste management plan (U.S. EPA 1986, Chapter 3). (*See also* U.S. EPA 1986, Chapters 4 and 5 and 1990b, Section 2; U.S. Congress, Office of Technology Assessment 1988, Chapter 3; Boecher et al. 1989; Keene 1989; Reinhardt and Gordon 1991, Chapter 16; Drum and Bulley 1994)

TOPICS FOR REVIEW OR DISCUSSION

1. Red-bagged wastes are usually placed in a rigid container for shipment. Why is this necessary?
2. How do criteria for ultimate disposal of RCRA hazardous wastes differ from those for infectious waste?
3. Why are sharps considered so dangerous to infectious waste handlers? Why must unused discarded sharps be managed as if they had been used?
4. The van body of an infectious waste transport truck is not acceptable as a "rigid container." Why not?
5. What is meant by starved air incineration, as in infectious waste incineration? Why is it considered good design for an infectious waste incinerator?
6. What is the major concern regarding atmospheric emissions from infectious waste incinerators?

REFERENCES

Boecher, Frederick W., David C. Guzewich, and Michael H. Diem. 1989. "Infectious Waste Management at Army Health Care Facilities, Past and Present." *Hazardous Materials Control* November-December:73ff.

Drum, Donald A., and Mike Bulley. 1994. "Medical Waste Disposal," White Paper, Medical Waste Committee (WT-3), Air & Waste Management Association. *Journal of Air & Waste Management Association* October:1176ff.

Green, Alex E. S. 1992. *Medical Waste Incineration and Pollution Prevention.* Van Nostrand Reinhold, New York.

Jenkins, Pamela R. 1990. *AIDS Infection Control, and the Effective Management of Medical Waste.* Environmental Resource Center, Fayetteville, NC.

Johnson, Jeff. 1995. "Incinerators Targeted by EPA." *Environmental Science and Technology* January:33ff.

Keene, John H. 1989. "Medical Waste Management: Public Pressure Versus Sound Medicine." *Hazardous Materials Control* September-October:29ff.

Reinhardt, Peter A., and Judith G. Gordon. 1991. *Infectious Medical Waste Management.* Lewis Publishers, Chelsea, MI.

U.S. Congress, Office of Technology Assessment. 1988. *Issues in Medical Waste Management — Background Paper.* Superintendent of Documents, Government Printing Office, Washington, D.C. OTA-BP-O-49.

U.S. Environmental Protection Agency. 1986. *EPA Guide for Infectious Waste Management.* Office of Solid Waste and Emergency Response, Washington, D.C. EPA 530-SW-86-014.

U.S. Environmental Protection Agency. 1990a. *Medical Waste Management in the United States — Second Interim Report to Congress.* Solid Waste and Emergency Response, Washington, D.C.

U.S. Environmental Protection Agency. 1990b. *Guides to Pollution Prevention: Selected Hospital Waste Streams.* Center for Environmental Research Information, Cincinnati, OH. EPA 625/7-90-009.

U.S. Environmental Protection Agency, et al. 1991. *Medical Waste Management and Disposal.* Noyes Data Corporation, Park Ridge, NJ.

U.S. Environmental Protection Agency. 1994. EPA news release, September 13, 1994.

13 RADIOACTIVE WASTE MANAGEMENT

OBJECTIVES

At completion of this chapter, the student should:

- be conversant with basic radioactivity, uses of nuclear energy, and problems of nuclear waste contamination.
- understand the basic physiological and human health effects of penetrating ionizing radiation and approaches to protection from exposure.
- have an understanding of the magnitude of the nuclear waste management problem in the United States, the causes, and the impediments to timely remedy thereof.
- be conversant with the four separate and distinct types of radioactive wastes and with the management and regulatory approach to each.

INTRODUCTION

U.S. News and World Report (Satchell 1989) featured an article entitled "Uncle Sam's Toxic Folly." The lead paragraph begins: "Cleaning up radioactive and chemical waste at the nation's nuclear weapons plants and military installations looms as the biggest, toughest and most expensive task of ecological restoration in American history. It presents technical challenges equal to the Apollo moon landing and space shuttle programs, and it will cost roughly as much, about $130 billion... ."

In 1895, William Konrad Roentgen, professor of physics at the University of Wurtzburg, Germany, showed that the X-rays he had discovered could penetrate matter which was impervious to ordinary light and could produce fluorescence in various substances, such as glass and calcite (Pauling 1958, p. 63). In 1896, the

French physicist Henri Becquerel discovered that minerals containing uranium gave off rays which were capable of:

- penetrating black paper and blackening a photographic plate.
- producing fluorescence in certain substances (zinc sulfide and barium platinocide).
- "ionizing" air and other gases and discharging on an electroscope.
- passing through plates of metal.

He called these rays "Becquerel rays" and observed that they were similar to X-rays. About two years later, it was discovered that thorium and its compounds possess properties similar to those of uranium and its compounds. The name "radioactivity" was coined and applied to these extraordinary properties.

Madame Curie and her husband, Professor Curie, working with Pitchblende* discovered polonium and by 1910, had isolated a new element which was at least one million times as active as uranium. They called the new element *radium* (Foster and Alyea 1948, p. 295ff).

Thereafter, the development of nuclear technology progressed through refinement of the X-ray, illumination of timepiece dials, development of tracers, treatment of cancers and allied diseases, fission and fusion weapons, and power generation. These developments brought about unprecedented medical advances, saved thousands of lives by significantly shortening World War II, played a major role in the post-World War II industrial miracles, probably prevented World War III, provided potentially the most environmentally benign source of electrical power, and (to the subject of this chapter) saddled the major world powers with nuclear waste management problems of staggering proportions.

Radioactive waste ("radwaste") management is not a new problem. It began with the Manhattan Project** and was recognized, in global terms, during the first conference on Peaceful Uses of Atomic Energy in Geneva in 1955. But environmental concerns with nuclear energy and weapons were focused on the anticipated "nuclear winter" which was expected to follow a nuclear war, testing of nuclear weapons, and fears of accidents at nuclear power generation stations. Meanwhile, the nation accumulated a massive amount of nuclear waste. In 1989, U.S. Department of Energy (DOE) officials spoke of some radwaste sites being so severely contaminated that abandonment as "national sacrifice zones" might be necessary. In following years, DOE representatives have been unwilling to discuss such a concept, but have recently openly discussed levels of cleanup criteria linked to "restricted use" of contaminated sites.

In March 1995, the DOE released the *Environmental Management 1995* report and an executive summary entitled *Estimating the Cold War Mortgage — The 1995 Baseline Environmental Management Report-Executive Summary*. These documents

* Pitchblende is an ore, containing uraninite and uranium (U_3O_8), which is found in Bohemia, a region and former province of Czechoslovakia.

** Technically, the "Manhattan District," a U.S. Army Corps of Engineers unit, was established in 1942 to administer the project that produced the first nuclear bombs.

speak clearly of sites which can be remediated only partially. In several cases, the technology does not exist to achieve even that end. Some of these sites will remain closed to public access; others will be suitable only for restricted use; a few have radioactive contaminants that cannot be removed from groundwater. The entire operation is now expected to require 75 years, and the "mid-range" cost estimate has grown to $230 billion (U.S. DOE 1995a, 1995b).

During the present and next decades, many thousands of engineers, scientists, technicians, administrators, and project managers will be engaged in the radioactive waste cleanup effort. Accordingly, we here devote appropriate space to provide an overview of the problem and the effort to manage it.

Background

How is it possible that the United States could let such a problem grow to such proportions? The history is complex and should not be oversimplified, but four factors seem to stand out.

1. The defense/energy establishment's first priority, for three decades, was the development, production, and modernization of nuclear weapons. The work was carried out behind a wall of secrecy that made it possible for environmental considerations to be "postponed," while weapons imperatives were pursued.
2. The nature of the waste — it is not biodegradable. It is not destroyed by incineration or other conventional treatment techniques. It began accumulating during times in which burial was considered good waste management.

During the first three decades of the nuclear era, scientists, regulators, and promoters of nuclear power tended to view waste management as a technical problem for which modern technology would provide a solution ... It was not until the late 1970s that the federal government allocated substantial funds and personnel to develop a plan for the long-term management of nuclear wastes (League of Women Voters 1985).

---

3. During the 1970s, President Carter, expressing proliferation concerns, imposed bans on commercial reprocessing of spent nuclear fuel rods. The ban had the effect of causing significantly more high-level radwaste to accumulate than would have been the case without the ban. In 1981, President Reagan lifted the ban, but the industry has declined to make the commitment to reprocessing because (1) of uncertainty about future governmental policies regarding reprocessing and (2) uranium is now so cheap that industry cannot afford to reprocess spent fuel rods.
4. As will be discussed, attempts to develop permanent or temporary repositories are hamstrung by public outcry, political power, court decisions, and technical difficulties. Each delay is compounded in further delays, exponentially higher costs, and ever-increasing frustration on the part of all involved.

Table 13.1 Half-Lives of Some Radioisotopes

Radioisotope	Half-Life
Iodine 132	2.4 hours
Rhodium 105	36.0 hours
Xenon 133	5.3 days
Barium 140	12.8 days
Cerium 144	284 days
Cesium 137	30 years
Carbon 14	5,730 years
Uranium 234	250,000 years
Uranium 235	704,000,000 years[a]
Uranium 238	4,470,000,000 years[a]
Helium 4	12,500,000,000 years

[a]Tang and Saling (1990, p. 20).

Source: Enger et al. (1989).

With neither reprocessing capability nor long-term storage and disposal available, the nation's inability to manage high-level, transuranic, and low-level wastes is approaching crisis status. The nation must soon find additional storage space for spent nuclear fuel or begin shutting down nuclear-power-generating facilities. Cleanup operations at the weapons facilities cannot proceed without repositories. The most promising scenario for keeping former Soviet Union warheads out of terrorist hands is to bring the warheads to the United States for demilitarization, but facilities are overburdened with U.S. weapons slated for demilitarization. The numbers and complexities of the issues that attend radwaste management are such that public attitudes and political postures are shaped by fears — legitimate and unfounded. Pasternak (1995) provides an excellent lay-language summary of the DOE's demilitarization/reprocessing vs. environmental management quandry.

The Nature, Effects, and Measurement of Radioactivity

Radioactivity

Some atoms are unstable (radioactive) and undergo a spontaneous decay process, emitting radiation until they reach a stable form. Such atoms are called radioisotopes. The decay process may last from a fraction of a second to billions of years, depending upon the type of atom. The rate of radioactive decay is measured in half-lives, the time required for half the atoms in a sample to spontaneously decay to another form. Table 13.1 shows the variability in half-lives of some atoms.

Nuclear energy is released by the processes of fission and fusion. During fission the nucleus of an atom is split into two smaller nuclei, called fission products, releasing neutrons, radiation, and heat in the process. The released neutrons can cause nearby atoms to split, and if sufficient fissionable material is present, a chain reaction can begin. Such a chain reaction generates heat from the fission process and from the

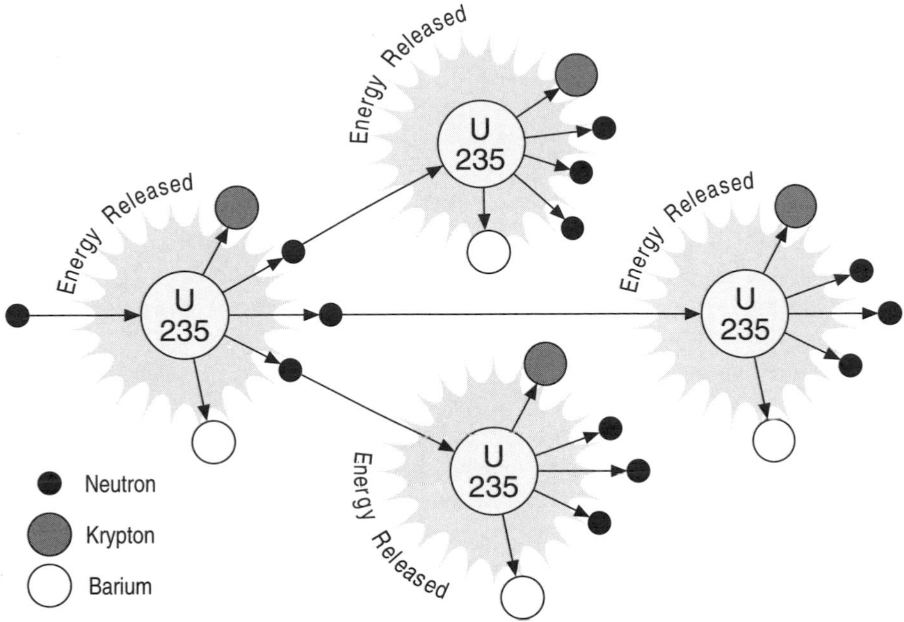

FIGURE 13.1 Schematic of the nuclear fission process. (Adapted from Enger, Eldon D., J. Richard Kormelink, Bradley F. Smith, and Rodney J. Smith, 1989. *Environmental Sciences: The Study of Interrelationships*. Wm. C. Brown Publishers, Dubuque, IA. With permission.)

decay of radioactive products. An uncontrolled nuclear chain reaction can progress to an atomic explosion (Office of Technology Assessment 1985). The fission process is illustrated in Figure 13.1.

The fusion process involves the combination of small atomic nuclei to form more massive nuclei, instability of one or both nuclei, and the simultaneous release of energy. Figure 13.2 illustrates three possible types of fusion.

The fission process is harnessed to provide intense heat for steam generation, which in turn powers turbine generators in a nuclear power facility (Figure 13.3). Both fusion and fission processes are employed in nuclear weapons to create massive uncontrolled chain reactions.

Types of Radiation

The radioactive isotopes found in radwaste emit three types of penetrating ionizing radiation — alpha (α) and beta (β) particles and gamma (γ) rays. Radioactivity is a process in which a nucleus spontaneously disintegrates or "decays," resulting in a release of one or more types of ionizing radiation.* The following are examples of the decay and energy release processes of nuclear reactions:

* Radiation that has enough energy to cause a change in the atomic balance of substances it passes through is called ionizing radiation.

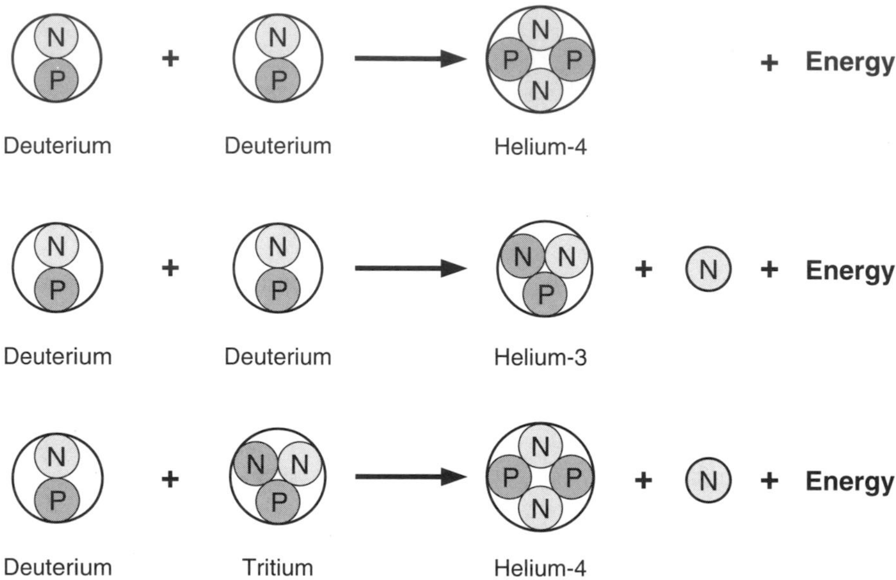

FIGURE 13.2 Schematic of the nuclear fusion process. (Adapted from Enger, Eldon D., J. Richard Kormelink, Bradley F. Smith, and Rodney J. Smith, 1989. *Environmental Sciences: The Study of Interrelationships*. Wm. C. Brown Publishers, Dubuque, IA. With permission.)

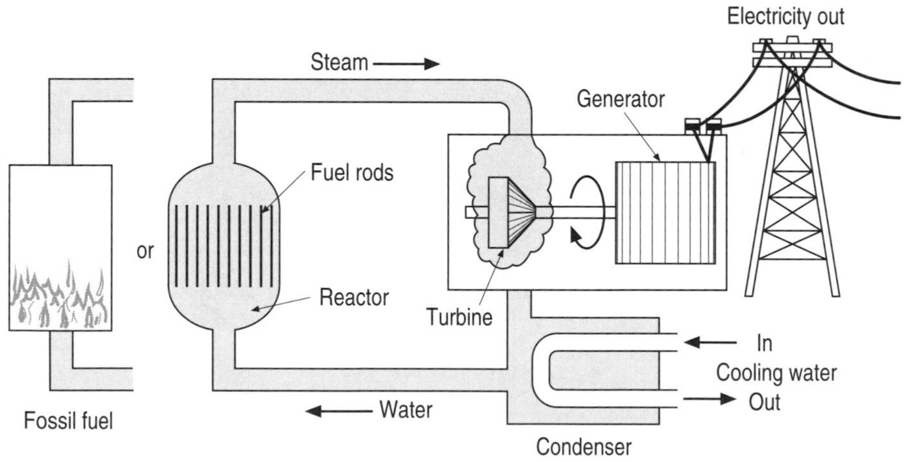

FIGURE 13.3 Schematic of nuclear power generation. (Adapted from Enger, Eldon D., J. Richard Kormelink, Bradley F. Smith, and Rodney J. Smith, 1989. *Environmental Sciences: The Study of Interrelationships*. Wm. C. Brown Publishers, Dubuque, IA. With permission.)

Uranium 238 → Thorium 234 + α particle

Iodine 131 → Xenon 131 + ß particle

Cobalt 60 → Nickel 60 + ß particle + γ ray

Alpha particles are positively charged ions propelled from the nucleus of atoms at about 10% of the speed of light. Alpha radiation is the most energetic (densely ionizing), but the least penetrating type of radiation. An alpha particle can be stopped by a sheet of paper. Alpha particles are unable to penetrate human skin, but can be very harmful if an alpha emitter enters the body by ingestion or inhalation (Ehlers and Steel 1958, p. 490). When an element emits an alpha particle, the product has the properties of an element two places to the left of the parent in the periodic table (Sawyer and McCarty 1978, p. 258).

Beta particles are negatively charged particles moving at velocities ranging from 30 to 99% of the speed of light. They may penetrate human skin, but like alpha particles, their most serious effect is caused by ingestion or inhalation of beta-emitting isotopes (Ehlers and Steel 1958, p. 490). Most fission products in spent-fuel assemblies and reprocessed waste (e.g., iodine 131, cesium 137, and strontium 90) are beta emitters (NCRP 1980, Chapter 2). When an element emits a beta particle, the product has the properties of an element one place to the right of the parent in the periodic table (Sawyer and McCarty 1978, p. 258).

Gamma radiation is a type of electromagnetic energy wave, like X-rays, light, and radio waves. It has the greater penetrating power of the emissions and can pass through relatively thick layers of concrete or metal (Foster and Alyea 1948, p. 299). Gamma radiation can penetrate and damage critical organs in the body. Most fission products are gamma emitters as well as beta emitters (Sawyer and McCarty 1978, p. 266).

Neutrons are composed of high-energy neutral particles, which are released in a nuclear detonation and in laboratory research. Since neutrons have no charge, they can travel long distances in air and other materials and are similar in degree of hazard to gamma radiation (Corbitt 1990, p. 9.87). Fortunately, neutron activity is not normally encountered in waste management operations.

Measurement of Radioactivity

The intensity of radioactivity in a sample is determined by the number of emissions, or disintegrations, per second and is usually measured in curies. The curie (Ci) is the standard unit for this measurement and is based on the amount of radioactivity contained in 1 g of radium. Numerically, 1 Ci is equal to 3.7×10^{10} disintegrations per second. The amounts of radioactivity that people normally work with are in the millicurie (1 thousandth of a curie) or microcurie (1 millionth of a curie) range. Elements with shorter half-lives (e.g., thorium 234 at 24.1 days) are more radioactive than those with longer half-lives (e.g., uranium 238 at 4.5 billion years).

Radiation exposure is measured in rem,* a unit that indicates the amount of radiation received and the biological implications of the exposure. In one year, the average person in the United States is exposed to approximately 160 millirems (thousandths of a rem) of radiation, two thirds of which comes from natural background sources such as mineral ores, cosmic radiation from outer space, and the radioactive carbon and potassium found in most living things. Slightly less than one third of this annual exposure comes from medical sources (i.e., X-rays) (U.S. Office of Technology Assessment 1985, pp. 21–23).

Human Health Effects of Exposure to Radiation

Radiation is converted to other forms of energy when it is absorbed by matter. Because of this energy conversion, damage occurs at a cellular, tissue, organ, or organism level when organisms are irradiated. Radiation effects on man are classified as *somatic* or *genetic*. Somatic effects are those which cause damage to the exposed individual and include anemia, fatigue, loss of hair, cataracts, skin damage, and cancer. Genetic effects include inheritable changes resulting from mutations in reproductive cells (Sawyer and McCarty 1978, p. 266). The degree and kind of damage varies with the kind and amount of radiation, the duration of the exposure, and the particular type of cells irradiated.

Ingestion and inhalation are frequent forms of chronic exposure. Several historic cases provide classic examples:

- Madame Curie was felled by cancer, at the age of 47, due to her exposure while working with radioactive substances. Irene Joliet-Curie, who continued her mother's research, also died with cancer at age 59.
- Workers in clock factories, during the period of 1915–1935, painted the numerals and hands with fluorescent radium to give them night visibility. The workers twirled the paint brushes on their tongues to provide a very sharp point. The workers experienced very high incidences of bone sarcoma and carcinomas of the head and paranasal sinuses (National Academy of Sciences 1972, p. 126ff). (*See also* Martland 1929)
- The high incidence of lung cancer among uranium miners has been widely reported and documented. The incidence is most strongly associated with miners having the highest exposure to radon and radon daughters, and who are also cigarette smokers (National Academy of Sciences 1972, p. 146).

An acute radiation dose — 50 rems or more over a 24-hour period — results in radiation sickness within one hour to several weeks. The chance of death is nearly 100% from a dose greater than 1000 rems, 90 to 100% from 600 to 1000 rems, and 50% from 400 rems. Survival is almost certain if the dose is 200 rems or less.

* *Rem* — 10 CFR 20.1004 defines the rem as "a measure of the dose of any ionizing radiation to body tissues in terms of its estimated biological effect relative to a dose of one roentgen of X-rays." In more practical terms, a rem is the amount of radiation that is required to produce the same biological effect as one roentgen of gamma or X-radiation. (For further discussion, *see* Sawyer and McCarty 1978, p. 259; Corbitt 1990, p. 9.87; Meyer 1989, p. 480.)

Other consequences range from gastrointestinal and circulatory system disorders to long-term effects such as cancer, birth abnormalities, genetic defects, and poor general health. Long-term effects also result from chronic exposure to low-level radiation. In radioactive waste disposal, the concern centers on the possibility of such chronic low-level exposure caused by releases of radioactive waste (U.S. Office of Technology Assessment 1985, p. 21). (*See also* Miller and Majumdar 1985; Tang and Saling 1990, Chapter 2)

Radiation Protection

A basic understanding of the nature of radioactivity and protection of human health and the environment from adverse impacts of radioactivity is a major thrust of this chapter. But we shall devote only limited time and space, under this heading, to the topic of protection. As we shall shortly see, there are actually *four* types of radioactive waste and four separate and distinct radioactive waste management problems. Each has its own set of standards, regulations, and practices, including waste management.

A few concepts and principles apply to all or most of the four types. We now take up those concepts.

Permissible Dose Concepts and Applications

In 1964, the International Commission on Radiological Protection (ICRP) defined "permissible dose" as

> that dose, accumulated over a long period of time, or resulting from a single exposure which, in the light of present knowledge, carries a negligible probability of severe somatic or genetic injuries. Furthermore it is such a dose that any effects that ensue more frequently are limited to those of a minor nature that would be considered unacceptable by the exposed individual and by competent medical authorities.

Occupational groups are limited by 10 CFR 20 to permissible doses per year, as follows:

- Total effective dose equivalent (TEDE) 5 rems
- Any organ other than the lens of the eye 50 rems
- Hands and forearms; feet and ankles 50 rems
- Skin of the whole body 50 rems

The general population is provided a higher level of protection by an annual limit of 0.1 rem.

The ALARA Concept

In 1975, the U.S. Nuclear Regulatory Commission (NRC) published Regulatory Guide 8.8, entitled *Information Relevant to Assuring That Occupational Radiation*

Exposures at Nuclear Power Plants Will Be As Low As Reasonably Achievable, or ALARA. The concept is based upon the assumption that the relationship between dose and biological effect is linear and that no threshold effect is involved. The 1977 revision provides the ALARA philosophy as follows:

1. Merely controlling the maximum dose to the individual is not sufficient; the collective dose to the group (measured in person-rems) must be kept as low as is reasonably achievable.
2. "Reasonably achievable" is judged by considering the state of technology and the economics of improvement in relation to all of the benefits from these improvements.
3. Under the linear, nonthreshold concept, restricting the doses to individuals at a fraction of the applicable limit would be inappropriate if such action would result in the exposure of more persons to radiation and would increase the total person-rem dose (Tang and Saling 1990, p. 41).

(*See also* Sabo 1985; Berlin and Stanton 1989, pp. 79–84)

Pathways of Dispersion and Human Exposure

To the extent that radioactive particles enter the human body by ingestion (i.e., eating, drinking, and breathing), it is necessary to isolate the source of radioactivity or to render it harmless. Account must be taken of all pathways to humans, including ingestion of water, food crops, milk, and fauna (e.g., livestock, fish); direct and indirect exposure to radioactive materials; and background (natural) exposure.

The impact potential of a release of radioactive materials is measured in terms of the concentration and release rate to a dispersion pathway. The seriousness of a release depends upon a number of factors:

- The initial concentration of radionuclides in the source material. Greater concentrations can be subjected to greater dispersion and remain at dangerous levels.
- The physical form of the matrix in the waste stream in which the radionuclides are bound. Considerable variation in emission rate occurs due to moisture content, density, permeability, particle size, etc.
- The nature and intensity of the release mechanism. Atmospheric releases tend to be more mobile and to be dispersed rapidly. Surface water releases may be channeled and diluted or impounded. Groundwater releases may be slowly but broadly dispersed.

The nuclear fuel cycle, diagrammed in Figure 13.4, illustrates a dispersion pathway by which radionuclides may reach the human population. Each process, movement, or use of the material embodies actual or potential release(s) of radioisotopes. [*See* Berlin and Stanton (1989, Chapter 4) for a detailed discussion of the mobilization and dispersion of radioactive waste sources.]

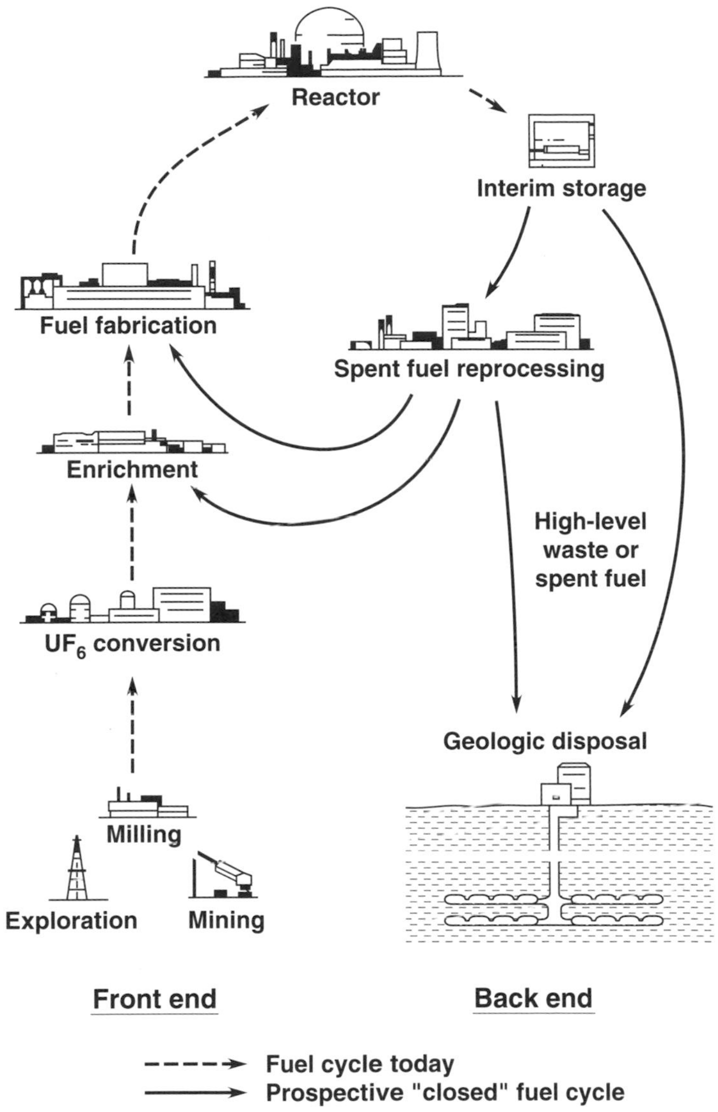

FIGURE 13.4 Schematic of the nuclear fuel cycle (EPA).

Physical Protection

Radioactive material having a short half-life may be stored, if properly shielded and isolated, until it decays to an acceptable level. If in solution, the material may be diluted below the maximum permissible concentration (MPC) and treated or stored. Materials having longer half-lives require long-term storage in deep repositories. These requirements are overviewed in subsequent sections of this chapter.

Protection against external radiation exposure of the body requires consideration of three factors: distance, time, and shielding. Distance between the source and receptor humans should be maximized, time of exposure should be minimized, and shielding should be provided by the greatest density and thickness of shielding material that is practicable.

Radiological Monitoring Programs

Radiological monitoring is conducted at radwaste facilities to verify that there is no unacceptable migration of pollutants through pathways that could lead to man. The monitoring is necessary to ensure that safe working conditions are maintained for onsite employees,and that safe environmental conditions are maintained for the general public. Monitoring programs are also designed and operated to:

- assess the level of impact of site operations on the environment and the public.
- determine if the site is in compliance with applicable regulations, standards, and performance objectives.
- enable timely detection of migration.
- enable long-term predictions of waste isolation capabilities that will be important in the post-closure period for the site.
- establish a database for use in the design of future waste disposal sites and monitoring programs.
- evaluate the effectiveness of effluent control measures and equipment.

A facility radiological monitoring program has three components:

1. Baseline monitoring prior to facility construction is conducted to document the concentration of radionuclides in the soil, water, air, and biota prior to disturbance of the land.
2. Environmental monitoring at the site boundaries and adjacent to the site is conducted to detect any changes from baseline conditions. Monitoring parameters are those pertinent to the radioactive materials, chemically toxic substances, and leachate indicators managed at the site.
3. Effluent monitoring is designed to determine concentrations and release rates of the gaseous and liquid effluents that are released by the facility. The data is used to assess (1) the effectiveness of control systems and engineered barriers in preventing releases and (2) compliance with environmental regulations.

In addition, radiation safety monitoring programs, including external radiation surveys, airborne radiation surveys, and internal radiation monitoring, are conducted to measure radiation rates and exposure indicators throughout the facility and among workers (Berlin and Stanton 1989, Chapter 4) (*See also* Jester and Yu 1985; Tang and Saling 1990, Chapter 2)

Regulatory Structures

Historical Development of Policies and Statutes

In the previous section, we noted that four different classifications of radioactive wastes present separate and distinct management problems and are regulated accordingly. The four are:

1. High-level waste (HLW)
2. Transuranic waste (TRU)
3. Low-level waste (LLW)
4. Uranium mine and mill tailings

Although the four "levels" of radwaste are regulated separately, a general view regarding responsibility prevailed in Congress and among the states during the early years of the nuclear era. That view was to the effect that, due to the long half-lives of some radwaste constituents, only the most durable and permanent of institutions can be counted upon to carry out the continuing responsibilities associated with radwaste management. Accordingly, the task was assigned to governments — federal and state (Gehr 1990). That view was reflected in the 1982 Nuclear Waste Policy Act (NWPA) assignment of responsibility for management of HLW to the federal agencies. Hindsight, and the experience of other countries, raises substantial questions regarding the wisdom of that policy:

> Foreign nuclear utilities generally have more responsibility for waste disposal than their American counterparts. Proponents of this approach believe that placing the burden of implementing waste disposal solutions on the waste producers may encourage better managerial and financial accountability for the program (U.S. GAO 1994, p. 12).

Nevertheless, the original concerns regarding security of materials that can be converted to weaponry remain as valid now as in 1982. It remains to be seen how effectively the other countries' security systems will perform with respect to controlling materials adaptable to weaponry.

Much of the TRU is generated by military programs. The management of TRU has thus evolved as a federal government program.

Management of LLW was originally assigned to the Atomic Energy Commission (AEC), but growing concerns on the part of the states wherein storage was taking place moved Congress, in 1959, to amend the basic legislation. The new legislation authorized states to enter into agreements with the AEC to regulate LLW under regulations and standards set by the AEC. As a result, existing LLW disposal sites are licensed and regulated by host states, since all are in "agreement states." Any proposed site in nonagreement states would be regulated by the federal government.

In 1980, Congress passed new LLW legislation mandating decentralized responsibility, making the disposal of commercial LLW a state responsibility. States were free to build their own dump sites or could form regional compacts with the approval of Congress to establish burial sites. The legislation provided for refusal by regional groups to accept waste from noncompact states after 1985 (Friedman 1985).

After years of no management, Congress in 1978 assigned responsibility for management of uranium mill tailings piles to the DOE. These responsibilities are discussed further in the following sections.

Statutory and Regulatory Framework

The NWPA, as amended in 1987 by the Nuclear Waste Policy Act Amendments (NWPAA), establishes the framework and assigns responsibility for management of HLW. The two acts:

- assign responsibility for accepting and disposing of waste from privately owned reactors in the United States to the DOE.
- establish a schedule for the siting, construction, and operation of an HLW repository.
- authorize the DOE to site, construct, and operate one monitored retrievable storage (MRS) facility.
- authorize the DOE to develop a system for transporting high-level nuclear waste to an MRS facility and repository.
- define the working and decisionmaking relationships between the federal and state governments and the Indian tribes.
- require the establishment of a fund to cover nuclear waste disposal costs (U.S. GAO 1993).

The original provisions for HLW repositories, contained in NWPA, were amended to consider only the Yucca Mountain, NV site as the first geologic repository. The original act also called for a MRS facility at Oak Ridge, TN. The amendment canceled the Oak Ridge siting proposal and established an MRS Review Commission to evaluate the need for the MRS (Tang and Saling 1990, Chapter 1). These delays in bringing both temporary and permanent disposal facilities to operational status, and the resultant accumulations of HLW, have been the source of great concern and controversy.

The U.S. Environmental Protection Agency (EPA) is charged with responsibility to develop and promulgate environmental standards for protection of public health and the environment from radioactive materials. Such standards may include limits on radiation exposures to workers and members of the general public and concentrations or quantities of radioactive materials in uncontrolled areas (Berlin and Stanton 1989, pp. 79–80).

The NRC and DOE regulate radiation control within, and in areas affected by, facilities which they license or operate. The DOE regulates the activities of contractors at the weapons-related facilities.

Regulatory responsibilities for radwaste are shared by the NRC, EPA, and U.S. Department of Transportation (DOT). The NRC regulates and licenses all waste handling/processing and disposal activities. The EPA sets standards for exposure of the general public to radiation and reviews impact statements for major projects. The

DOT establishes packaging, marking, and labeling standards; sets qualifications for carrier personnel; and monitors transportation. (*See also* U.S. Office of Technology Assessment 1985, Chapters 4 and 5)

Department of Energy Management of Cleanup Programs

The Energy Reorganization Act of 1974 abolished the AEC and transferred the agency's waste management and remedial action functions to the DOE. The DOE retained many of AEC's personnel, policies, priorities, and attitudes. By 1988, the DOE was generally discredited with regard to attitudes and progress toward environmental responsibilities. Although the focus was upon the major weapons facilities, all DOE operations having to do with cleanup and waste management were under congressional scrutiny. In January 1989, President Bush nominated retired Admiral James D. Watkins as Secretary of Energy. Watkins, a veteran of Admiral Hyman Rickover's nuclear navy programs, brought organizational and technical skills to bear and began the difficult process of refocusing the DOE from weapons production to cleanup of the sites. The following years were characterized by a top to bottom overhaul and shakeup of the agency. Although the environmental management program has focused and achieved some order and problem-solving ability, budget, administrative, political, and technical problems continue to hamstring the cleanup program, including the repository projects.

High-Level Radioactive Waste Management

HLW Defined and Described

The NRC description of HLW includes spent fuel from reactors in civilian power-generating plants, naval propulsion units, and obsolete nuclear weapons; the highly concentrated wastes from reprocessing fuel rods; and the solids generated in fuel reprocessing. This classification is frequently divided into "commercial" and "defense" subcategories. However, Goranson (1978) asserts:

> Separation of high-level wastes into 'commercial' and 'defense' has meaning only to the technologist concerned about specific chemical composition (acid vs. neutralized waste) and heat generation. The public and the media use the terms interchangeably.

HLW Treatment and Disposal

From the earliest days of the nuclear era, development and implementation of suitable treatment and disposal for radwastes have lagged their production. The evolution of scientific and engineering knowledge has brought about several alternative concepts, including deep geologic repositories, ocean disposal, disposal in thick Antarctic ice, disposal in deep space, and highly theoretical transmutation schemes. Prior to 1970, the United States disposed of much of the generated HLW in the ocean. The United States and other nations had placed 90,000 barrels of radioactive waste on the ocean floor when a moratorium halted this practice in 1970. Other nations have continued the practice in disregard of several international agreements and conventions (*see* Chapter 7).

Reprocessing has been proven technically feasible for significant reduction of the quantities of HLW that are otherwise destined for disposal. As noted earlier, reprocessing of commercial spent nuclear fuel (SNF) was halted in 1977 by President Carter, primarily because of concerns regarding control of plutonium and the proliferation of nuclear weapons. Reprocessing of military SNF continues at three sites. Reprocessing is not, however, a panacea. It is very costly, produces large volumes of TRU, and is a major source of HLW (Tang and Saling 1990, p. 6, 47). Nevertheless, France, Germany, and Japan have proceeded with reprocessing SNF and apparently intend to continue the practice.

As noted earlier, the NWPA, enacted in 1982, and the 1987 amendments have focused on the design, site selection, and construction of an HLW repository. The 1987 amendments added provision for a MRS facility, but conditioned construction of the MRS upon NRC authorization for construction of the permanent repository. Repository construction was expected to require six years, but public opposition, disapproval of the project by the state of Nevada and subsequent legal maneuvering, a large number of technical difficulties, and inadequate funding have delayed the project. In 1989, the DOE announced a schedule to begin operating the MRS in 1998 and the repository in 2010. The DOE schedule incorrectly assumed that a site would be found for the MRS and that the NRC license would be issued in time to maintain that schedule. The U.S. General Accounting Office (GAO) now estimates that, if the present pace continues, it is unlikely that the repository will begin operation until 2007, and possibly not before 2014 (U.S. GAO 1993, p. 28).

Meanwhile, HLW must be stored in safe, secure facilities. The DOE is attempting to safely store 396,000 m^3 of previously generated HLW. Liquid HLW is stored in tanks and buried in drums at various DOE facilities and leakage has reached disastrous proportions at some DOE sites. The agency's environmental management (EM) program is responsible for identifying and reducing risks and for managing wastes at 137 sites in 34 states. The amount of waste generated will increase as weapons are dismantled, facilities are disassembled and remediated, and contaminated sites are restored (U.S. DOE 1994a, pp. 1–5).

HLW, including spent fuel rods, must be rendered immobile and insoluble prior to disposal. Liquid HLW may be subjected to one of a number of calcination processes that produce a reduced-volume, stable, dry solid. The calcined material may then be incorporated into a molten glass mixture and solidified. Other wastes may be immobilized in the borosilicate glass as well (U.S. DOE 1994b, p. 23ff).

Nuclear power plants in the United States have stored spent fuel rods removed from their reactor cores in water pools at the power generation sites. Water is a convenient storage medium because it is inexpensive, available, can cool by natural circulation, provides shielding from radiation, and provides visibility for handling. Most utilities are nearing storage capacity and are insisting that the DOE has a statutory and contractual responsibility to accept the wastes in 1998.

The DOE is examining a variety of options for operating an above-ground temporary storage facility, including multi-purpose canisters for transportation, storage, and disposal of spent fuel rods (*Environment Reporter*, June 3, 1994, p. 237).

SNF assemblies must be disassembled in concrete "hot" cells that provide shielding of workers. The fuel rods will be consolidated in canisters and stored while decay processes reduce heating, after which they will be placed in 200-ton (empty) casks for disposal. (*See also* Organization for Economic Co-operation and Development 1984; U.S. Office of Technology Assessment 1985, Chapter 3; League of Women Voters 1993, pp. 21–23; Nebel and Wright 1993, Chapter 22); U.S. GAO 1994)

Transuranic Waste Management

TRU Defined and Described

TRU elements are those having atomic numbers greater than 92 (i.e., having more protons than uranium). TRU waste is defined in the United States as radwaste that is not classified as HLW, but contains an activity of more than 100 nCi/g from alpha-emitting TRU isotopes having half-lives greater than 20 years (Tang and Saling 1990, p. 173). TRU waste typically includes metal tools, gloves, lab coats, rags, scrap, equipment, debris, etc. contaminated with plutonium during laboratory and facility operations (U.S. DOE 1994c, p. 0036P). Much of the TRU contains reprocessing residues, solvents, and other organics which cause it to meet the definition of a Resource Conservation and Recovery Act (RCRA) "mixed waste." As such, TRU is subject to EPA regulations with respect to treatment and disposal.

TRU waste may contain sufficiently high concentrations of gamma-emitting nuclides that remote handling is necessary.* Most TRU wastes contain primarily alpha-emitters and, when packaged, are safe for contact handling.* Nevertheless, great care must be taken to avoid damage to containers because of the dangers of ingestion of spilled or leaked alpha-emitters. Since TRU wastes, by definition, have long half-lives, the most suitable method for disposal is isolation in geologic repositories.

TRU Disposal

Prior to 1970, large, but imprecisely known, quantities of TRU wastes were buried at various sites owned by the federal government. Since 1974, TRU waste has been stored in steel, concrete, or wooden boxes on surface storage pads (Tang and Saling 1990, Chapter 5). The DOE acknowledges that TRU wastes are presently stored at ten sites, primarily in Washington, Idaho, New Mexico, and South Carolina (U.S. DOE 1995b).

The Waste Isolation Pilot Plant. In 1979 Congress authorized studies and development operations preliminary to construction of the Waste Isolation Pilot Plant (WIPP). The facility was to be constructed in the Salado Formation, near Carlsbad, NM, if the early investigative and planning phases showed that the project was feasible. This 3000-ft-thick rock salt formation is in a seismically stable area and is devoid of circulating groundwater. The facility was designated "a research and development facility to demonstrate the safe disposal of radwaste resulting from the

* This dichotomy has given rise to still another classification: contact-handled (CH) TRU has sufficient restrictions on radioactive content and packaging that personnel can work in the immediate vicinity without shielding; remote-handled (RH) TRU requires nearby personnel to be shielded.

defense activities and programs of the U.S. exempted from regulation by the NRC." The intent was to provide a laboratory for demonstration and validation of disposal of defense radwastes in salt formations. The project was to have begun radioactive waste operations in October 1988 (Khareis 1990).

As the operational date approached, a variety of delays caused the 1988 startup date to be missed, and the schedule continues to recede further into the future. As noted earlier, the refocusing effort at the DOE is having a positive effect, but problems continue to impede progress. Some examples at WIPP are:

1. The TRU wastes, having biodegradable content, including organic solvents and refuse, are RCRA mixed waste and must meet the requirements of 40 CFR 191. The deposited wastes are to be contained in 55-gallon drums; they will be backfilled by "blown-in" granular salt to absorb any gases that may be released from the drums. DOE officials petitioned the EPA for a variance from the RCRA requirement for venting so that the test phase could proceed. The petition was opposed by local environmentalists. EPA representatives and a National Academy of Science review panel agreed that the test phase should go forward. The issue now awaits submission of a 40 CFR 268 "No Migration Variance" petition by the DOE to EPA and the EPA's response to the petition. The DOE was to have submitted the petition in May 1995. The expectation is that the EPA will issue the variance approximately two years later.
2. Several aspects of the project required resolution by Congress. The Bureau of Land Management (BLM) land had to be transferred to the DOE. Funding for state construction of roads and other facilities was to be appropriated. A bill to accomplish those ends failed in 1989 and was not brought to the floor in 1990. Congress passed the Waste Isolation Plant Land Withdrawal Act (WIPP LWA) in 1992. In addition to accomplishing the necessary land withdrawl, the act required the EPA to promulgate specific criteria for determination if the facility complies with the EPA's generic HLW and TRU waste disposal standards. The EPA proposed the criteria in January 1995; the approval process is expected to require approximately one year, and the earliest date that WIPP could begin accepting waste is now said to be June 1998 (*Environment Reporter*, January 20, 1995, p. 1798).

If the project continues in the original format, the DOE hopes to demonstrate that TRU waste can be safely stored in a deep-bedded salt formation 2150 ft below ground surface. If the demonstration is successful, the WIPP will be operated as a repository for an additional 20 years. Figure 13.5 is a schematic showing the configuration of the shafts, tunnels, and storage areas of the WIPP. The scientific knowledge that is expected to result from WIPP will greatly enhance knowledge of management technology for safe handling and storage of radioactive wastes. (*See also* Berlin and Stanton 1989, pp. 107–110; U.S. DOE 1994a, pp. 35–37 and 1994c, p. 0036P).

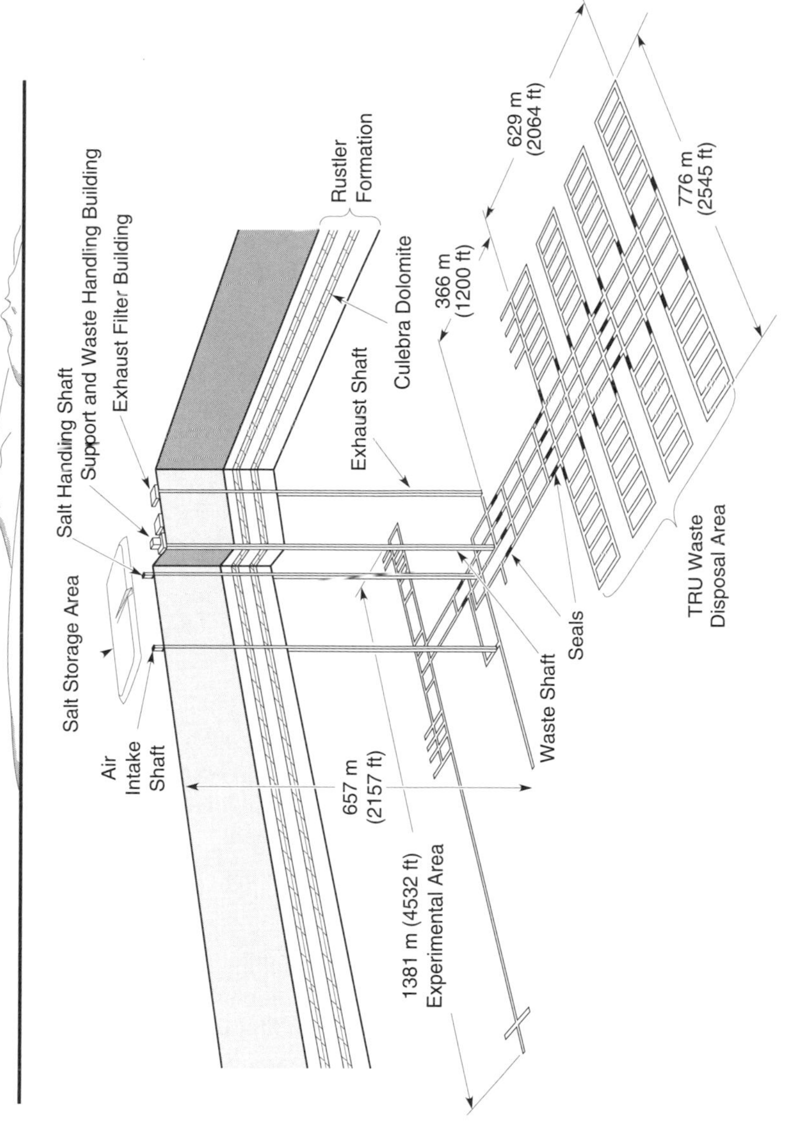

FIGURE 13.5 Schematic of the configuration of the WIPP (DOE).

Table 13.2 NRC Waste Classification System Maximum Radionuclide Concentration (μCi/cc) or (Ci/m³)

Radionuclide	Class A	Class B	Class C
H-3	40	MC	—
Co-60	700	MC	—
Ni-63	3.5	70	700
Ni-63 (in activated metal)	35	700	7,000
Sr-90	0.04	150	7,000
Cs-137	1	44	4,600
C-14	0.8	—	8
C-14 (in activated metal)	8	—	80
Ni-59 (in activated metal)	22	—	220
Nb-94 (in activated metal)	0.02	—	0.2
Tc-99	0.3	—	3
I-129	0.008	—	0.08
Total all radionuclides with <5 year half-life	700	MC	—
Alpha-emitting TRU with half-life >5 years	10*		100*
Pu-241	350*		3,500*
Cm-242	2,000*		20,000*

Note: MC = maximum concentration (all waste above Class A limit is Class B). — = no limit is applicable for this class. * = units are nanocuries/gram (nCi/g).

Source: Adapted from Dornsife (1985) and 10 CFR 61.55.

Low-Level Waste Management

LLW Defined and Classified

LLWs are defined by the Low-Level Radioactive Waste Policy Act (LLRWPA) as "radioactive waste not classified as high-level waste, transuranic waste, spent nuclear fuel, or mill tailings." LLW often contains small amounts of radioactivity dispersed in large amounts of material. It is generated by uranium enrichment processes, reactor operations, isotope production, and medical and research activities. The 1980 LLRPA assigned responsibility for management of this category of waste to the states, authorizes states to enter into compacts for the development of regional disposal facilities, and provided statutory authority for states to refuse acceptance of wastes generated outside their regional borders after 1986. By 1984, it became evident that no new disposal facilities would be available by 1986. In an effort to establish a sense of urgency among states, Congress enacted the Low-Level Radioactive Waste Policy Amendments Act of 1985, requiring states and compacts to comply with strict timetables for establishing LLW disposal sites (U.S. DOE 1994c, p. 0186P).

LLW is defined so broadly that some waste streams may meet the definition, but contain some radionuclides which may not be suitable for disposal in near-surface facilities. Accordingly, the NRC has developed a classification scheme which is implemented by 10 CFR 61. The classifications are summarized in Table 13.2.

Treatment and Disposal of LLW

The general nature of LLW includes items and materials incidental to, and contaminated during, radwaste handling, including dry trash, plastics, paper, glass, clothing, discarded tools and equipment, wet sludges, and organic liquids (Tang and Saling 1990, p. 195).

Some forms of LLW may be concentrated by evaporation, crystallization, and drying. Some may be amenable to incineration, calcination, or compaction. Much of the waste goes directly to near-surface land disposal. Class B and C wastes receive deeper burial, more cover, and/or incremental protection.

By 1994, only two sites — Barnwell, SC and Richland, WA — were accepting LLW, and in June 1994 Barnwell closed to contributors other than the Southeast Compact states. Moreover, Barnwell is to close to compact states by the end of 1995, and the replacement facility in North Carolina will not be ready to accept LLW until mid-1997 (*Environment Reporter*, September 23, 1994). The compacts, member states, and host states are presently aligned as indicated in Table 13.3.

Siting of LLW disposal facilities is proving to be as difficult as the HLW and TRU waste siting has been. The Ward Valley site in southeastern California is a case in point. The site is intended to serve the Southwest Compact for 30 years. In July 1992, California, host state for the Southwest Compact, applied to then-Interior Secretary Manuel Lujan to purchase the site from the BLM. In August 1993, newly appointed Secretary Bruce Babbitt notified Governor Pete Wilson that he proposed selling the land to California based upon the outcome of narrowly focused public hearings. In September 1993, the California Department of Health Services (DHS) issued a disposal facility operating license for the Ward Valley site to U.S. Geology, the contractor retained by the state for initial work on the site. This would normally have triggered construction of the site.

One month after the license was issued, Senator Barbara Boxer of California announced that an unreviewed report (the "Wilshire report") by three U.S. Geological Survey (USGS) geologists "found 'significant potential' for radioactive contamination of the groundwater and eventual contamination of the Colorado River." Both DHS and U.S. Ecology took strong issue with the report, noting that it had not been subjected to the normal internal USGS review process and that the authors had relied upon faulty and incomplete information to support their conclusions.

In October 1993, opponents filed two lawsuits claiming that improper procedures had been followed in the issuance of the operating license and that the Wilshire report provided significant new evidence showing the unsuitability of the Ward Valley site. Shortly thereafter, Secretary Babbitt notified the governor that he was "postponing further action pending final resolution of the litigation." In February 1994, Senator Boxer reiterated her request to Secretary Babbitt that "the work of the three USGS geologists be expanded and subjected to a thorough and objective scientific review." DHS retained environmental consultants who reviewed the technical data and concluded that contamination of the Colorado River by releases from the Ward Valley site would be "impossible." Secretary Babbitt then asked the National Academy of Sciences (NAS) to review the issues raised in the Wilshire report. The NAS report is expected to be completed in the spring of 1995.

Table 13.3 Low-Level Radioactive Waste Disposal Compact Membership

Compact	Host State	Member State(s)
Northeast	Connecticut	New Jersey
Appalachia	Pennsylvania	West Virginia
		Maryland
		Delaware
Southeast	South Carolina[a]	Florida
	North Carolina[b]	Georgia
		Tennessee
		Alabama
		Mississippi
		Virginia
Central states	Nebraska	Arkansas
		Louisiana
		Kansas
		Oklahoma
Midwest	Ohio	Wisconsin
		Indiana
		Iowa
		Minnesota
		Missouri
Central Midwest	Illinois	Kentucky
Rocky Mountain[c]		Nevada
		Colorado
		New Mexico
Southwest	California	Arizona
		North Dakota
		South Dakota
Northwest	Washington	Idaho
		Oregon
		Utah
		Alaska
		Hawaii
		Montana
		Wyoming
Texas	Texas	Maine
		Vermont

Unaligned — New Hampshire, New York, Massachusetts, Rhode Island, Puerto Rico, District of Columbia, Michigan

[a] Current host state.

[b] Future Host state.

[c] Northwest accepts Rocky Mountain LLW per agreement between compacts.

Source: Adapted from Dornsife (1985) and 10 CFR 61.55.

Meanwhile, in May 1994, the Superior Court combined the two lawsuits and dismissed all of the allegations except one, ruling that DHS should reexamine the licensing decision in the light of the Wilshire report. The matter now awaits a California Supreme Court Decision.

Further impediments grow from concerns for the Desert Tortoise, a threatened species. U.S. Ecology and a Desert Tortoise Task Force submitted a plan to the U.S. Fish and Wildlife Service (USFWS) in 1990 to mitigate impacts of the site on the tortoise. The plan includes installation of several miles of tortoise-proof fencing along Interstate 40 to eliminate road kills, which is the leading cause of mortality for tortoises in the northern portion of Ward Valley. The plan was expected to more than compensate for the loss of the 80 acres that would be used for the LLW facility. The USFWS received the mitigation plan favorably, but two organizations sued the agency to force creation of a critical habitat for the tortoise. In February 1994, the USFWS designated a critical habitat that included land in which the proposed disposal site was located. The decision will require DHS to seek another biological opinion from USFWS. Because the site is now located within a critical habitat, the EPA and several other federal agencies must be consulted.

The NAS, which had been asked by Secretary Babbitt to review the *geological* issues raised in the Wilshire report, has now entered objections that the habitat should not be fragmented by projects like the Ward Valley disposal facility. Project opponents, who have threatened to sue the Department of the Interior if it transfers the land to DHS for the facility, are expected to argue that the NAS opinions constitute "new information" requiring reevaluation under the California Environmental Quality Act and the National Environmental Policy Act (summarized from DOE news releases of July 18, 1994 and January 16, 1995). Meanwhile, LLW generators within the Southwest Compact must continue to store their wastes onsite.

Uranium Mine and Mill Tailings Management

Tailings Defined, Described, and Characterized

Uranium mine tailings usually consist of waste rock and low-grade ores which may be piled near or in the mine or may be used in construction of the mill tailings pond(s). The uranium mine tailings generally contain low levels of radioactive materials, are considered to be subject to the Bevill Amendment,* and have not been brought under RCRA control.

Uranium mill tailings are the sandy residue of the uranium extraction processes. Much of the ore contains less than 1% uranium, so that extraction produces large volumes of bulky wastes. Estimates place the waste-to-product ratio at 1300:1. After extraction of the uranium, the tailings contain other natural radionuclides such as thorium 230, radium 226, and radon 222. The tailings are discharged, in a slurry, to a basin or impoundment where the solids are retained behind a manmade dam. The liquid overflows or is pumped to a waste treatment facility where the radium is coprecipitated with barium sulfate (Hare and Aikin 1984).

* *See* Bevill Amendment in Glossary.

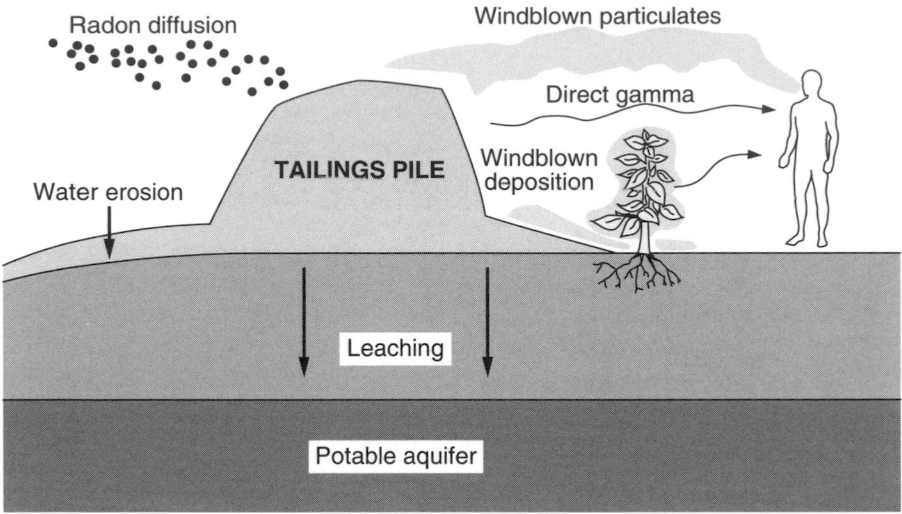

FIGURE 13.6 Schematic of the potential exposure pathways originating in uranium mill tailings piles. (Adapted from Enger, Eldon D., J. Richard Kormelink, Bradley F. Smith, and Rodney J. Smith, 1989. *Environmental Sciences: The Study of Interrelationships*. Wm. C. Brown Publishers, Dubuque, IA. With permission.)

The tailings have accumulated in huge piles in several uranium-producing areas of the United States and Canada. The piles have been poorly controlled and, where control has not been established, are acknowledged to constitute a health and environmental hazard (Figure 13.6). Where control has not been established, the remaining radionuclides are subject to dispersion in wind-blown tailings, and the remaining radium is leached from the piles by rainfall. The effectiveness of remediation efforts has not been convincingly demonstrated. Seepage from the piles may contain radium in concentrations exceeding criteria. Radium is easily taken up by plants and ingested by animals. The pathway to humans via these introductions to the food chain can be direct or short. Figure 13.6 is a schematic showing pathways of migration from a uranium mill tailings pile.

Treatment and Control

The uranium industry grew rapidly during the early days of the nuclear era, and large numbers of tailings piles were generated. However, the expected growth in nuclear power generation failed to materialize, and many of the mills closed. At the peak of the domestic industry, 28 uranium mills were operating. All are now closed and many were abandoned. Abandoned (and uncontrolled) tailings piles became numerous. When present in populated areas, the tailings present a potential long-term health hazard because they emit small amounts of radon gas and contain other radioactive contaminants that can pollute groundwater (U.S. DOE 1994c). During the nearly three decades of the existence of the AEC, the officials of the commission claimed that the AEC had no jurisdiction to assert control over tailings management.

The Uranium Mill Tailings Radiation Control Act of 1978 (UMTRA) made the DOE responsible for management of the tailings piles at 24 inactive sites in 10 states where uranium was produced for the national defense programs. Remedial actions taken at these sites are site specific and hinge upon the requirement that the site and surrounding areas comply with EPA standards. Actions taken range from stabilization onsite, to removal of the tailings for stabilization onsite, to removal of the tailings for stabilization elsewhere. By the end of 1993, remedial actions had been completed at 11 sites, and cleanup was underway or scheduled at the remaining sites (U.S. DOE 1994c).

In January 1995, the EPA issued new disposal and cleanup standards which may enable the DOE to accelerate the schedule and reduce some remediation costs. The new standards allow for some aspects of cleanup criteria to be avoided if the affected groundwater is not a current source or expected to be a source within the next 100 years or if the water (groundwater quality) would be expected to restore itself naturally (*Environment Reporter*, January 13, 1995. p. 1751).

Tailings were used in construction and as backfill around building foundations in several Colorado, Utah, New Mexico, and Idaho communities. Persons living and working in the buildings were exposed to radon gas concentrations exceeding maximum allowable levels for uranium miners. Some 13,555 potential cleanup sites were originally surveyed to determine if they were contaminated. More than 5000 of the 5199 properties found to be contaminated had been remediated by the end of 1993.

Uranium mill tailings were dispersed in other ways that endangered human health. Several disastrous failures of tailings dams allowed tailings to be washed into streams. Mine and mill owners were required to retrieve the tailings, but the effectiveness of the cleanup is questionable. (*See also* Rustum 1982; Tang and Saling 1990, Chapter 7; League of Women Voters 1993; U.S. DOE 1994a)

TOPICS FOR REVIEW OR DISCUSSION

1. The text discusses four types of radiation, three of which may be of concern in managing radioactive waste. One type probably will not be encountered on a radioactive waste site. Discuss.
2. If alpha particles are so easily attenuated (i.e., by a paper barrier), why is this type of radiation a concern to hazardous or radioactive waste workers?
3. Physiological effects of radiation on man are classified as *somatic* or *genetic*. Explain the terms and their implications.
4. Occupational exposure to radioactive materials is limited, by 40 CFR 20, to 50 rems per year to each of several organs, but only 5 rems total body exposure. Explain!
5. There are three radioactive repository/storage sites in various stages of development (in the United States). Identify them and the types of wastes to be managed at each.
6. What is meant by RCRA "mixed waste"? Why is it a major problem (1) from a technical standpoint and (2) from a regulatory standpoint?

7. Most TRU wastes are relatively mild in terms of radioactivity. Why, then, is TRU to be managed in deep underground repositories? What special management problems attend TRU wastes?
8. Some of the LLW disposal compact memberships are not noteworthy for geographical contiguity nor proximity. What problems do you foresee in this regard?
9. Considering overall history of development, what problems do the Yucca Mountain, WIPP, and Ward Valley sites have in common? As a future policymaker/implementer, how would you develop and implement plans for a future site in a manner that would avoid the controversies that now attend the three planned sites?

REFERENCES

Berlin, Robert E., and Catherine C. Stanton. 1989. *Radioactive Waste Management.* John Wiley & Sons, New York.

Corbitt, Robert A. 1990. "Hazardous Waste." *Standard Handbook of Environmental Engineering,* Robert A. Corbitt, Ed. McGraw-Hill, New York.

Dornsife, William P. 1985. "Classification of Radioactive Materials and Wastes." *Management of Radioactive Materials and Wastes.* Pennsylvania Academy of Science.

Ehlers, Victor M., and Ernest W. Steel. 1958. *Municipal and Rural Sanitation.* McGraw-Hill, New York.

Enger, Eldon D., J. Richard Kormelink, Bradley F. Smith, and Rodney J. Smith. 1989. *Environmental Science: The Study of Interrelationships.* Wm. C. Brown Publishers, Dubuque, IA.

Environment Reporter January 20, 1995. p. 1798. Bureau of National Affairs, Washington, D.C.

Environment Reporter June 3, 1994. p. 237. Bureau of National Affairs, Washington, D.C.

Environment Reporter September 23, 1994. Bureau of National Affairs, Washington, D.C.

Environment Reporter January 13, 1995. p. 1751. Bureau of National Affairs, Washington, D.C.

Foster, William, and Hubert N. Alyea. 1948. *An Introduction to General Chemistry.* D Van Nostrand, New York.

Friedman, Robert S. 1985. "Political Considerations of Nuclear Waste Disposal Policy." *Management of Radioactive Materials and Wastes.* Pennsylvania Academy of Science.

Gehr, Arthur C., Esq. December 4, 1990. Partner, Snell and Wilmer. Personal communication. Phoenix, AZ.

Goranson, Richard B. 1978. "Long-Term Management of Defense High-Level Waste." Waste Management and Fuel Cycles '78. Proceedings of the Symposium on Waste Management, March 6–8, Tucson, AZ.

Hare, F. Kenneth, and A. M. Aikin. 1984. "Nuclear Waste Disposal Technology and Environmental Hazards." *Nuclear Power-Assessing and Managing Hazardous Technology,* Martin J. Pasqualetti and K. David Pijawka, Eds. Westview Press, Boulder, CO.

Jester, William A., and Charley Yu. 1985. "Environmental Monitoring of Low-Level Radioactive Materials." *Management of Radioactive Materials and Wastes.* Pennsylvania Academy of Science.

Khareis, Tarek. 1990. U.S. Department of Energy, WIPP Project. Personal communication. July 31.

League of Women Voters. 1985. *The Nuclear Waste Primer.* Nick Lyons Books, New York.

League of Women Voters. 1993. *The Nuclear Waste Primer*. League of Women Voters Education Fund, Washington, D.C.

Martland, H. S., and R. E. Humphries. 1929. "Osteogenic Sarcoma in Dial Painters Using Luminous Paint." *Archival Pathology* Vol. 7.

Meyer, Eugene, 1989. *Chemistry of Hazardous Materials, Second Edition*. Prentice-Hall, Englewood Cliffs, NJ.

Miller, E. Willard, and Shyamal K. Majumdar. 1985. "Environmental and Biological Effects of Ionizing Radiation." *Management of Radioactive Materials and Wastes*. Pennsylvania Academy of Science.

National Academy of Sciences. 1972. The Effects on Populations of Exposure to Low Levels of Ionizing Radiation. Report of the Advisory Committee on the Biological Effects of Ionizing Radiation (BEIR Report), Washington, D.C.

National Council on Radiation Protection and Measurements (NCRP). 1971. *Basic Radiation Protection Criteria*. NCRP, Washington, D.C. NCRP-59.

National Council on Radiation Protection and Measurements (NCRP). 1980. *Management of Persons Accidentally Contaminated with Radionuclides*. NCRP, Washington, D.C. NCRP-65.

Nebel, Bernard J. and Richard T. Wright. 1993. *Environmental Science*. Prentice-Hall, Englewood Cliffs, NJ.

Organization for Economic Co-operation and Development. 1984. *Geological Disposal of Radioactive Waste*. Nuclear Energy Agency, Paris.

Pauling, Linus. 1958. *General Chemistry*. W.H. Freeman and Company, San Francisco, CA.

Pasternak, Douglas. 1995. "Give Us Your Spent Fuel, Your Warheads." *U.S. News and World Report* March 20, pp. 42–43.

Rustum, Roy. 1982. *Radioactive Waste Disposal*. Pergamon Press, New York.

Sabo, A. T. 1985. "Radiation Protection Standards and Radiation Risks." *Management of Radioactive Materials and Waste*. Pennsylvania Academy of Science.

Satchell, Michael. 1989. "Uncle Sam's Folly." *U.S. News and World Report* Vol. 106, No. 12, March 27. p. 20ff.

Sawyer, Clair N., and Perry L. McCarty. 1978. *Chemistry for Environmental Engineers, Third Edition*. McGraw-Hill, New York.

Tang, Y. S., and James H. Saling. 1990. *Radioactive Waste Management*. Hemisphere Publishing Corporation, New York.

U.S. General Accounting Office (GAO). 1993. *NUCLEAR WASTE—Yucca Mountain Project Behind Schedule and Facing Major Scientific Uncertainties*. U.S. GAO, Washington, D.C. GAO/RCED-93-124.

U.S. General Accounting Office (GAO). 1994. *NUCLEAR WASTE-Foreign Countries' Approaches to High-Level Waste Storage and Disposal*. U.S. GAO, Washington, D.C. GAO/RCED-94-172.

U.S. Office of Technology Assessment. 1985. *Managing the Nation's Commercial High-Level Radioactive Waste*. U.S. Congress, Superintendent of Documents, Government Printing Office, Washington, D.C.

U.S. Department of Energy. 1994a. *Environmental Management 1994*. Office of Environmental Management Information, Washington, D.C. DOE/EM-0119.

U.S. Department of Energy. 1994b. *Committed to Results: DOE's Environmental Management Program*. Office of Environmental Restoration, Washington, D.C. DOE/EM-0152P.

U.S. Department of Energy. 1994c. *Environmental Fact Sheets*. Office of Environmental Management, Washington, D.C.

U.S. Department of Energy. 1995a. *Environmental Management 1995*. Center for Environmental Management Information, Washington, D.C. DOE/EM-0228.

U.S. Department of Energy. 1995b. *Estimating the Cold War Mortgage — The 1995 Baseline Environmental Management Report-Executive Summary*. Office of Environmental Management, Washington, D.C.

14 UNDERGROUND STORAGE TANK MANAGEMENT

OBJECTIVES

At completion of this chapter, the student should:

- understand the nature and magnitude of the environmental threat of leaking underground storage tanks.
- understand the causes of underground storage tank and piping failures.
- be familiar with the theories and practice of internal tank testing and external monitoring for leaks.
- be familiar with remediation measures, tank rehabilitation procedures, and requirements for new tank installations.
- be conversant on the Resource Conservation and Recovery Act (RCRA) Subtitle I requirements for underground storage tank management.

INTRODUCTION

Several million underground storage tank (UST) systems in the United States contain petroleum or hazardous chemicals. The U.S. Environmental Protection Agency (EPA) estimates that about 1.2 million USTs buried at more than 500,000 sites are subject to federal regulation. [U.S. EPA 1994(d)]. Tens of thousands of these tanks, including their piping, have leaked or are currently leaking. The EPA reports that by July 1994 the number of releases confirmed since the beginning of the regulatory program had reached 262,000. Moreover, the agency expects the total number of releases to reach 400,000 during the next few years [U.S. EPA 1994(c)]. The typical condition of steel tanks being removed in corrective actions is shown in Figures 14.1 and 14.2. Many older tanks, and the associated piping, are of unprotected steel construction and can be expected to develop leaks unless they are removed or rehabilitated.

Leaking USTs can cause fires or explosions and/or contaminate groundwater. More than 50% of the population in the United States depend upon groundwater for domestic use. Thus, leaking USTs are a major threat to the public health and safety and to the environment.

FIGURE 14.1 Corroded USTs after removal (Arizona Instrument Corporation, 1100 E. University Drive, Tempe, AZ 85280).

FIGURE 14.2 Corroded USTs after removal (Arizona Department of Environmental Quality).

In the Hazardous and Solid Waste Amendments of 1984 (HSWA), Congress added a new Subtitle I to the RCRA to address the problem of leaking underground tanks used for storage of petroleum and hazardous *substances*. The implementing federal regulations are found in 40 CFR 280 and 281. (Tanks used for storing hazardous *wastes* are regulated by 40 CFR 264 and 265.)

In this chapter we will overview the nature and causes of the problem, the related technologies, and the regulatory structure.

Leaking Underground Storage Tanks — Problems and Causes

As noted, large numbers of the older USTs are of "bare" steel construction. Older tanks, especially those more than ten years old and/or unprotected from corrosion, are likely to develop leaks. A leak from a UST, if undetected or ignored, can cause very large amounts of petroleum product to be lost to the subsurface. In a recent case, a tank at a city-owned vehicle maintenance facility lost an estimated 500,000 gallons of gasoline to a producing aquifer. In another case, a major oil company found it necessary to buy and vacate all of the residences on a city block adjacent to a company-owned service station. Leaking gasoline had migrated from the underground tanks at the station, and liquid gasoline and vapors entered basements on the block. Water supply wells adjacent to older service stations are frequently contaminated with gasoline.

USTs usually release contaminants into the subsurface environment as a result of one or more of four factors: corrosion, faulty installation, piping failure, or spills and overfills. Galvanic corrosion, or the breakdown of hard, refined steel, is the most common cause of release from bare steel UST systems. Because the majority of older UST systems are of bare steel, corrosion is believed to be the leading cause of releases (U.S. EPA 1990, p. IV-2). This may not be true, however, in areas of the arid southwestern United States

Galvanic Corrosion

The rate and severity of corrosion varies depending upon a number of site-specific factors (e.g., soil conductivity) that are almost always present when bare steel is placed underground. Steel is, by definition, an alloy of iron and carbon, containing other constituents such as manganese, chromium, nickel, molybdenum, copper, tungsten, or cobalt. These metals have differing electromotive activities, and the more active metals tend to displace the less active. Dissimilar metals may be present in the soil surrounding a steel tank. Most commonly, part of the tank becomes negatively charged with respect to the surrounding area. The negatively charged part of the UST acts as a negative electrode and begins to corrode at a rate proportional to the intensity of the current (U.S. EPA 1990, p. IV-2). Galvanic corrosion always occurs at a specific point on a tank or pipe where the current exits. As the current passes through this point, the hard steel is transformed into soft ore, a hole forms, and the leak occurs. The hole, so formed, is usually small (Figure 14.3), but large quantities of liquid may be released. (For a thorough discussion of the galvanic corrosion of steel underground tanks, *see* Cole 1992, Appendix A.)

FIGURE 14.3 Typical pinhole leak caused by galvanic activity (EPA).

Faulty Installation

Installation failure encompasses a wide variety of problems such as inadequate backfill, allowing movement of the tank, and separation of pipe joints. Mishandling of the tank during installation can cause structural failure of fiberglass-reinforced plastic (FRP) tanks or damage to steel tank coatings and cathodic protection. Cole lists the causes of failure that are related to backfill (Cole 1992, p. 49):

- Using improper, inhomogeneous (*sic*) backfill material
- Inadequate or improper compaction
- Rocks or debris left in excavation
- Voids left under tank
- Failure to prevent migration of backfill
- Placing a tank directly on a concrete slab or hard native soil

Piping Failures

The underground piping which connects tanks to each other, to delivery pumps, and to fill drops is even more frequently of unprotected steel (Figure 14.4). EPA studies indicate that piping failure accounts for 50 to 80% of spills at UST facilities. The piping failures are caused equally by poor workmanship and corrosion. Threading of galvanized steel pipe exposes electrically active metal and creates a strong tendency to corrode if not coated and cathodically protected. The problem is compounded if the fittings and valves used in the system are of dissimilar metals. Improper layout of piping runs, incomplete tightening of joints, inadequate cover pad

FIGURE 14.4 Typical corroded piping at a UST leak investigation site (Fuel Tech Distributing Company, 1809 W. 4th Street, Tempe, AZ 85281).

construction, and construction accidents can lead to failure of delivery piping. Figure 14.5 diagrams a typical service station tank and piping layout (Cole 1992, p. 2; Munter et al. 1995, p. 190).

Spills and Overfills

Spills and overfills contribute to the release problem at UST facilities. In addition to the direct contamination effect, repeated spills of petroleum products or hazardous wastes can intensify the corrosiveness of soils. Spills and overfills are almost totally attributable to human error. These mistakes can be avoided by following the correct tank filling practices and by providing spill and overfill protection. EPA regulations require catchment basins to contain spills and the installation of automatic shutoff devices, overfill alarms, or ball float valves [U.S. EPA 1994(a)].

Compatibility of UST and Contents

Another possible cause of tank failure has become a concern in areas of the nation that are experimenting with alternative (automotive) fuels in the hope of achieving improved air quality. The rush to replace steel tanks has enhanced the popularity of FRP tanks and tank liners to the end that large numbers of them have been put into service. Some FRP tanks or liners may not be compatible with some methanol-blended (and possibly some ethanol-blended) fuels.

Compatibility for tanks means that the fuel components would not change the physical or mechanical properties of the tank. Compatibility for liners requires that

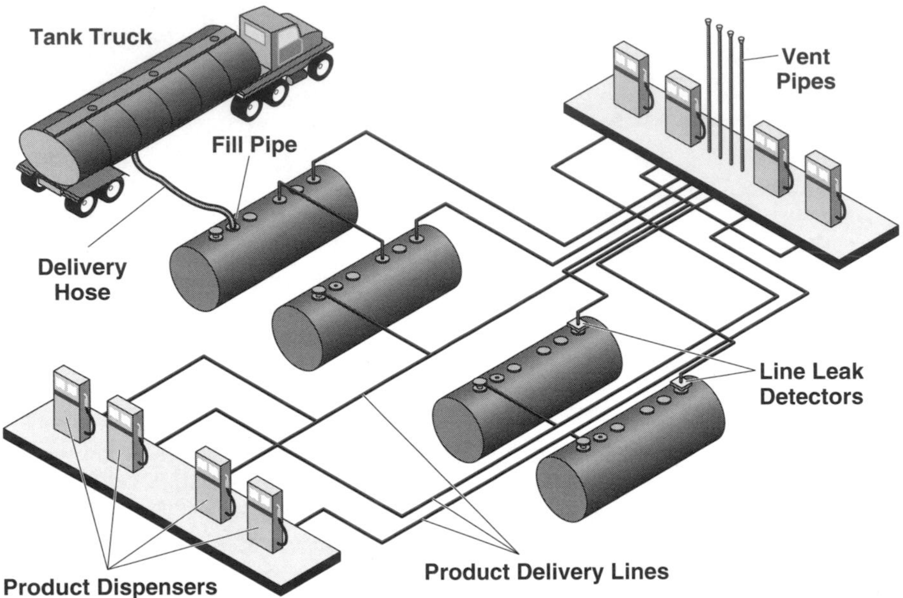

FIGURE 14.5 Typical service station tank and piping layout (EPA).

the fuel components not cause blistering, underfilm corrosion, or internal stress or cracking. Owners/operators of FRP-constructed or -lined tanks should consult the appropriate standards of the American Petroleum Institute (API) (Leiter 1989, p. 55).

Mobility of Leaked Hydrocarbon Fuels

Motor fuels, when leaked, are acted upon by gravitational forces which act to draw the fluid downward. Other forces act to retain the fuel, which is either adsorbed to soil particles or trapped in soil pores. The amount of fuel retained in the soil is of primary importance, as it will determine both the degree of contamination and the likelihood of subsequent contaminant transport to groundwater (Bauman 1989, p. 3). Upon reaching the saturated zone, some of the lighter components may dissolve in water, but large quantities can float on the water surface, sliding downgradient over great distances. This mobility frequently causes remediation of leaking UST sites to be costly, involving many recovery wells and large-scale separation of pumped water and recovered product.

Protection of Tanks and Piping from Corrosion

As noted earlier, unprotected steel USTs are frequently damaged by corrosion. Galvanic corrosion is the most common cause of release from bare steel UST systems. Steel tanks and piping can be protected by coating them with a corrosion-resistant coating and by using "cathodic" protection. Cathodic protection reverses the electric current that causes corrosion and can be applied in the form of sacrificial anodes or as an impressed current.

Protection by Sacrificial Anode

Sacrificial anodes are pieces of metal that are more electrically active than steel in the UST to which they are attached. Because the anodes are more active, the electric current will exit from them rather than from the steel tank. Thus, the tank becomes the cathode and is protected from corrosion while the attached anode is sacrificed.

Protection by Impressed Current

An impressed current protection system introduces an electric current into the ground through a series of anodes that are not attached to the UST. Since the electric current flowing from these anodes to the tank system is greater than the corrosive current attempting to flow from it, the UST is protected from corrosion [U.S. EPA 1988(d), p. 31]. (*See also* Cole 1992, Appendix A)

Protection by Cladding or Dielectric Coating

Steel-FRP composite tanks are adequately protected from corrosion by the thick outside layer (or cladding) of FRP (Figure 14.6). Cathodic protection is not needed with this method of protection (40 CFR 280.20). New steel tanks for petroleum storage must be coated with a dielectric coating (asphalt or paint) and cathodically protected (40 CFR 280.20). Care must be taken, during installation, to protect the coating from damage. Any separation ("holiday") of the coating from the tank tends to focus the galvanic forces, accelerates corrosion, and may cause a release (Leiter 1989, p. 22).

Protection of Piping

The UST regulations require that piping in contact with the ground be constructed entirely of FRP or, if of steel, be cathodically protected by:

- coating with suitable dielectric material.
- field-installed cathodic protection system designed by a corrosion expert.
- impressed current system.
- cathodic protection conforming with listed codes and standards (40 CFR 280.20).

Detection of Leaks From Underground Storage Tank Systems

There are seven general methods of leak detection for USTs. There are many variations on some of the methods. Practitioners and tank testing companies vigorously argue the merits of particular methods and the supporting technologies. The RCRA Subtitle I regulations allow owners or operators of UST facilities to choose between leak detection methods and impose specific requirements on the use of each method. The student should refer to Figure 14.7 as the methods are briefly described.

FIGURE 14.6 Composite steel-FRP tanks (JOOR Industries, 1189 Industrial Avenue, Escondido, CA 92029).

Automatic Tank Gauging (1)

This method uses monitors which are permanently installed in the tank and an external control device to monitor product level and inventory control. During a test period of several hours, when nothing is put into or taken from the tank, the gauging system automatically calculates the changes in product volume that can indicate a leaking tank. This method cannot be used on piping [U.S. EPA 1994(b)]. (*See also* Leiter 1989, p. 174; Wilcox 1990, pp.119ff)

Groundwater Monitoring (2)

This method is used to detect the presence of gasoline or other liquid product floating on the groundwater. Monitoring wells are placed at strategic locations in the ground near the tank and piping runs. The wells may be sampled periodically by hand or continuously with permanently installed equipment. The method is effective only at sites where groundwater is within 20 ft of the surface [U.S. EPA 1994(b)].

Soil Vapor Monitoring (3)

Leaked petroleum product releases vapors into the soil surrounding the UST. Vapor monitoring around the tank and piping senses the presence of vapors from leaked product. The method requires that tanks be backfilled with porous soils and that monitoring locations be carefully planned. Vapor monitoring can be performed

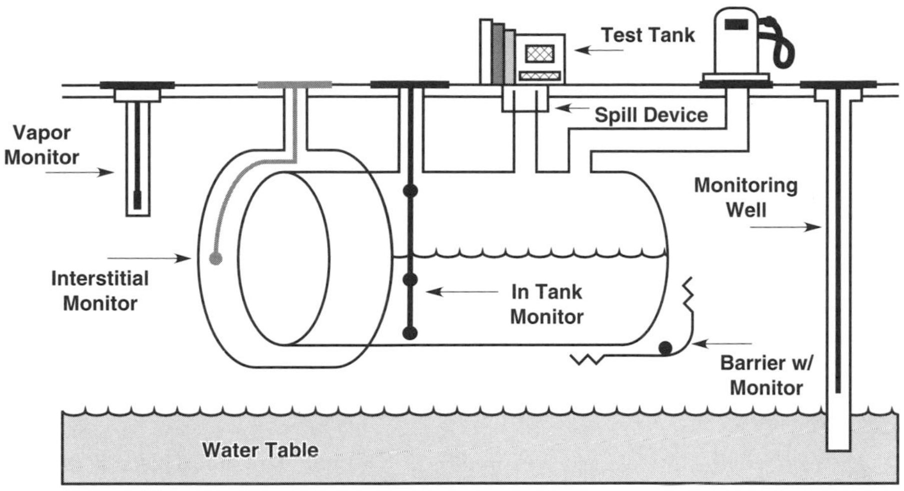

FIGURE 14.7 UST leak detection alternatives (EPA).

manually on a prescribed frequency or continuously using permanently installed equipment [U.S. EPA 1994(b)].

Secondary Containment and Interstitial Monitoring (4)

Secondary containment is achieved by placing a barrier between the UST and the environment. The barrier may be a vault, liner, or double-walled structure. Leaked product from the UST is detected by monitoring of the space between the tank and the barrier. Interstitial monitoring methods range from a simple dip stick to automated vapor or liquid sensors permanently installed in the system. New USTs holding hazardous substances must use this method [U.S. EPA 1994(b)].

Statistical Inventory Reconciliation (5)

This method uses sophisticated computer software to determine whether a tank system is leaking. The computer conducts a statistical analysis of inventory, delivery, and dispensing data collected over a period of time and provided by the operator to a vendor [U.S. EPA 1994(b)].

Manual Tank Gauging (6)

Manual gauging can be used only on tanks of 2000 gallons capacity or smaller. The method requires taking the tank out of service for at least 36 hours each week to take measurements of the tank's contents. Tanks of not more than 1000 gallons capacity may use this method alone. Tanks of 1001 to 2000 gallons capacity must also use periodic tank tightness testing and for only ten years after installation or upgrade of the UST. After ten years, these USTs must use one of the other detection methods listed in Items 1 through 5 [U.S. EPA 1994(b)].

Tank Tightness Testing with Inventory Control (7)

The method combines manual inventory control information (measured daily and compiled monthly) with tank tightness testing every five years. Tightness testing requires taking the UST out of service and the temporary installation of test equipment to measure changes in liquid level or volume over time. This method may only be used in new or upgraded tanks during their first ten years of operation (or until 1998, whichever is later). Tanks which have not been upgraded may be placed under inventory control and subjected to *annual* tightness testing until upgraded or until 1998, whichever is earlier. Thereafter, one of the methods listed in Items 1 through 5 must be used [U.S. EPA 1994(b)].

Detection of Leaks in Pressurized Underground Piping

An automatic line leak detector is required. The automatic line leak detector uses combinations of flow restrictors and flow shutoffs to monitor pressure in a line. Automatic line leak detection must be accompanied by one of the following methods: groundwater monitoring, vapor monitoring, secondary containment and interstitial monitoring, or an annual tightness testing of the piping [U.S. EPA 1994(b)].

Detection of Leaks in Underground Suction Piping

Leak detection is not required if the suction piping meets the following basic design requirements:

- Below-grade piping is sloped so that the contents of the piping will drain back into the storage tank if suction pressure is released
- Only one check valve is included in each suction line and it is located directly below the suction pump in the dispensing unit

Suction piping which does not meet the above requirements must be subjected to one of the following [U.S. EPA 1994(b)]:

- Line tightness tests every three years
- Groundwater monitoring
- Soil vapor monitoring
- Secondary containment and interstitial monitoring

For an exhaustive review of UST technology, *see* Gangadharan et al. (1988).

RCRA Subtitle I Regulations and Requirements

Background

In recognition of the leaking UST problem, Congress included the original Subtitle I in the 1984 HSWA. Subtitle I contained provisions prohibiting installation of new tanks that were not designed to prevent releases due to corrosion, structural failure, or incompatibility and imposed notification requirements upon owners of UST facilities.

The implementing regulations (40 CFR 280) were significantly broadened and strengthened in 1988. The new regulations established (1) technical standards that new and existing UST facilities must meet and (2) financial assurance requirements which require owners or operators to demonstrate that they can pay for cleanup of leaks from their UST facilities.

The goals of the UST regulations are:

- to prevent leaks and spills.
- to detect leaks and spills if and when they occur.
- to ensure that owners and operators can pay for correction of problems created by leaks that may occur.
- to ensure that state regulatory programs for USTs impose regulations that are as strict or more strict than the federal regulations.

Implementation Schedule

The regulations impose differing requirements upon owners or operators of "new" and "existing" UST systems. *New* UST systems are those that are installed after December 1988. *Existing* systems are those installed before December 1988.

Requirements for New Petroleum UST Systems

Owners or operators of UST systems that were installed after December 1988 must meet four technical requirements. They must:

- certify that the tank and piping are installed properly according to applicable industry codes.
- equip the UST with devices that prevent spills and overfill, and follow correct tank filling practices.
- protect the tank and piping from corrosion.
- equip both tank and piping with leak detection [U.S. EPA 1988(b), p. 7ff].

The corrosion protection requirement may be met by one of the following performance standards:

- Tank and piping completely made of noncorrodible material, such as fiberglass
- Tank and piping made of steel having a corrosion-resistant coating *and* having cathodic protection
- Tank made of steel clad with a thick layer of noncorrodible material (this option does not apply to piping) [U.S. EPA 1994(a)]

Requirements for Existing UST Systems

As noted previously, an *existing* UST system is one that was installed prior to December 1988. The implementation schedule for existing systems requires immediate adoption of tank filling procedures that will prevent spills and overfills. By December 1998 (ten years following promulgation of the UST regulations), systems that were installed before December 1988 must have:

- corrosion protection for steel tanks and piping.
- devices that prevent spills and overfills.

The corrosion protection requirement for *existing* tanks may be met by achieving one of the performance standards for *new* tanks, listed previously; by meeting one of the upgrade options listed here; or by closing properly [U.S. EPA 1994(a)]:

- Add cathodic protection to a tank that has been proven to be structurally sound. For existing tanks, this option may best be met by adding an impressed current system that protects the UST by introducing an electrical current to the surrounding soil.
- Add a thick layer of noncorrodible material to the interior of the tank. This interior lining must be periodically inspected.
- Combine cathodic protection and interior lining. USTs for which this option has been selected do not require periodic inspection of the interior lining.

Corrective Action Requirements

The release investigation and corrective action requirements pertaining to UST releases are found at 40 CFR 280, Subparts E and F. The EPA regulations are carefully worded to defer to the implementing (state or local) agency, but also establish minimum standards for release responses. The standards, paraphrased,* require owners and operators to:

- report to the implementing agency, within 24 hours, discovery of a release, unusual operating conditions, or monitoring results that indicate that a release may have occurred.
- conduct appropriate tests; repair, replace, or upgrade the defective unit; and begin corrective action as required by Subpart F.
- contain and immediately clean up spills and overfills.
- report releases equal to or in excess of reportable quantities of hazardous substances to the National Response Center.
- investigate the extent of the release, and monitor and mitigate fire and safety hazards.

* The Subpart E and F requirements are condensed here for overview knowledge. They are extensive and subject to augmentation by the implementing agency. The practitioner should become fully familiar with the contents of Subparts E and F, as well as applicable state and/or local codes.

- remedy hazards posed by contaminated soil and groundwater.
- conduct free product removal and abate free product migration. (40 CFR 280, Subparts E and F)

Financial Responsibility Requirements

Subpart H (40 CFR 280.90 through 280.111) establishes extensive and complex financial assurance requirements which either the owner or operator of a UST system must meet. The intent of these regulations is to ensure that money is available to pay for cleanup of releases of petroleum product and to compensate third parties for bodily injury and property damage resulting from a release.

The financial responsibility regulations require:

- petroleum marketers to have coverage in the amount of $1 million.
- those who are not a marketer, coverage of $500,000.

The required coverage may be shown in one of the following ways:

- By passing one of two financial tests, if the firm has a tangible net worth of at least $10 million
- By obtaining insurance coverage in the required amount
- By obtaining a guarantee from a corporate entity which can pass one of the financial tests
- By obtaining a surety bond in the required amount
- By obtaining a letter of credit for the required amount
- By setting up a fully funded trust fund
- By the use of another state-approved method, such as a risk retention group
- By a combination of the above, with aggregate coverage in the required amount [U.S. EPA 1988(a), p. 6]

The LUST Trust Fund

The Leaking Underground Storage Tank (LUST) Trust Fund was created by Congress in the 1986 amendments to RCRA Subtitle I and was reauthorized for five more years in 1990. The fund provides money for:

- overseeing corrective action taken by a responsible party — usually the owner or operator of the leaking UST.
- cleanups at UST sites where the owner or operator is unknown, unwilling, or unable to respond or which require emergency action.

The fund is financed by a 0.1 cent per gallon tax on motor fuel sold in the United States By May 1994, the fund had collected about $1.2 billion and had disbursed about $475 million to the EPA. The agency has passed through about $410 million to state programs for use in administration, oversight, and cleanup work. The states have used the trust fund and state funds to:

- confirm more than 262,000 releases.
- oversee or conduct more than 7800 emergency responses.
- oversee or initiate more than 202,000 cleanups.
- oversee or complete more than 101,000 cleanups.
- oversee or conduct more than 892,000 closures [U.S. EPA 1994(d)].

Closure of Underground Storage Tank Facilities

In keeping with RCRA requirements for closure of hazardous waste sites, the UST regulations also require formal closure when use ends or is suspended.

Permanent Closure

Tanks that are not protected from corrosion and which are unused for more than 12 months or tanks to be permanently closed must conform to the required procedures for permanent closure. The requirements, in brief, are:

- The regulatory agency must be notified at least 30 days prior to closure.
- An assessment must be made to determine if leakage has occurred. The requirement may be satisfied if one of the external release detection methods (soil vapor or groundwater monitoring) is in operation at the time of closure and indicates that no release has occurred. If contamination is detected, corrective actions must be taken in accord with Subpart F (40 CFR 280.60 through 280.67).*
- The tank must be emptied and cleaned by removing all liquids, dangerous vapors, and accumulated sludge.**
- The tank must be removed from the ground or closed in place. Closure in place requires filling with a harmless and chemically inactive solid [U.S. EPA 1994(a)].

Exceptions to Permanent Closure

Requirements for permanent closure may not apply if the following occur:

- If the tank meets requirements for a new or upgraded UST, it may remain "temporarily" closed indefinitely, provided it meets the requirements (below) for temporary closure.
- The regulatory authority grants an extension beyond the 12-month limit on temporary closure of tanks that are unprotected from corrosion. In this case, a site assessment must be accomplished.

* Some states have taken exception to this federal regulation. State regulations should also be followed in a tank closure activity.

** An extremely hazardous activity; *see* Chapter 15 in this edition; Bridge 1988.

- The stored contents are to be changed to an unregulated substance. The regulatory agency must be notified of the change; the cleaning and assessment procedures for permanent closure must be followed; and any release must be corrected per Subpart F.

Temporary Closure

Tanks not in use for 3 to 12 months must meet requirements for temporary closure. These requirements, which are contained in the Subpart G regulations, are, in brief:

- Operation and maintenance of corrosion protection equipment must be continued, and any detection of a release must be corrected per Subpart F.
- All vent lines must remain open and functioning.
- All other lines must be capped; pumps, manways, and other ancillary equipment must be secured (40 CFR 280.70).

(*See also* Bridge 1988)

TOPICS FOR REVIEW OR DISCUSSION

1. There are four factors which result in releases from underground petroleum storage tanks. What are the factors? One of these is believed to be the most common cause of releases. Which is it?
2. Describe/explain the galvanic corrosion process as it affects steel USTs.
3. How do sacrificial anodes protect USTs and piping? What other methods of corrosion protection/prevention are available for USTs.
4. Is the piping associated with USTs also subject to galvanic activity?
5. Why is testing of underground pressurized and suction piping, associated with USTs, considered to be so important?
6. The RCRA Subtitle I regulations (40 CFR 280) provide several leak detection options. What is meant by interstitial monitoring?
7. Under what circumstances is leak detection not required for UST piping? What is the rationale for that exception?
8. You have been notified by the attorney for your late uncle Harry that he left his old service station property to you. It has been padlocked since 1976. You decide to look the place over and find that there are at least two USTs that apparently have some petroleum product in them. What must be one of the first things that you do?

REFERENCES

Bauman, Bruce J. 1989. "Soils Contaminated by Motor Fuels: Research Activities and Perspectives of the American Petroleum Institute." *Petroleum Contaminated Soils: Remediation Techniques, Environmental Fate, and Risk Assessment,* Paul T. Kostecki and Edward J. Calabrese, Eds. Lewis Publishers, Chelsea, MI. Chapter 1.

Bridge, Jennie. 1988. *Tank Closure Without Tears: An Inspector's Safety Guide*. New England Interstate Water Pollution Control Commission, Boston, MA.

Cole, G. Mattney. 1992. *Underground Storage Tank Installation & Management*. Lewis Publishers, Chelsea, MI.

Gangadharan, A. C., et al. 1988. *Leak Prevention and Corrective Action Technology for Underground Storage Tanks*. Noyes Data Corporation, Park Ridge, NJ.

Munter, Florence, et al. 1995. "Hazardous Wastes." *Accident Prevention Manual for Business and Industry — Environmental Management*. National Safety Council, Itasca, IL. Chapter 8

Leiter, Jeffrey L. Editor-in-Chief. 1989. *Underground Storage Tank Guide*. Thompson Publishing Group, Salisbury, MD.

U.S. Environmental Protection Agency. 1988(a). *Dollars and Sense*. Office of Underground Storage Tanks, Washington, D.C. 530/UST-88/005.

U.S. Environmental Protection Agency. 1988(b). *Musts for USTs*. Office of Underground Storage Tanks, Washington, D.C. 530/UST-88/00.

U.S. Environmental Protection Agency. 1990. *RCRA Orientation Manual, 1990 Edition*. Superintendent of Documents, Government Printing Office, Washington, D.C.

U.S. Environmental Protection Agency. 1994(a). *UST Program Facts Preventing Releases*. Office of Solid Waste and Emergency Response, Washington, D.C. EPA 510-F-94-004.

U.S. Environmental Protection Agency. 1994(b). *UST Program Facts Detecting Releases*. Office of Solid Waste and Emergency Response, Washington, D.C. EPA 510-F-94-005.

U.S. Environmental Protection Agency. 1994(c). *UST Program Facts Cleaning Up Releases*. Office of Solid Waste and Emergency Response, Washington, D.C. EPA 510-F-94-006.

U.S. Environmental Protection Agency. 1994(d). *UST Program Facts Overview of the UST Program*. Office of Solid Waste and Emergency Response, Washington, D.C. EPA 510-F-94-008.

Wilcox, H. Kendall. 1990. "In-Tank Leak Detection Methodologies." *Underground Storage Systems — Leak Detection and Monitoring,* Todd G. Schwendeman and H. Kendall Wilcox, Eds. Lewis Publishers, Chelsea, MI.

15 HAZARDOUS WASTE WORKER HEALTH AND SAFETY

OBJECTIVES

At completion of this chapter, the student should:

- understand the types of hazards which may be encountered by workers on hazardous waste sites.
- be familiar with actions and preventive measures which may or should be taken to minimize impacts of those hazards during both routine and emergency conditions.
- be familiar with regulatory requirements for protection of worker health and safety on hazardous waste sites.

INTRODUCTION

Item: Labor Secretary Robert B. Reich proposes penalties of $1,597,000 against Rhone-Poulenc AG Co. of Institute, WV for violations of the OSHA Chemical Process Safety Standard and the Hazardous Waste and Emergency Response Standard. One worker was killed, and two other sustained lung and skin injuries as a result of a fire and explosion on August 18, 1993 (OSHA news release, February 17, 1994).

Item: Cedric Jackson, a concrete finisher, decided to make a little extra money to support his wife and four children by helping Jerry Martin remove two 10,000-gallon tanks from Martin's Automotive Shop property. A Florida Department of Environmental Regulation official had earlier advised Martin to contact a pollution specialty contractor to remove the fuel from the tanks, dismantle the system, and remove the tanks. Instead, Martin hired Jackson, who had never worked on underground storage tanks, at $5 per hour, to undertake the project. Jackson either slipped or was thrown between the tanks when one of the tanks rolled. It took fire and rescue teams more than five hours to secure the tanks and remove Jackson's body from beneath the concrete anchor in the muddy, fuel-contaminated tank hole (Petroleum Equipment Institute 1992).

Item: Workers using organic solvents and detergents to remove polychlorinated biphenyl contamination from a poorly ventilated factory basement experienced "grossly abnormal" neurologic symptoms. One worker developed headache, memory impairment, and acute confusion after three days of work with the solvents. His mental status — which was clinically normal before his employment — was judged abnormal by the same physician after the work with the solvents. Neuropsychiatric testing performed 9 and 20 months after job completion "demonstrated severe deficits in attention, memory, and concentration." Another worker who developed similar symptoms was tested 20 months later and showed deficits in attention, concentration, and memory. Complaints from both engineers and laborers indicated that work conditions were poor, ventilation was inadequate, respirator use was minimal, skin protection was ineffective, and cleaning agents were mixed together and used in higher-than-recommended concentrations (*Occupational Safety and Health Reporter*, July 29, 1992).

Item: OSHA proposed penalties greater than $2 million against Southern Scrap Metals, which employs 150 workers to process scrap and waste materials. The company was cited for 40 willful violations related to employee exposure to lead, 21 violations related to cadmium exposure, violations of various safety requirements, and 4 repeat safety violations. Many of the violations involved temporary Mexican workers who spoke little English.* The alleged violations include overexposure of seven workers to lead, failure to monitor lead exposures, lack of a written compliance plan, work surfaces contaminated with lead, no change or shower facilities, no lunch room free from lead dust, no medical surveillance program, and no employee training. The OSHA Baton Rouge area director said the worst incident at the plant involved one worker who was exposed to 400 μg of lead per cubic meter of air, eight times OSHA's permissible limit (*Occupational Safety and Health Reporter*, October 5, 1994).

Workers face a formidable array of workplace hazards and potential hazards as they perform the many routine and nonroutine tasks associated with the practice of hazardous waste management. Whether collecting wastes from satellite collection points for transfer to a central collection point, or remediating an abandoned chemical storage facility, the hazardous waste worker is challenged by known and unknown hazards, to an extent and extreme matched by few other workplace activities. In earlier times, the worker was characteristically ill-prepared, in terms of intellect, literacy, training, instruments, equipment, and supervision, to perform the required tasks with relative safety to him/herself, fellow workers, the public, and the environment. Commendable progress has been made toward improving workplace safety for the hazardous waste worker, but the improvements are not consistent among employers and workplaces as noted previously, and much remains to be done to improve awareness and minimize the hazards on hazardous waste workplaces.

Owners and operators of hazardous waste facilities and managers and supervisors of hazardous waste workers are similarly on a rising curve, with respect to effective management, supervision, training, and equipping of workers and/or facilities. Some have taken the necessary steps to achieve the required compliance status. Others have demonstrated extraordinary leadership by going beyond mere compliance, in terms of providing well-trained and experienced supervisors, adequate resources and equipment, and management emphasis. Unfortunately, some owners,

* For an exploration of ethnic populations in "high-hazard, low-wage" jobs, *see* Robinson (1991, Chapter 6).

operators, managers, and supervisors linger at the lower end of the curve. A frequent example of the latter is observed by trainers and faculty in the person of the employee having inadequate or no background or experience in worker safety and health who arrives at work one morning and is informed that he/she is the new health and safety (environment and safety, compliance, etc.) officer or specialist. Company and employee then initiate a hasty search for some quick training that will lend some legitimacy to the appointment. There is no satisfactory substitute for in-depth training in safety, industrial hygiene, hazardous waste/materials management, environmental compliance, and other disciplines related to the specific appointment.

Hazards Encountered on Hazardous Waste Sites

The designation of a site as a hazardous waste site leaves much unsaid, insofar as worker health and safety is concerned. The hazards present include, but may also far exceed, those attributable to the hazardous waste which is cause for the site designation. A great variety of possible or potential hazards assert themselves, and it is difficult to construct an organized listing. The following ordering of onsite hazards is adapted and summarized from the *Occupational Safety and Health Guidance Manual for Hazardous Waste Site Activities*, prepared by the U.S. National Institute for Occupational Safety and Health (NIOSH), the Occupational Safety and Health Administration (OSHA), the U.S. Coast Guard (USCG), and the U.S. Environmental Protection Agency (EPA). This manual, frequently referred to as "the four agency manual," is an excellent resource and is here highly recommended for inclusion in the professional libraries of hazardous waste management practitioners (HHS 1985).

Chemical Exposure

As discussed in Chapter 4, chemicals exert toxic effects on humans by gaining access to the cells and tissues. The three major routes of exposure are ingestion, inhalation, and dermal absorption. Entry may also occur in the form of a puncture wound or entry through mucous membranes of the eyes or nasal passages. Exposures may be chronic or acute (as discussed earlier), may be temporary and reversible, or may be permanent.

Inhalation is frequently the potential exposure route of greatest concern on hazardous waste sites. The human respiratory system has the function of quickly facilitating the absorption of oxygen into the bloodstream, where it is efficiently distributed to the vital organs of the body. The toxic chemical, whether or not a threat to the lungs, may be absorbed and distributed in a similar manner. Some toxic chemicals may not be detected by the human senses, i.e., they may be colorless, odorless, tasteless, or nonirritating, and their toxic effects may not produce immediate symptoms. Respiratory protection is therefore extremely important where the workplace atmosphere may contain hazardous substances.

Absorption by the skin and mucous membrane are important routes of exposure. Chemicals may directly injure the skin or may pass through the skin where they are transported to vulnerable organs. Skin absorption is enhanced by wounds, heat, and/or moisture. Contact with body orifices is an important route of entry. Airborne chemicals can dissolve in the moist surface of the eye, be absorbed by the near-surface capillaries, and be carried through the bloodstream. Workers must wear protective equipment, avoid using contact lenses in contaminated atmospheres, keep hands away from the face, and minimize skin contact with liquid and solid chemicals.

Ingestion is thought of as the least likely route of exposure at hazardous waste sites, but workers should be aware of the possibility and the means. Personal habits such as chewing gum or tobacco, drinking, eating, or smoking cigarettes while onsite may provide a route of entry and should be prohibited. Particulate material may accumulate in the bronchial passages, be brought to the throat by the natural cleansing processes, and then be swallowed.

Injection of chemicals through puncture wounds may occur from stepping on, or other contact with, sharp objects. Protection from injection hazards can be improved by wearing safety footwear, by avoiding physical hazards, and by taking common sense precautions.

Explosion and Fire

The potential causes of fires and explosions on hazardous waste sites are as listed in Chapter 4. They include:

- chemical reactions that produce explosion, fire, or heat, including those attributable to pyrophoric and water reactive substances.
- ignition of explosive or flammable chemicals.
- ignition of materials due to oxygen enrichment.
- agitation of shock- or friction-sensitive compounds.
- sudden release of material under pressure.

Hazardous wastes may spontaneously ignite or explode. The more frequent causes include activities such as movement of drums, accidental mixing of incompatible chemicals, attainment of auto-ignition temperatures, or the introduction of an ignition source into an explosive or flammable environment. Such events not only pose the obvious hazards of intense heat, open flame, smoke inhalation, and destructive shock waves and flying objects, but may also release toxic chemicals into the environment. Threats to onsite personnel, as well as the public, may be minimized by field monitoring for explosive atmospheres and flammable vapors; identifying and verifying incompatible materials; keeping potential ignition sources away from flammable or explosive environments; using nonsparking, explosion-proof equipment; remotely handling unknown materials and suspect containers; and avoiding practices that might result in agitation or release of chemicals.

Oxygen Deficiency

The oxygen content of normal air is approximately 21%. Humans experience physiological effects when oxygen concentrations in the air are depressed to 16% at sea level. The effects include impaired attention, judgement, and coordination and increased breathing and heart rate. To provide for individual physiological responses and errors in measurement, oxygen deficiency is considered to be indicated at 19.5% or lower concentration. OSHA is currently proposing new oxygen deficiency criteria, in which deficiency remains at 19.5% for altitudes up to 14,000 ft above sea level, but the oxygen-deficient, immediately dangerous to life or health (IDLH) scales up from 16.0% at 0 to 3000 ft to 19.5% at altitudes above 8000 ft (*see* 59 FR 58884, November 15, 1994).

Oxygen deficiency may result from the displacement of oxygen by another gas, by the consumption of oxygen by a chemical or biological reaction, or at higher altitudes as noted previously. Confined spaces and low-lying areas are characteristically vulnerable to oxygen deficiency and should be monitored as entry operations begin and frequently thereafter. Workers in oxygen-deficient atmospheres must be trained in respirator use and wear air-supplying respirators. Air-purifying respirators should never be used in oxygen-deficient atmospheres and should only be used where the seven required conditions (discussed later in this chapter) are met.

Ionizing Radiation

Health impacts and physiological effects of ionizing radiation on humans is summarized in Chapter 13. Use of protective clothing, coupled with scrupulous personal hygiene and decontamination, affords good protection against alpha and beta radiation.

Chemical protective clothing affords no protection against gamma radiation; however, use of respiratory and other protective equipment can provide some protection against entry of radiation-emitting materials from entering the body by inhalation, ingestion, injection, or skin absorption.

Sites having radiation greater than background levels should be entered only after consultation with a health physicist. At levels greater than 2 rems per hour,* all site activities should cease until the site has been assessed by a health physicist (ICRP 1977).

Biologic Hazards

Medical and infectious wastes, as described in Chapter 12, are a significant hazard if encountered onsite and, like other wastes, are subject to wind and water dispersion. Other biologic hazards that may be present on hazardous waste sites include poisonous plants, insects, reptiles, animals, and indigenous pathogens (e.g., hanta virus). Protective clothing and respiratory equipment can help reduce the chances of exposure. Thorough washing of any exposed body parts and equipment will help protect against infection.

* Criteria originally published by the International Commission of Radiological Protection in "Basic Safety Standards for Radiation Protection" (ICRP-26), more recently by the EPA in the form of an "Action Guide: For Hazardous Waste Site Workers."

Safety Hazards

A wide variety of safety hazards are found on hazardous waste sites, including variations on the following:

- Holes or ditches
- Excavations and steep grades (cave-in hazards)
- Overhead and buried utilities
- Bins, silos, and other containment structures (engulfment hazards)
- Confined spaces
- Underground storage tanks being lifted or positioned
- Precariously positioned objects, such as drums that may fall
- Sharp objects such as nails, metal shards, and broken glass
- Slippery surfaces
- Steep grades
- Uneven terrain
- Unstable surfaces such as walls or floors that may fail

OSHA has promulgated health and safety standards for many of these workplace hazards. See Appendix A, to this chapter, for a listing of the standards.

Safety hazards are also created as a result of the work in progress on the site. Movement of heavy equipment involves physical hazards as well as noise. Protective equipment can impair worker agility, hearing, and vision, in turn creating increased risk of accidents. Increased chemical exposure hazard is caused when protective equipment is damaged. Workers onsite must continually observe each other and the work area for potential safety hazards and immediately inform supervisors of any new or previously undiscovered hazards .

Electrical Hazards

Overhead power lines, downed electrical wires, and buried cables all pose a danger of shock or electrocution if workers contact or sever them during site operations. Electrical equipment used onsite may also be a hazard to workers. Low-voltage equipment with ground-fault interrupters and water-tight, corrosion-resistant connecting cables should be used to minimize this hazard. Weather conditions should be monitored so that work may be suspended during thunder storms, thereby eliminating the lightning hazard. Capacitors found onsite may retain a charge and should be grounded before handling. Underground storage tank removals frequently involve electrical cables and/or other electrical apparatus in the same trench or in close proximity to petroleum fuel or natural gas lines.

Heat Stress

Heat stress is a major hazard for workers wearing protective clothing. The protective clothing materials that serve to shield the body from chemical exposure also limit the dissipation of body heat and moisture. Depending upon the ambient conditions and the work being performed, heat stress can develop very rapidly — within as little as 15 minutes. It can pose a danger to worker health as great as that of chemical exposure. Heat stress can initially cause rashes, cramps, discomfort, and drowsiness, resulting in impaired functional ability that threatens the safety of both the individual and coworkers. Continued heat stress can lead to heat stroke and death. Avoiding overprotection, careful training and frequent monitoring of personnel who wear protective clothing, shade and ventilation, judicious scheduling of work and rest periods, and frequent replacement of fluids can provide protection against this hazard. Employees and employers must be trained and alert to recognize symptoms of heat stress.

Cold Exposure

Cold injury (frostbite and hypothermia) and impaired ability to work are dangers at low temperatures and when the wind chill factor is low. To guard against them, managers and supervisors should ensure that workers wear appropriate clothing, have warm shelter readily available, carefully schedule work and rest periods, and monitor workers' physical conditions.

Noise Hazard

Onsite activity, in proximity to heavy equipment and machinery, may create a noise environment that is hazardous. Workplace noise is measured in decibels (dBA) on an "A-weighted" scale. The scale gives greater weight to the sound pressures in the more damaging frequencies (approximately 2000 Hz) and less weight to sound pressures outside this range (Martin 1994, p. 522). Effects of excessive noise may include:

- workers being startled, annoyed, or distracted.
- physical damage to the ear, pain, and temporary and/or permanent hearing loss.
- communication interference that may increase potential hazards due to the inability to warn of danger and the proper safety precautions to be taken.

If employees are subjected to noise exceeding an eight-hour, time-weighted average sound level of 90 dBA, feasible administrative or engineering controls must be utilized. In addition, whenever employee noise exposures equal or exceed an eight-hour, time-weighted average sound level of 85 dBA, employers must administer a continuing, effective hearing conservation program as described in 29 CFR 1910.95.

Other Physical Hazards

A variety of other physical hazard encounters are possible on hazardous waste sites. Vibrations, misused or malfunctioning hand tools, repetitive motion injury, and workplace violence are examples. Hazardous waste management activity requires intense focus on the primary objective. Employers and employees must be alert to the unexpected.

Hazardous Waste Operations and Emergency Response

Background

OSHA was created in December 1970* by enactment of the Occupational Safety and Health Act, PL 91-596, and began operations in April 1971 (Miller, 1985, Chapter 8). OSHA (the agency), under authorities of the original act and subsequent amendments, undertook the promulgation of workplace health and safety standards as specified by Section 6(g) based upon the needs of specific "industries, trades, crafts, occupations, businesses, workplaces, or work environments." In the years to follow, OSHA issued a variety of proposed standards, and some were made final. Standards dealing incidentally with activities of hazardous waste workers were promulgated, e.g., exposure standards for specific chemicals, standards governing handling of compressed gases, etc. In 1986, as Congress deliberated the Superfund Amendments and Reauthorization Act (SARA), Section 126 was added to Title I, requiring the Secretary of Labor to promulgate a hazardous waste worker health and safety standard. Interim final standards were issued on December 19, 1986. The final Hazardous Waste Operations and Emergency Response standards were published on March 6, 1989 (54 FR 9317) and were codified at 29 CFR 1910.120.

The Hazardous Waste Operations and Emergency Response standard, frequently referred to as the HazWOpER, became effective on March 6, 1990. It is intended to protect hazardous waste workers who are private employees, federal employees, and state and local government employees in states having delegated OSHA programs. In 40 CFR 311, state and local government employees engaged in hazardous waste operations and emergency response, in states that do not have an OSHA-approved state plan, are brought under the standard (Levine et al. 1994, p. 3). The scope of the HazWOpER encompasses three clearly defined groups of workers, those engaged in:

- cleanup sites, whether being cleaned up as a Superfund site, a RCRA Corrective Action site, or a voluntary cleanup site, are subject to paragraphs (a) through (o) of the standard.
- treatment, storage, and disposal facilities (RCRA permitted or interim status facilities) are subject to paragraph (p) of the standard.
- emergency response operations for releases of, or substantial threats of releases of, hazardous substances without regard to the location of the hazard are subject to paragraph (q) of the standard.

Generators who store hazardous wastes for less than 90 days and small quantity generators having emergency response teams that respond to releases of (or substantial threats of releases of) hazardous substances are required to comply only with paragraph (p)(8) of the standard. This requirement for an emergency response plan

* OSHA was created by amendment to an existing statute during the same month that the EPA was created by President Nixon's Reorganization Order No. 3 of 1970 (an executive order). OSHA was buried in the Department of Labor bureaucracy; the EPA was made an independent agency in the executive department (the administrator reports to the president). OSHA was organized primarily as an enforcement organization, with most of the staff as inspectors; the EPA was to be staffed with a mix of administrative, program management, research, and enforcement personnel.

does not apply to generators and small quantity generators who do not have emergency response teams if they provide an emergency action plan complying with 29 CFR 1910.38(a).

The Department of Labor has issued letters,* interpretations, and policy statements to the effect that employees who conduct leaking underground storage tank remediation are required to comply with 29 CFR 1910.120, including the training requirements.

In the following summary, the salient features of the standard are covered within the framework of the three groupings noted earlier. Space does not permit detailed explanation or discussion. The intent here is, as in previous chapters, to provide an introduction and oversight to and of the practice of hazardous waste management. The beginning practitioner should carefully read, at a minimum, the standard and the four-agency manual.

The HazWOpER Summarized

Standards Applicable to Cleanup Sites

The following are summarizations of subparagraphs of 29 CFR 1910:120:

(a) Scope, Application, and Definitions. The standard applies to mandatory cleanup operations involving hazardous substances at *uncontrolled* hazardous waste sites such as National Priority List (NPL) sites; RCRA corrective action sites; voluntary cleanup operations at sites which are uncontrolled; and emergency response operations involving hazardous substances without regard to location. *See* paragraph (a)/(2) for specific definitions.

(b) Safety and Health Program. Employers are required to develop and implement a written safety and health program, which must incorporate the following:

- An organizational structure
- A comprehensive workplan
- A site-specific safety and health plan, including an emergency response plan
- The safety and health training program
- The medical surveillance program

* Department of Labor memorandum of August 31, 1990 to OSHA regional administrators states, in part, "Activity under Subtitle I of RCRA could fall under the following scope sections of 29 CFR 1910.120":

1. Cleanup operations — 1910.120 (a)(1)(i) and (a)(1)(iii)
2. Corrective actions — 1910.120 (a)(1)(ii)
3. Emergency response operations — 1910.120 (a)(1)(v)

Leak detection, leak prevention, tank cleaning, and closure activity are covered by 29 CFR 1910.120 if any of the following apply:

1. A government body requires the tank to be removed because of the potential threat to the environment or the public.
2. The activities are necessary to complete a corrective action.
3. A governmental body has recognized the site to be uncontrolled hazardous waste.
4. There is a need for emergency response procedures.

- The employer's standard operating procedures for safety and health
- Coordination of general safety and health program and site-specific activities

Contractors and subcontractors must be informed regarding all hazards onsite. The written health and safety plan must be made available to contractors and to regulatory personnel having authority over the site.

(c) Site Characterization and Analysis. Sites where cleanup operations are planned must be evaluated to identify specific hazards and to determine safety and health control procedures needed to protect employees from the identified hazards. The process proceeds with a preliminary evaluation, in which a qualified person determines initial levels of personal protection necessary, followed by a more detailed evaluation of the site's specific hazards. The next step involves development of detailed physical, chemical, biological, and toxicological data on the site. Monitoring of radiation and air quality is accomplished with direct reading instruments. Risk identification associated with the identified substances is then determined and communicated to all employees involved in the project.

(d) Site Control. The site is closely controlled with respect to work zones, the use of a "buddy system," onsite communications, standard operating procedures, and identification of the nearest medical assistance. Continuous or periodic air quality monitoring is performed to detect changes that may have occurred since initial entry. A site map is used to communicate current and new information regarding the site as shifts change or as new contractors arrive.

(e) Training. All employees working onsite must receive training on:

- names of personnel responsible for site safety and health.
- safety, health, and other hazards onsite.
- use of personal protective equipment.
- work practices by which the employee can minimize risks from hazards.
- safe use of engineering controls and equipment onsite.
- medical surveillance.
- contents of the site safety and health plan.

General site workers (such as equipment operators, general laborers, and supervisors) engaged in hazardous substance removal or other activities which expose or potentially expose them to hazardous substances and health hazards must receive 40 hours* of instruction off the site and an additional three days* actual experience under the direct supervision of a trained, experienced supervisor. Workers only occasionally or regularly onsite in areas which are characterized as having minimal exposure hazards must receive 24 hours* of training offsite and one day* of actual experience under a trained, experienced supervisor. Onsite managers and supervisors must receive the 40 or 24 hours (as above) of offsite training and three days or one day (as above) of supervised field experience, plus 8 additional hours** of special-

* Employees who may be required to perform emergency response tasks at hazardous waste cleanup sites must receive training in appropriate response to emergencies that may arise on the site.

** Hourly classroom and field experience requirements are stated as minimum requirements.

ized training pertaining to their duties. All such employees must receive eight hours of refresher training annually.

Trainers must meet the qualifications of 29 CFR 1910.120(e)(5), requiring specific training in the subjects taught or appropriate academic credentials. On January 28, 1990, the EPA proposed an accreditation standard under a new 29 CFR 1910.121 (55 FR 2790). The rule was never finalized, but an expanded, nonmandatory Training Curriculum Guideline was published as Appendix E to 1910.120 on August 22, 1994 (59 FR 43270). Employers or others seeking the required training should ascertain that prospective training sources are in substantial adherance to the guidelines.

(f) Medical Surveillance. Employers of employees engaged in hazardous waste operations who:

- are or may be exposed above permissible exposure limits, without regard to the use of respirators, for more than 30 days per year.
- wear a respirator for 30 days or more per year.
- are injured due to overexposure from an emergency incident involving hazardous substances or health hazards.
- are members of HAZMAT teams.

must institute a medical surveillance program including a preassignment examination, annual or more frequent medical examinations and consultations, and medical examinations and consultations at the time of termination or transfer of the employee to an assignment which would not be subject to these requirements. These examinations and consultations must also be provided, at no cost to the employee, as soon as possible upon notification by an employee of detection of signs or symptoms of overexposure to hazardous substances or health hazards or that the employee has been injured or exposed above permissible limits. The frequency of examinations may be increased or decreased, as determined by the examining physician, but may not exceed two years. Employees of excepted generator facilities and who have no emergency response assignments, are injured, receive health impairments, develop symptoms of exposure to hazardous substances, or are exposed to concentrations above permissible or published limits, while not using appropriate personal protective equipment, must be provided the required examinations and consultations. The content of the examinations is to be determined by the physician, but must include a medical and work history. The employer must furnish a copy of the physician's written opinion regarding the examination, but the opinion may not reveal specific findings or diagnoses unrelated to occupational exposures.

(g) Engineering Controls, Work Practices, and Personal Protective Equipment for Employee Protection. The title phrases of this subparagraph are the three elements of a hierarchy of preferable approaches to hazardous waste worker protection. The preferred solution to an exposure or injury hazard is to reduce or "engineer" the problem out of existence by preventing, containing, isolating, or removing the hazard. Examples include enhanced ventilation, remotely operated devices for operating material handling equipment, use of pressurized cabs or control booths on equipment, elimination of sources of excess noise, or smoothing the paths of forklifts carrying hazardous chemicals. Work practices (also referred to as administrative

FIGURE 15.1 Level A (training) — totally encapsulating chemical protective suits and self-contained or supplied-air respirators.

controls) are also considered preferable to the use of protective clothing and equipment. Examples include removing all nonessential personnel from a worksite while drums are being opened, scheduling operations to take advantage of cooler temperatures to reduce heat stress hazards, wetting down dusty operations, or locating employees upwind of airborne hazards. Only if the hazard cannot be eliminated by engineering controls and/or work practices should protective clothing and equipment (PPE) be the protective option (*see also* Wallace 1994, p. 208).

Selection of levels of PPE must be based upon an evaluation of the performance characteristics of the PPE *relative to the identified and potential hazards onsite*.* Totally encapsulating chemical protective suits and self-contained or supplied-air respirators (Level A) (Figure 15.1) are required where skin absorption of a hazardous substance may result in a substantial possibility of death, immediate serious illness or injury, or impair the ability to escape. Level B, consisting of self-contained or supplied-air respirator and chemical-resistant protective clothing which is not fully encapsulating, inner and outer gloves, chemical-resistant safety boots, and optional boot covers, hard hat, or face shield (figure 15.2), is worn where the highest level of respiratory protection, but a lesser level of skin protection is needed. Level C (Figure 15.3), consisting of an air-purifying respirator (APR) and clothing similar to that of Level B, may be worn when concentration(s) and types of airborne substance(s) are known and all criteria for use of APRs are met. *In all cases, the chemical resistance characteristics of the protective clothing, as provided by the manufacturer, must be*

* The importance of this linkage between site characterization and level of PPE selection cannot be overemphasized.

FIGURE 15.2 Level B (training) — self-contained or supplied-air respirator and chemical-resistant protective clothing which is not fully encapsulating, inner and outer gloves, chemical-resistant safety boots, and optional boot covers, hard hat, or face shield.

FIGURE 15.3 Level C (training) — air-purifying respirator (APR) and clothing similar to that of Level B.

compatible with the known chemical hazards on the site and with the solvent(s) to be used in decontamination.

Level of PPE decisions must balance protection, worker productivity, worker comfort, and cost. Neither overcautiousness, overconfidence, nor indifference have a place in the decision. For example, the degree of worker protection achieved by a supervisor's decision to require wearing of Level A vs. Level B, in many scenarios, is primarily in the degree of skin protection achieved. The supervisor must balance the reality of the splash or vapor hazard against the extreme stresses and limitations imposed on the worker by a Level A outfit. In no case, however, should the PPE selection criteria of Chapter 8 of the four-agency manual, Subtitle I of 29 CFR 1910, or the *NIOSH Pocket Guide to Chemical Hazards* be disregarded or overridden.

The appendices to 29 CFR 1910.120, the applicable standards of Subpart I, and the four-agency manual must be read and understood before the use of PPE.* Employees must not be assigned to onsite tasks requiring PPE before receiving the required training summarized in subparagraph (e). (*See also* Schwope and O'Leary 1994, Chapter 9; Goldman 1994, Chapter 10).

(h) Monitoring. Initial and periodic air quality monitoring are performed where there may be a question of employee exposure to hazardous concentrations of hazardous substances in order to assure proper selection of engineering controls, work practices, and PPE. Upon initial entry, air monitoring is conducted to identify any IDLH condition, exposure over permissible or published exposure levels, exposure over a radioactive material's dose limits, or other danger such as the presence of flammable atmospheres or oxygen-deficient environments. Periodic monitoring is conducted when there is the possibility (or actuality) of chemical concentrations in excess of a ceiling, an IDLH condition or flammable atmosphere, or an indication that exposures may rise over permissible limits. Individual high-risk employees are monitored during the actual cleanup operations, e.g., when soil, surface water, or containers are moved or disturbed.

(i) Informational Programs. Employees, contractors, and subcontractors must be informed of the nature, level, and degree of exposure likely in their participation in hazardous waste operations.

(j) Handling Drums and Containers. The subparagraph (j) standards pertaining to drums are lengthy and do not lend themselves to summarization. In general, drums and other containers used during cleanup operations must meet appropriate U.S. Department of Transportation (DOT), OSHA, and EPA regulations for the wastes to be contained. Drums must be inspected and their integrity assured before moving. Leaking or damaged drums must be overpacked or have contents transferred prior to being moved. Drums with old labels and unlabeled drums should be considered to contain hazardous substances and be handled accordingly until the contents are positively identified and labeled. Containers suspected of containing radioactive materials must not be handled by workers until evaluated by an expert. Site opera-

* For a listing of other workplace standards which may apply to a particular site or set of conditions, see Appendix A to this chapter.

tions must be organized to minimize movement of drums. Exhumation of buried drums must be done with caution in order to prevent rupture (Chapter 11, Figure 11.7) and provision must be made for containing spills. Drums that are bulged must be opened remotely with the operator shielded and must not be moved until the cause of the bulging has been determined. Drums that show signs of crystalline material must be treated as shock sensitive until identification of the contents can be made.

(k) Decontamination. A decontamination procedure must be developed, communicated to employees, and implemented before any employees or equipment enter the exclusion zone (or areas where potential for exposure exists). The decontamination area or corridor must be located to provide a transition from contaminated to noncontaminated areas without exposing noncontaminated employees or equipment. Employees leaving a contaminated area must be decontaminated; contaminated clothing and equipment must be properly decontaminated or disposed of. Decontamination procedures must be monitored by the site safety officer to determine their effectiveness and to modify or correct them as necessary. Shower and change rooms must be provided where the decontamination procedure indicates need for regular showers. Showers must be used immediately where nonimpermeable clothing becomes wetted with hazardous substances or impermeable clothing becomes compromised. As indicated in Item 7, solvent(s) used in decontamination must be chemically compatible with protective clothing worn and with the contaminant(s) encountered. Solvents used in decontamination must be managed as hazardous waste until it can be shown that they are nonhazardous.

(l) Emergency Response by Employees at Uncontrolled Hazardous Waste Sites. Cleanup site employers must develop and implement an emergency response plan, which is a separate section of the site safety and health plan. The plan must be in writing and available for inspection and copying by employees, employee representatives, and regulatory agencies having relevant purview. Employers who will evacuate employees from the workplace when an emergency occurs and who do not permit any of their employees to assist in handling the emergency are exempt from this requirement if they provide an emergency action plan which complies with 29 CFR 38(a). Minimum requirements for an emergency response plan include:

- Preemergency planning
- Personnel roles, lines of authority, and communication
- Emergency recognition and prevention
- Safe distances and places of refuge
- Site security and control
- Evacuation routes and procedures
- Decontamination procedures not covered by the site safety and health plan
- Emergency medical treatment and first aid
- Emergency alerting and response procedures
- Critique of response and follow-up
- PPE and emergency equipment

In addition to the listed minimum requirements, emergency response plans must include site topography; layout; prevailing weather conditions; and procedures for reporting incidents to appropriate local, state, and federal agencies. The plan must be compatible and integrated with disaster, fire, and/or emergency response plans of local state and federal agencies and can be integrated with the RCRA Contingency Plan, Clean Water Act Spill Prevention Control and Countermeasures Plan, and OSHA Process Safety Emergency Action Plan. The plan must be rehearsed regularly and reviewed and amended as needed. An employee alarm system, as prescribed by 29 CFR 1910.165, must be installed and operated to inform employees of an emergency situation.

(m) Illumination. This standard identifies minimum criteria ranging from 3-ft candles in excavation and waste areas to 30-ft candles for first aid stations. The standard is summarized in Table H-120.1 of subparagraph m.

(n) Sanitation at Temporary Workplaces. The sanitation requirements cover potable water, containers, drinking cups, nonpotable water systems, toilets, food handling, temporary sleeping quarters, washing facilities, and showers and change rooms .

(o) New Technology Programs. This subparagraph requires employers to stay abreast of new technologies and equipment developed for protection of employees on cleanup sites, to provide procedures for the introduction of new technologies, and to implement them.

Standards Applicable to Treatment, Storage, and Disposal Sites

(p) Certain Operations Conducted Under the Resource Conservation and Recovery Act of 1976 (RCRA). The employer conducting operations at RCRA permitted or interim status TSDFs is required to provide and implement many of the same, or similar, standards as required of cleanup site employers. The TSDF is presumed to be controlled as differentiated from the cleanup site, which may be, or potentially is, uncontrolled. The site is presumed to be characterized, i.e., the hazards are known, and the employee is theoretically less likely to be exposed. The more apparent difference between the cleanup site and TSDF requirements are those pertaining to training. The TSDF employee must have 24 hours of initial training, plus an 8-hour annual refresher. The trainer providing the initial training must have satisfactorily completed a training course for teaching the required subjects or have equivalent academic credentials and instructional experience.

Standards Applicable to Emergency Response Teams

The separate and distinct "first responder" standards of subparagraph (q) are frequently the basis for confusion or misunderstanding. Subparagraph (a)(v) speaks of "Emergency response operations for releases of, or substantial threats of releases of, hazardous substances *without regard to location of the hazard*." However, subparagraph (q) begins with "This paragraph covers employers whose employees are engaged in emergency response no matter where it occurs except that it does not cover employees engaged in operations specified in paragraphs (a)(1)(i) through (a)(1)(iv)...," the latter being cleanup site and treatment, storage, and disposal site workers (referred to by NIOSH as "collateral duty responders"). In the nonmandatory

Appendix E, added in August 1994, the curriculum guidelines for subparagraph (q) emergency responders emphasized the concept that the training requirements of subparagraph (q) were aimed at the private sector (i.e., collateral duty) emergency responders. It further stated that the requirements could have an impact upon public responders, but that public responder training would be determined by the various state regulations. Many state and local governments require their public responders to have training far in excess of that required in subparagraph (q). The salience of the matter is that collateral duty responders must be trained specifically to deal with the hazards of the sites to which they are assigned by employment. They are not trained for public responder duties and should not be placed in public responder positions until they meet the applicable state and local training requirements.

(q) Emergency Response to Hazardous Substance Releases. OSHA defines five levels of response training, each of which is specific to assigned duties of the employee.

1. *First Responder Awareness Level* — Individuals likely to witness or discover a hazardous substance release and initiate the emergency response must demonstrate competency in such areas as recognizing the presence of hazardous materials in an emergency, ability to identify the hazardous material (if possible), the risks involved, and the outcomes associated with an emergency involving hazardous materials. The first responder assigned to "awareness" level tasks must understand that role in the employers emergency response plan and must be able to recognize the need for additional resources and make the appropriate notification(s). There is no specified number of hours of training required.
2. *First Responder Operations Level* — Individuals take defensive action to contain the release from a safe distance, keep it from spreading, and prevent exposures. In addition to demonstrating competencies of the "awareness level," the operations level responder must receive at least eight hours of training or demonstrate competency in basic hazard and risk assessment techniques; selection and use of appropriate PPE; hazmat terminology; basic control, containment, and confinement operations; decontamination procedures; and standard operating procedures.
3. *Hazardous Materials Technician* — The technicians are individuals who respond aggressively to releases or potential releases for the purpose of stopping the release. Hazardous materials technicians must receive at least 24 hours of training equal to the first responder operations level and must know how to implement the employer's emergency response plan; know the classification, identification, and verification of hazardous materials by using field instruments and equipment; know how to select and use specialized chemical protective equipment; understand hazard and risk assessment techniques; be able to perform advanced control, containment, and confinement operations; understand and implement decontamination and termination procedures; understand basic chemistry and toxicology; and be able to function within the Incident Command System.

4. *Hazardous Materials Specialist* — These individuals have duties parallel to those of the technician, but requiring more specific knowledge of the substances which may be encountered. The specialist must have at least 24 hours of training equal to the technician level; know the local and state emergency response plan; know how to implement the local plan; understand classification and identification of hazardous materials using advanced survey instruments and equipment; understand and use specialized chemical protective equipment; understand chemical, radiological, and toxicological terminology and behavior and in-depth hazard and risk assessment techniques; be able to develop a site safety and control plan; and be able to determine and implement decontamination procedures.
5. *On-Scene Incident Commander* — This individual must have at least 24 hours of training equal to the operations level; be able to implement the employer's incident command system, emergency response plan, and the local emergency response plan; know of the state emergency response plan and of the Federal Regional Response Team; and know and understand the hazards and risks associated with employees working in chemical protective clothing and the importance of decontamination procedures.

Employers must certify the training and/or competence of each individual assigned to one of these levels.

Other Important Topics and Compliance Issues

In this section, we attempt to alert managers and supervisors to three issues which are not clearly defined and\or explained by OSHA. They are issues which require a degree of monitoring by responsible individuals. In a more general context, managers and supervisors should be alert to a trend of ever-widening scope and detail of the OSHA regulatory structure. The trend is clearly toward more emphasis on hazard assessment and employee training. The April 6, 1994 final rule amendments to 29 CFR 1910.133 (eye and face protection), 1910.135 (head protection), 1910.136 (foot protection), and 1910.138 (hand protection) are recent examples.

Respirator Selection Criteria

Respiratory protection is of primary importance because inhalation is one of the major routes of exposure to chemical toxicant. As before, space does not permit a detailed presentation on respirator selection. However, widespread misuse of respirator equipment by hazardous waste workers is cause for concerns regarding emphasis, or adequacy of training, or both. All concerned with respirator selection should be thoroughly familiarized with 29 CFR 1910.134, the OSHA respirator standard, and the *latest update* of the source standard — ANSI* Z88.2.

Respirators which supply air to the user are called atmosphere-supplying respirators and consist of two types:

* The American National Standards Institute, 11 West 42nd Street, New York, NY 10036.

- Self-contained breathing apparatus (SCBA) which supply breathing-grade air from a source carried by the user
- Supplied-air respirators (SAR) (or airline respirators) which supply breathing-grade air from a source located some distance away, through an airline, to the user

APRs do not provide air from a separate source. They provide ambient air which has been "purified" by a filtering element, e.g., a cartridge or canister.

Both types of respirators are further classified as to positive or negative pressure. Positive pressure respirators, as the name implies, maintain slightly positive pressure inside the face piece. Negative pressure respirators depend upon the negative pressure created inside the respirator when the user inhales.

NIOSH, in 1976, recommended seven distinct conditions which should be met in order for the user to safely use an APR (Bollinger and Schultz, 1987). These conditions have been restated in a variety of publications which do not have regulatory authorities. The original seven conditions are:

- Ambient air has at least 19.5% oxygen, by volume.
- Concentrations of known contaminants are less than IDLH levels.
- The known contaminants have adequate warning properties; the threshold odor concentrations are less than the permissible exposure limit (PEL).
- Identity and concentrations of chemical contaminants are known (requires regularly scheduled monitoring).
- Respirator (face piece and cartridge or canister) is NIOSH/MSHA* approved for the known contaminants at the measured concentrations.
- Protection factor is adequate to keep exposure at concentrations less than PELs of known contaminants.
- Wearer is properly fit tested.

Moreover, APR cartridges have finite lifespans based upon the saturation rates of the absorbent materials and must be replaced before breakthrough occurs. The service life of a cartridge is dependent upon respiratory rate, contaminant concentration, cartridge efficiency, and humidity. (*See also* ANSI Z88.2 1992; four-agency manual 1985, p. 8-7; Schwope and O'Leary 1994, p. 223ff; Jones 1994, Chapter 4)

In the current 29 CFR 1910.134, OSHA has by reference to ANSI Z88.2 (1969) codified two of the seven conditions. In proposed amendments** to 1910.134, OSHA has used language suggestive of three of the NIOSH seven conditions. At this writing, the proposed amendments await final publication, and it is questionable which, if any, of the seven can be enforced.

The recommended seven conditions are obviously well grounded and legitimate. Yet workers are regularly seen wearing APRs while engaged in hazardous waste activity where it is clear that one or more of the conditions are not met. This is particularly true with respect to identification and concentrations of chemical con-

* U.S. Mine Safety and Health Administration.
** 59 FR 58884, November 15, 1994.

stituents, protection factors, and adequate warning properties. The manager/supervisor should carefully consider the ramifications of anything less than full adherence to the recommendations.

Applicable Air Contaminant Standards

Soon after enactment of the Occupational Safety and Health Act, in 1970, OSHA promulgated permissible exposure limits (PELS) for many substances, per Section 6(a) of the act. The standards can be traced back to 1968 threshold limit values (TLVs) of the American Conference of Governmental Industrial Hygienists (ACGIH) and to the American Standards Association, the predecessor of ANSI. By 1989, significant data had accumulated, to the effect that the existing 400 substances regulated were inadequate, but OSHA lacked resources to rigorously develop substance-by-substance rulemaking and elected to engage in "generic" rulemaking to achieve the desired improvements. The 1989 rulemaking covered a total of 600 substances, including PELs for 164 new substances, adoption of more protective PELs for 212 substances, no changes for 160 substances, and lesser adjustments. [Adapted from the Introduction to OSHA Publication 3112 (U.S. Department of Labor 1989).]

A July 1992 federal appeals court decision vacated the 1989 rulemaking and forced OSHA to roll back exposure limits for many hazardous chemicals to less protective 1971 levels and eliminate exposure limits for dozens of other substances that had been unregulated prior to 1989 (*Environment Reporter*, June 30, 1993, p. 108). The enforceable PELs are those now listed in Tables Z-1, Z-2, and Z-3 of 29 CFR 1910.1000. OSHA can be expected to promulgate new limits on new and presently regulated substances in the earlier substance-by-substance mode. The manager/supervisor is thus faced with at least two additional quandaries: (1) the necessity to maintain close observation of seemingly insignificant promulgations pertaining to single substances and (2) the question of adequacy of the present PELs to protect his/her employees.

Chemical Hazard Communication

Employer recognition of need, as well as OSHA requirements, have brought hazard communication to the forefront of workplace safety management. The Hazard Communication Standard, or HAZCOM (29 CFR 1910.1200), establishes uniform requirements to ensure that the hazards of all chemicals imported into, produced, or used in workplaces are evaluated by the employer and that this hazard information is transmitted to affected employers and to employees that are at risk of exposure. The requirements of the standard focus upon use of the Material Safety Data Sheet (MSDS) and labels as the primary means of communicating chemical hazard information. The standard requires training of employees regarding their rights under the standard, health effects of chemicals being used, how to read and use the labels and MSDSs in terms of available controls, and use of PPE. Competent and conscientious owners, operators, managers, and supervisors of facilities using toxic chemicals have generally met or exceeded requirements of the HAZCOM. Some go beyond the requirement by using MSDSs to screen out highly hazardous chemicals and find less toxic substitutes.

For hazardous waste workers, hazard communication takes on a different meaning. The HAZCOM [29 CFR 1910.1200(b)(6)(i),(ii)] excludes RCRA hazardous waste and Comprehensive Environmental Response, Compensation, and Liability Act (CERCLA) hazardous substances from applicability of the standard. Nevertheless, hazard communication requirements are threaded throughout the HAZWOPER, and worker health and safety courses regularly include discussion of the MSDS, the types of information contained, responsibilities of the chemical manufacturer/importer, the distributor, and the employer. MSDSs may occasionally be located and obtained for identified hazardous waste constituents. Moreover, waste chemicals such as used solvents may be chemically similar to the virgin product, whereby the original MSDSs would suffice for HAZCOM purposes. Wherever waste constituents can be identified on cleanup sites, the MSDS will be a valuable source of information, particularly with regard to incompatibility, ignitability, and toxicity. But cleanup sites frequently involve chemical mixtures, decay products, and reaction products that are numerous and/or unidentified. Thus, the MSDS for hazardous wastes found on cleanup sites may be nonexistent, and the manager/supervisor frequently must perform the required risk assessments using very limited chemical data. This circumstance may lead to a false sense of security on the part of the worker and unwarranted relaxation of the PPE regimen.

APPENDIX A. OSHA WORKPLACE STANDARDS WHICH MAY APPLY TO HAZARDOUS WASTE SITES

Document: CFR Part 1910 — Occupational Safety and Health Standards

Subpart C — General Safety and Health Provisions

- 1910.20 Access to Employee Exposure and Medical Records

Subpart D — Walking-Working Surfaces

- 1910.21 Definitions
- 1910.22 General Requirements
- 1910.23 Guarding Floor and Wall Openings and Holes
- 1910.24 Fixed Industrial Stairs
- 1910.25 Portable Wood Ladders
- 1910.26 Portable Metal Ladders
- 1910.27 Fixed Ladders
- 1910.28 Safety Requirements for Scaffolding
- 1910.29 Manually Propelled Mobile Ladder Stands and Scaffolds (Towers)
- 1910.30 Other Working Surfaces
- 1910.31 Sources of Standards
- 1910.32 Standards Organizations

Subpart E — Means of Egress

- 1910.35 Definitions
- 1910.36 General Requirements
- 1910.37 Means of Egress, General

1910.38 Employee Emergency Plans and Fire Prevention Plans
1910.39 Sources of Standards
1910.40 Standards Organizations
Appendix To Subpart E — Means of Egress

Subpart F — Powered Platforms, Manlifts, and Vehicle-Mounted Work Platforms
1910.66 Powered Platforms for Building Maintenance
1910.67 Vehicle-Mounted Elevating and Rotating Work Platforms
1910.68 Manlifts
1910.69 Sources of Standards
1910.70 Standards Organizations

Subpart G — Occupational Health and Environmental Control
1910.94 Ventilation
1910.95 Occupational Noise Exposure
1910.96 Ionizing Radiation
1910.97 Nonionizing Radiation
1910.98 Effective Dates
1910.99 Sources of Standards
1910.100 Standards Organizations

Subpart H — Hazardous Materials
1910.101 Compressed Gases, General Requirements
1910.102 Acetylene
1910.103 Hydrogen
1910.104 Oxygen
1910.105 Nitrous Oxide
1910.106 Flammable and Combustible Liquids
1910.107 Spray Finishing Using Flammable and Combustible Materials
1910.108 Dip Tanks Containing Flammable or Combustible Liquids
1910.109 Explosives and Blasting Agents
1910.110 Storage and Handling of Liquified Petroleum Gases
1910.111 Storage and Handling of Anhydrous Ammonia
1910.112–1910.113 [Reserved]
1910.114 Effective Dates
1910.115 Sources of Standards
1910.116 Standards Organizations
1910.119 Process Safety Management of Highly Hazardous Chemicals
1910.120 Hazardous Waste Operations and Emergency Response

Subpart I — Personal Protective Equipment
1910.132 General Requirements
1910.133 Eye and Face Protection
1910.134 Respiratory Protection
1910.135 Occupational Head Protection
1910.136 Occupational Foot Protection
1910.137 Electrical Protective Devices
1910.138 Hand Protection
1910.139 Sources of Standards
1910.140 Standards Organizations

Appendix A to Subpart I — References for Further Information (Non-Mandatory)

Appendix B to Subpart I — Non-Mandatory Compliance Guidelines for Hazard Assessment and Personal Protective Equipment Selection

Subpart J — General Environmental Controls

1910.141 Sanitation
1910.142 Temporary Labor Camps
1910.143 Nonwater Carriage Disposal Systems
1910.144 Safety Color Code for Marking Physical Hazards
1910.145 Specifications for Accident Prevention Signs and Tags
1910.146 Permit-Required Confined Spaces
1910.147 The Control of Hazardous Energy (Lockout/Tagout)
1910.148 Standards Organizations
1910.149 Effective Dates
1910.150 Sources of Standards

Subpart K — Medical and First Aid

1910.151 Medical Services and First Aid
1910.152 [Reserved]
1910.153 Sources of Standards

Subpart L — Fire Protection

1910.155 Scope, Application, and Definitions Applicable to This Subpart
1910.156 Fire Brigades

Portable Fire Suppression Equipment

1910.157 Portable Fire Extinguishers
1910.158 Standpipe and Hose Systems

Fixed Fire Suppression Equipment

1910.159 Automatic Sprinkler Systems
1910.160 Fixed Extinguishing Systems, General
1910.161 Fixed Extinguishing Systems, Dry Chemical
1910.162 Fixed Extinguishing Systems, Gaseous Agent
1910.163 Fixed Extinguishing Systems, Water Spray and Foam

Other Fire Protection Systems

1910.164 Fire Detection Systems
1910.165 Employee Alarm Systems

Appendices to Subpart L

Appendix A to Subpart L — Fire Protection

Appendix B to Subpart L — National Concensus Standards

Appendix C to Subpart L — Fire Protection References For Further Information

Appendix D to Subpart L — Availability of Publications Incorporated by Reference in Section 1910.156 Fire Brigades

Appendix E to Subpart L — Test Methods for Protective Clothing

Subpart M — Compressed Gas and Compressed Air Equipment
- 1910.166–1910.168 [Reserved]
- 1910.169 Air Receivers
- 1910.170 Sources of Standards
- 1910.171 Standards Organizations

Subpart N — Materials Handling and Storage
- 1910.176 Handling Materials — General
- 1910.177 Servicing Multi-Piece and Single Piece Rim Wheels
- 1910.178 Powered Industrial Trucks
- 1910.179 Overhead and Gantry Cranes
- 1910.180 Crawler Locomotive and Truck Cranes
- 1910.181 Derricks
- 1910.182 Effective Dates
- 1910.183 Helicopters
- 1910.184 Slings
- 1910.189 Sources of Standards
- 1910.190 Standards Organizations

Subpart O — Machinery and Machine Guarding
- 1910.211 Definitions
- 1910.212 General Requirements for All Machines
- 1910.213 Woodworking Machinery Requirements
- 1910.214 Cooperage Machinery
- 1910.215 Abrasive Wheel Machinery
- 1910.216 Mills and Calenders in the Rubber and Plastics Industries
- 1910.217 Mechanical Power Presses
- 1910.218 Forging Machines
- 1910.219 Mechanical Power-Transmission Apparatus
- 1910.220 Effective Dates
- 1910.221 Sources of Standards
- 1910.222 Standards Organizations

Subpart P — Hand and Portable Powered Tools and Other Hand-Held Equipment
- 1910.241 Definitions
- 1910.242 Hand and Portable Powered Tools and Equipment, General
- 1910.243 Guarding of Portable Powered Tools
- 1910.244 Other Portable Tools and Equipment
- 1910.245 Effective Dates
- 1910.246 Sources of Standards
- 1910.247 Standards Organizations

Subpart Q — Welding, Cutting, and Brazing
- 1910.251 Definitions
- 1910.252 General Requirements
- 1910.253 Oxygen-Fuel Gas Welding and Cutting
- 1910.254 Arc Welding and Cutting
- 1910.255 Resistance Welding
- 1910.256 Sources of Standards
- 1910.257 Standards Organizations

Subpart S — Electrical

1910.301 Introduction. Design Safety Standards for Electrical Systems
1910.302 Electric Utilization Systems
1910.303 General Requirements
1910.304 Wiring Design and Protection
1910.305 Wiring Methods, Components, and Equipment for General Use
1910.306 Specific Purpose Equipment and Installations
1910.307 Hazardous (Classified) Locations
1910.308 Special Systems
1910.309–1910.330 [Reserved]

Safety-Related Work Practices

1910.331 Scope
1910.332 Training
1910.333 Selection and Use of Work Practices
1910.334 Use of Equipment
1910.335 Safeguards for Personnel Protection
1910.336–1910.360 [Reserved]

Safety-Related Maintenance Requirements

1910.361–1910.380 [Reserved]

Safety Requirements for Special Equipment

1910.381–1910.398 [Reserved]

Subpart Z — Toxic and Hazardous Substances

1910.1000 Air Contaminants
1910.1001 Asbestos
1910.1002 Coal Tar Pitch Volatiles; Interpretation of Term
1910.1003 4-Nitrobiphenyl
1910.1004 Alpha-Naphthylamine
1910.1005 [Reserved]
1910.1006 Methyl Chloromethyl Ether
1910.1007 3,3-Dichlorobenzidine (and Its Salts)
1910.1008 *bis*-Chloromethyl ether
1910.1009 Beta-Naphthylamine
1910.1010 Benzidine
1910.1011 4-Aminodiphenyl
1910.1012 Ethyleneimine
1910.1013 Beta-Propiolactone
1910.1014 2-Acetylaminofluorene
1910.1015 4-Dimethylaminoazobenzene
1910.1016 *N*-Nitrosodimethylamine
1910.1017 Vinyl Chloride
1910.1018 Inorganic Arsenic
1910.1025 Lead
1910.1027 Cadmium

1910.1028	Benzene
1910.1029	Coke Oven Emissions
1910.1030	Bloodborne Pathogens
1910.1043	Cotton Dust
1910.1044	1,2-Dibromo-3-Chloropropane
1910.1045	Acrylonitrile
1910.1047	Ethylene Oxide
1910.1048	Formaldehyde
1910.1050	Methylenedianline
1910.1200	Hazard Communication
1910.1201	Retention of DOT Markings, Placards, and Labels
1910.1450	Occupational Exposure to Hazardous Chemicals in Laboratories
1910.1499	Source of Standards
1910.1500	Standards Organizations

TOPICS FOR REVIEW OR DISCUSSION

1. Hazardous waste site workers may be confronted with any of five routes of chemical exposure. Review the five and examples of how each may occur.
2. One of the routes is generally considered to be the most likely route of chemical exposure. Which and why?
3. If air at higher altitudes, say 8000 ft, contains 19.5% oxygen, why is that considered a respiratory problem by OSHA?
4. If alpha particles can be attenuated or stopped by a sheet of paper or light clothing, why are they considered a major hazard on sites having alpha sources?
5. Heat stress is a major hazard for hazardous waste workers. Give some examples of work practices or administrative controls that might be appropriate for prevention of heat stress.
6. Under what circumstances are underground storage tank workers considered to be subject to the HAZWOPER?
7. Discuss some examples of confined spaces. Why are they considered so hazardous?
8. Discuss ways in which an MSDS might be useful on a hazardous waste site (even though RCRA hazardous waste is not covered by the HAZCOM standard).
9. The seven criteria for use of an air-purifying respirator, while working in potentially hazardous atmospheres, are ____ , ______ , ______ , ______ , ______ , ______ , and ______ .
10. There is an extremely important linkage between site characterization and selection of PPE. Explain.

REFERENCES

American Conference of Governmental Industrial Hygienists. 1993. *Threshold Limit Values for Chemical Substances and Physical Agents and Biological Exposure Indices.* Technical Affairs Office, Cincinnati, OH.

American National Standards Institute. 1992. *American National Standard for Respiratory Protection.* ANSI Z882.2-1992. New York.

Bollinger, Nancy J. and Robert H. Schutz. 1987. *NIOSH Guide to Industrial Respiratory Protection.* Division of Safety Research, National Institute for Occupational Safety and Health, Cincinnati, OH.

Environment Reporter June 30, 1993. p. 108. Bureau of National Affairs, Washington, D.C.

Goldman, Ralph F. 1994. "Heat Stress in Industrial Protective Encapsulating Garments." *Protecting Personnel at Hazardous Waste Sites*, Butterworth-Heinemann, Stoneham, MA. Chapter 10.

International Commission on Radiological Protection (ICRP). 1977. *Recommendations of the International Commission on Radiological Protection,* ICRP Publication 26. Pergamon Press, Oxford, England.

Jones, Frank E. 1994. *Toxic Organic Vapors in the Workplace.* CRC Press, Boca Raton, FL.

Levine, Steven P., Rodney D. Turpin, and Michael Gochfeld. 1994. "Protecting Personnel at Hazardous Waste Sites: Current Issues," Chapter 1. In *Protecting Personnel at Hazardous Waste Sites,* Butterworth-Heinemann, Stoneham, MA.

Martin, William, F. 1994. "Site Health and Safety Plans," Chapter 16. In *Protecting Personnel at Hazardous Waste Sites,* Butterworth-Heinemann, Stoneham, MA.

Miller, Marshall Lee. 1985. "Occupational Safety and Health," Chapter 8. In *Environmental Law Handbook.* Government Institutes, Inc., Rockville, MD.

Occupational Safety and Health Reporter October 5, 1994. Bureau of National Affairs, Washington, D.C.

Occupational Safety and Health Reporter July 29, 1992. Bureau of National Affairs, Washington, D.C.

Petroleum Equipment Institute. 1992. *Tulsaletter* July 28. Tulsa, OK.

Robinson, James C. 1991. *Toils and Toxics.* University of California Press, Los Angeles.

Schwope, Arthur D., and Christopher C. O'Leary. 1994. "Personal Protective Equipment." *Protecting Personnel at Hazardous Waste Sites*, Butterworth-Heinemann, Stoneham, MA. Chapter 9.

U.S. Department of Health and Human Services. 1985. *Occupational Safety and Health Guidance Manual for Hazardous Waste Site Activities.* Superintendent of Documents, Government Printing Office, Washington, D.C. (cited in text as the "four-agency manual").

U.S. Department of Labor. 1989. *Air Contaminants — Permissible Exposure Limits* (29 CFR 1910.1000). Occupational Safety and Health Administration, Washington, D.C. OSHA-3112.

U.S. National Institute for Occupational Safety and Health. 1994. *NIOSH Pocket Guide to Chemical Hazards.* Government Printing Office, Washington, D.C.

U.S. Occupational Safety and Health Administration (OSHA). 1994. News release, February 17.

Wallace, Lynn P. 1994. "Site Layout and Engineered Controls." Chapter 8. In *Protecting Personnel at Hazardous Waste Sites*, Butterworth-Heinemann, Stoneham, MA.

GLOSSARY

There are three conventions in this glossary:

1. Definitions using the word "means" are those taken directly from the Resource Conservation and Recovery Act (RCRA), the implementing regulations, and other pertinent statutes and regulations. Definitions without the word "means" are those commonly used and accepted in the hazardous waste management field.
2. Acronyms are mixed throughout, rather than being compiled separately, because many require definition as well as explanation.
3. Words in the masculine gender also include the feminine and neuter gender; words in the singular include the plural; and words in the plural include the singular.

Absorption — the process whereby one or more gaseous contaminants are dissolved into a relatively nonvolatile liquid and may be characterized as chemical or physical. Chemical absorption occurs when there is a reaction between the absorbed gas and the liquid solvent. Physical absorption occurs when the absorbed gas merely dissolves in the liquid solvent.

Active life means the period from the initial receipt of hazardous waste at a facility until the regional administrator receives certification of final closure.

Active portion means that portion of a facility where treatment, storage, or disposal operations are being or have been conducted after the effective date of 40 CFR 261, and which is not a closed portion. (*See also* **closed portion** and **inactive portion**)

Acute effect — an adverse effect on the receptor organism, with symptoms of severity coming quickly to a crisis.

Acutely hazardous waste — wastes listed in 40 CFR 261.31 and which are followed by the symbol (H), and all of the "P" wastes listed in 40 CFR 261.33(e).

Administrator means the Administrator of the Environmental Protection Agency or his designee.

Adsorption — a physical phenomenon which refers to the ability of certain solids to attract and collect organic substances from the surrounding medium. Granular activated carbon is widely used to absorb organic components from liquid and gaseous waste streams.

Aerobic decomposition — the natural decay and breakdown of organic matter by bacteria which utilize oxygen in respiration.

Alpha particle — a positively charged particle composed of two neutrons and two protons released by some atoms undergoing radioactive decay. The particle is identical to the nucleus of a helium atom.

Anaerobic decomposition — the natural decay and breakdown of organic matter by bacteria which do not require oxygen for respiration.

Aquifer means a geologic formation, group of formations, or part of a formation capable of yielding a significant amount of groundwater to wells or springs.

Artesian — the occurrence of groundwater under greater than atmospheric pressure.

Artificial recharge — the addition of water to the groundwater reservoir by activities of man.

Asphyxiant — a chemical that can deny oxygen to cells of the host organism, thereby slowing or halting metabolism.

Audit (environmental) — a systematic, documented, periodic, and objective review by regulated entities of facility operations and practices relate to meeting environmental requirements. The audit may verify compliance with environmental requirements, evaluate the effectiveness of environmental management systems already in place, or assess risks from regulated and unregulated materials and practices.

Base flow — the portion of the flow, in surface streams, that has been discharged to the stream as influent groundwater.

Beta particle — negatively charged particles (electrons) emitted by radioactive decay processes. Beta particles travel at 30 to 99% of the speed of light, but have low mass and relatively low penetrating power.

Bentsen Amendment — RCRA Section 3001(b)(2)(A-C), by then-Sen. Lloyd Bentsen, enacted on Oct. 21, 1980, which postponed RCRA regulation of drilling fluids, produced waters, and other wastes associated with the exploration, development, or production of crude oil or natural gas, pending a study by the administrator. The exclusions remain in effect at this writing. The implementing regulations are found at 40 CFR 261.4(b)(5).

Bevill Amendment — RCRA Section 3001(b)(3)(A-C), by Rep. Tom Bevill of Alabama, enacted on Oct. 21, 1980, which postponed regulation of fly ash waste, bottom ash waste, slag waste, flue gas emission control waste, solid waste from the extraction, beneficiation, and processing of ores and minerals, including phosphate rock and overburden from the mining of uranium ore, and cement kiln dust, pending a study by the administrator. The exclusions remain in effect at this writing. The implementing regulations are found at 30 CFR 261.4(b)(2-4).

BIFs — See **boilers** and **industrial furnaces**.

Bioaccumulation — the retention and concentration of a substance by an organism.

Biodegradation — decomposition of a substance into more elementary compounds by the action of microorganisms such as bacteria.

Biological treatment — a treatment technology that uses bacteria to consume waste constituents in municipal or industrial wastewaters.

Bioreclamation — a technique for treating contaminated areas by enhancing the natural microbial degradation of organic contaminants, thereby reducing the toxicity of the target compounds. The term was originally meant to imply the use of microbial degradation technology to "reclaim" the contaminated area, but is now apparently used interchangeably with **bioremediation.**

Bioremediation — a treatment process in which organic wastes in soils or other media may be seeded with soil microorganisms to alter or destroy the waste; or specific nutrients may be added to an organic waste to enhance naturally occurring (or extant) microorganisms and stimulate the activity.

Boiler — an enclosed device using controlled flame combustion, which is designed to recover and export thermal energy in the form of steam, heated fluids, or heated gases, and which meets the specifications of 40 CFR 260.10. Boilers and industrial furnaces **(BIFs)** are regulated by EPA when used to combust hazardous wastes for destruction of the waste, or when burning "hazardous waste fuel." See also **industrial furnace**.

CAA — Clean Air Act of 1970, 42 USC 7401 et seq. The act has been amended many times. *See also* **CAAA.**

CAAA — Clean Air Act Amendments of 1990, 42 USC 7404(d).

Carcinogen — an agent that has the potential to induce the abnormal, excessive, and uncoordinated proliferation of certain cell types, or the abnormal division of cells, i.e., a material that causes cancer cells to develop and proliferate.

CERCLA — the Comprehensive Environmental Response Compensation and Liability Act of 1980, 42 U.S.C. 9601 et seq. (*See also* **Superfund** and **SARA Title III**)

Certification means a statement of professional opinion based upon knowledge and belief.

CFCs — chlorofluorocarbon compounds, such as Freon—12 (CCl_2F_2), used chiefly as refrigerants. Their use as propellants for aerosols was prohibited in 1979 because of their depleting effect on stratospheric ozone.

CFR or **Code of Federal Regulations** — The CFR is the cumulation of executive agency regulations published in the *Federal Register* (*see* Glossary item) combined with regulations issued previously and remaining in effect. It is published annually by the Office of the Federal Register, National Archives and Records Service, Washington, D.C. The CFR is divided into 50 titles, each associated with a broad subject area (e.g., Title 40 contains most of the environmental regulations; Title 49, transportation; etc.). Citations may be by title and chapter, but most frequently are by title and part (e.g., 40 CFR 261.1). The citation is definitive in either form. Individual volumes of the code are revised each year, but are issued on a staggered quarterly basis. Thus, availability of a complete and current regulation may follow publication in the *Federal Register* by many months. Commercial publications and newsletters, which provide timely prints of newly revised or promulgated regulations, are available.

Chronic effect — an adverse effect upon a receptor organism, with symptoms which develop slowly over a long period of time or which recur frequently.

Closed portion means that portion of a facility which an owner or operator has closed in accordance with the approved facility closure plan and all applicable closure requirements. (*See also* **active portion** and **inactive portion**)

CNS — the central nervous system; the portion of the nervous system which consists of the spinal cord and the brain.

Conditionally exempt small quantity generator — a generator who generates no more than 100 kg of hazardous waste,and no more than 1 kg of acutely hazardous waste in any calendar month.

Confined aquifer means an aquifer bounded above and below by impermeable beds or by beds of distinctly lower permeability than that of the aquifer itself; an aquifer containing confined groundwater.

Container means any portable device in which a material is stored, transported, treated, disposed of, or otherwise handled.

Containment building means a hazardous waste management unit that is used to store or treat hazardous waste under the provisions of Subpart DD of 40 CFR 264 or 265.

Contamination — the degradation of natural water quality as a result of man's activities to the extent that its usefulness is impaired.

Contingency plan means a document setting out an organized, planned, and coordinated course of action to be followed in case of a fire, explosion, or release of hazardous waste or hazardous waste constituents which could threaten human health or the environment.

Corrosion expert means a person who, by reason of his knowledge of the physical sciences and the principles of engineering and mathematics acquired by a professional education and related practical experience, is qualified to engage in the practice of corrosion control on buried or submerged metal piping systems and metal tanks. Such a person must be certified by the National Association of Corrosion Engineers (NACE) or be a registered engineer who has certification or licensing that includes education and experience in corrosion control on buried or submerged metal piping systems and metal tanks.

Curie (Ci) means that quantity of radioactive material producing 37 million nuclear transformations per second. (The amount of radioactivity contained in one gram of radium.)

CWA — Clean Water Act of 1977, 33 USC 1251 et seq. The Clean Water Act is an amendment to the Federal Water Pollution Control Act of 1972.

Deactivation — as used with the **Land Disposal Restrictions,** means any of the recommended treatment technologies listed in 40 CFR 268, Appendix VI, or other technologies not listed, which are capable removal of the characteristics of ignitability, corrosivity, and reactivity from the wastes listed. *See* 40 CFR 268.42 and App. VI.

DDT — dichlorodiphenyltrichloroethane, a highly persistent insecticide which causes liver damage, is a suspect carcinogen and mutagen, and moves through the food chain to threaten higher forms of wildlife. DDT has been banned for use in the United States.

Designated facility — a hazardous waste treatment, storage, or disposal facility which has received an EPA permit (or a facility with interim status) that has been designated as such on the manifest pursuant to 40 CFR 262.20.

Dike means an embankment or ridge of either natural or manmade materials used to prevent the movement of liquids, sludges, solids, or other materials.

Dioxin — a term used to identify a group of polychlorinated compounds which vary greatly in the degree of toxicity. Those with four to six chlorinated atoms are the most active and have the greatest potential toxicity. 2,3,7,8-Tetrachlorodibenzo-*p*-dioxin (2,3,7,8-TCDD) has the greatest acute toxicity. The compound occurs as a side product contaminant in the pesticide 2,4,5-T (2,4,5-trichlorophenoxyacetic acid) and as an incomplete combustion product of the burning of chlorine-bleached materials.

Discarded material means any material which is abandoned, recycled, or considered inherently waste-like. (*See* 40 CFR 261.2).

Discharge or **hazardous waste discharge** means the accidental or intentional spilling, leaking, pumping, pouring, emitting, emptying, or dumping of hazardous waste into or on any land or water.

Disposal means the discharge, deposit, injection, dumping, spilling, leaking, or placing of any solid waste or hazardous waste into or on any land or water so that such solid waste or hazardous waste or any constituent thereof may enter the environment or be emitted into the air or discharged into any waters, including any groundwaters.

Disposal facility means a facility or part of a facility at which hazardous waste is intentionally placed into or on any land or water and at which waste will remain after closure.

Dose — the quantity of a chemical, or of radiation, absorbed by an organism. Quantitative — the mass of toxicant per mass of receptor (mg toxicant/kg animal). In radiology, the quantity of energy or radiation absorbed.

DRE — destruction and removal efficiency. The formula by which hazardous waste (and other) incinerators' performance is measured and regulated. The DRE (in percent) for each principal organic hazard constituent (POHC) is determined from the following equation:

$$DRE = \frac{\left(W_{in} - W_{out}\right)}{W_{in}} \times 100$$

where W_{in} is the mass feed rate of one POHC in the waste stream feeding the incinerator, and W_{out} is the mass feed rate of the same POHC present in exhaust emissions prior to release to the atmosphere. *See* 40 CFR 264, Subpart O.

Environmental audit (EA) — an investigative process to determine if the operations of an existing facility are in compliance with applicable environmental laws and regulations.

Environmental site assessment (ESA) — a process that seeks to determine or verify documented expectations regarding a parcel of real property by conducting interviews, reviewing records, and making first-hand observations. An ESA is generally less rigorous than an **EA**.

EPA hazardous waste number means the number assigned by the EPA to each hazardous waste listed in Subpart D of 40 CFR 261 and to each characteristic identified in Subpart C of 40 CFR 261.

EPA identification number means the number assigned by the EPA to each generator; transporter; and treatment, storage, or disposal facility.

EPA region means the states and territories found in any one of the ten standard federal regions of the U.S.

EPCRA — the Emergency Planning and Community Right-to-Know Act is Title III of the Superfund Amendments and Reauthorization Act (SARA) of 1986. The EPCRA requires emergency planning by local committees, notification of local and state authorities in the event of accidental releases of hazardous substances, community right-to-know reporting, and toxic chemical release reporting.

Existing hazardous waste management (HWM) facility or **existing facility** means a facility which was in operation or for which construction commenced on or before November 19, 1980. (*See* 40 CFR 260.10 for more detail)

Existing portion means that land surface area of an existing waste management unit, included in the original Part A permit application, on which wastes have been placed prior to the issuance of a permit.

Existing tank system or **existing component** means a tank system or component that is used for the storage or treatment of hazardous waste and that is in operation, or for which installation has commenced on July 14, 1986. (*See* 40 CFR 260.10 for more detail)

Facility means all contiguous land, structures, other appurtenances, and improvements on the land used for treating, storing, or disposing of hazardous waste. A facility may consist of several treatment, storage, or disposal operational units (e.g., one or more landfills, surface impoundments, or combinations of them).

Feasibility study (FS) means a study undertaken by the lead agency to develop and evaluate options for remedial action. The FS emphasizes data analysis and generally is performed concurrently and in an interactive fashion with the remedial investigation (RI) using data gathered during the RI. The term also refers to a report that describes the results of the study.

Federal Register (FR) — The medium by which federal government agencies make regulations and other legal documents of the executive branch available to the public. It is found in most public libraries. The FR, published daily by the Office of the Federal Register, National Archives and Records Service, Washington, D.C., includes both proposed and final regulations. Citations are by volume and page number (e.g., 43 FR 27736). Some writers prefer to include the date; however, the citation as shown is definitive. Once a regulation has completed the proposal and public comment phases, it is published in final form. If the published regulatory matter is a change to an existing regulation, the FR will publish only the change(s). To view the changed regulation in full, the reader must consult the *Code of Federal Regulations* (see Glossary item). This is a cause of frustration, since the CFR publications generally follow the FR publications by a year or more. There are a variety of commercial newsletters and trade publications which provide timely prints of regulations in full form.

FIFRA — Federal Insecticide, Fungicide, and Rodenticide Act of 1972, 7 USC 136 et seq.

Final closure means the closure of all hazardous waste management units at the facility in accordance with all applicable closure requirements so that hazardous waste management activities under 40 CFR 264 and 265 are no longer conducted at the facility.

Food chain crops means tobacco, crops grown for human consumption, and crops grown for feed for animals whose products are consumed by humans.

Freeboard means the vertical distance between the top of a tank or surface impoundment dike and the surface of the waste contained therein.

Free liquids means liquids which readily separate from the solid portion of a waste under ambient temperature and pressure.

Gamma radiation — electromagnetic energy waves, without mass, such as X-rays, which have great penetrating power and can penetrate and damage critical organs of the human body.

Generator means any person, by site, whose act or process produces hazardous waste identified or listed in 40 CFR 261, or whose act first causes a hazardous waste to become subject to regulation.

Gradient (groundwater or water table) — the slope of the piezometric surface. A positive slope is referred to as "up-gradient"; a negative slope is called "down-gradient." (There is lack of consistency in hyphenation.)

Groundwater — water below the land surface in a zone of saturation. In some early literature, a distinction was made between the terms *ground-water*, the hyphenated form, and *groundwater,* the combined term. The former was used as the noun and the latter as an adjective. Writers and users of the terms now use both forms without distinction. In this text, we have used the combined form, except where quoting or adapting from the works of sources who have used the separated or hyphenated form.

Half-life — the time required for the amount (concentration, strength, quantity, emission rate, etc.) of a substance to decrease, due to natural decay processes, to half of the original value.

Hazardous Air Pollutants (HAPs) — any of 189 chemicals listed pursuant to Title III of the Clean Air Act Amendments **(CAAA)** of 1990. The HAPs are suspected cancer-causing agents or other chemicals which are health or environmental hazards. EPA must set technology-based standards for HAPs.

Hazardous waste — The Solid Waste Disposal Act, as amended by the Resource Conservation and Recovery Act of 1976, [42 USC 6903(5)] defines "hazardous waste" as: "... a solid waste, or combination of solid wastes, which because of its quantity, concentration, or physical, chemical, or infectious characteristics may:

a. cause, or significantly contribute to an increase in mortality or an increase in serious irreversible, or incapacitating reversible, illness: or
b. pose a substantial present or potential hazard to human health or the environment when improperly treated, stored, transported, or disposed of, or otherwise managed."

The implementing regulations (40 CFR 261) define hazardous wastes as those solid wastes which:

- exhibit one or more of four the four characteristics described in Subpart C (ignitability, corrosivity, reactivity, or toxicity).
- are listed in Subpart D.
- are mixtures of solid and hazardous wastes.
- are derived from hazardous wastes.

Hazardous waste constituent — a constituent of a waste that causes the waste to be listed in Subpart D of 40 CFR 261, or a constituent listed in Table 1 of 40 CFR 261.24.

Hazardous waste management unit means a contiguous area of land on or in which hazardous waste is placed, or the largest area in which there is significant likelihood of mixing hazardous waste constituents in the same area. Examples of hazardous waste management units include a surface impoundment, a waste pile, a land treatment area, a landfill cell, an incinerator, a tank and its associated piping and underlying containment system, and a container storage area. A container alone does not constitute a unit; the unit includes containers and the land or pad upon which they are placed.

Hazard ranking system (HRS) means the method used by the EPA to evaluate the relative potential of hazardous substance releases to cause health or safety problems, or ecological or environmental damage. (The HRS is found at 40 CFR 300, Appendix A.)

Hazwaste — short or trade term for hazardous waste.

HazWOpER — Hazardous Waste Operations and Emergency Response – the OSHA workplace health and safety standard (29 CFR 1910.120) for hazardous waste workers. The Department of Labor has ruled that underground storage tank workers also may be covered by the standard. (*See* page 333 in text)

HLW or **high-level waste** — means the highly radioactive material resulting from the reprocessing of spent nuclear fuel, including liquid waste produced directly in reprocessing and any solid material derived from such other highly radioactive material that the Nuclear Regulatory Commission, by rule, requires permanent isolation.

HMTA — Hazardous Materials Transportation Act of 1975, 49 USC 1801 et seq. HMTA has been amended frequently, including HMTUSA (*see* Glossary item).

HMTUSA — Hazardous Materials Transportation and Uniform Safety Act of 1990, 49 USC 1802 et seq.

HSWA — the Hazardous and Solid Waste Amendments of 1984, which are major amendments to the Solid Waste Disposal Act. (*See also* RCRA)

Inactive portion means that portion of a facility which is not operated after the effective date of 40 CFR 261. (*See also* **active portion** and **closed portion**)

Incident — a broad catchall term used by government agencies and practitioners to denote an unscheduled event in which conditions hazardous or potentially hazardous to human health or the environment are present. Examples include collision, derailment, chemical spill or release, accident, cave-in, explosion, fire, building collapse, storm, flood, etc.

Incinerator means any enclosed device using controlled flame combustion that neither meets the criteria for classification as a boiler nor is listed as an industrial furnace.

Incompatible waste means a hazardous waste which is unsuitable for

a. Placement in a particular device or facility because it may cause corrosion or decay of containment materials (e.g., container inner liners or tank walls).

b. Comingling with another waste or material under uncontrolled conditions because the comingling might produce heat or pressure, fire or explosion, violent reaction, toxic dusts, mists, fumes, gases, or flammable fumes or gases. (*See* Appendix V of 40 CFR 265 for examples)

Industrial furnace — enclosed devices that are integral components of manufacturing processes and that use controlled flame devices to accomplish recovery of materials or energy, such as cement kilns, lime kilns, aggregate kilns, coke ovens, and blast furnaces. (*See* 40 CFR 260.10 for more detail)

Injection well means a well into which fluids are injected. (*See also* **underground injection** and **well**)

Inner liner means a continuous layer of material placed inside a tank or container which protects the construction materials of the tank or container from the contained waste or reagents used to treat the waste.

Interim status — hazardous waste treatment, storage, and disposal facilities that were in existence on November 19, 1980 and which met certain conditions were allowed to continue operating until their permit was issued or denied. Such facilities are said to have interim status.

IRIS — Integrated Risk Information System, an electronic database prepared and maintained by the EPA, containing both cancer and non-cancer chronic health hazard information on specific chemicals. IRIS is available to the public online through the National Library of Medicine's Toxicology Data Network (TOXLINE) and can be accessed by calling (301) 496-6531. The service is also available through the National Technical Information Service (NTIS) on diskette, furnished quarterly. The NTIS can be reached at (703) 487-4650.

Land disposal restrictions (LDRs) — restrictions placed on land disposal of hazardous wastes by the Hazardous and Solid Waste Amendments of 1984. (*See* 40 CFR 268)

Land treatment facility means a facility or part of a facility at which hazardous waste is applied onto or incorporated into the soil surface; such facilities are disposal facilities if the waste will remain after closure.

Landfill means a disposal facility or part of a facility where hazardous waste is placed into or on the land and which is not a pile, a land treatment facility, a surface impoundment, an underground injection well, a salt dome formation, a salt bed formation, an underground mine, or a cave (40 CFR 260.10). A disposal facility in which waste is deposited on the land or in trenches and is compacted and covered in layers or daily cells (author).

Landfill cell means a discrete volume of a hazardous waste landfill which uses a liner to provide isolation of wastes from adjacent cells or wastes. Examples of landfill cells are trenches and pits.

Leachate means any liquid, including any suspended components in the liquid, that has percolated through or drained from hazardous waste.

Leak-detection system means a system capable of detecting the failure of either the primary or secondary containment structure or the presence of a release of hazardous waste or accumulated liquid in the secondary containment structure. (*See* 40 CFR 260.10 for more detail)

Liner means a continuous layer of natural or manmade materials, beneath or on the sides of a surface impoundment, landfill, or landfill cell, which restricts the downward or lateral escape of hazardous waste, hazardous waste constituents, or leachate.

LOAEL — the lowest observed adverse effect level; the lowest dose in an experiment which produces an observable adverse effect.

Local emergency planning committee (LEPC) — LEPCs are appointed by state emergency planning commissions to carry out emergency planning at the local district (or county) level as required by the Emergency Planning and Community Right-to-Know Act (EPCRA).

Lower explosive limit — the concentration of a flammable compound, in air, below which a flame will not propogate if an ignition source is present. LEL is expressed as the percent of the flammable vapor, by volume, in air.

Low-level waste (LLW) — radioactive waste generated by uranium enrichment processes, reactor operations, isotope production, and medical and research activities. LLW often contains small amounts of radioactivity dispersed in large amounts of material.

Management or **hazardous waste management** means the systematic control of the collection, source separation, storage, transportation, processing, treatment, recovery, and disposal of hazardous waste.

Manifest means the shipping document EPA Form 8700-22 and, if necessary, EPA Form 8700-22A, originated and signed by the generator in accordance with the instructions included in the Appendix to 40 CFR 262.

Maquiladora — (twin) industrial facilities which are established in Mexico and in the U.S. and another country, usually to take advantage of significantly less stringent regulatory burdens and labor costs on the Mexican side. Work that is labor intensive, involves use of toxic chemicals, or produces hazardous waste is performed in the Mexican facility. Subassemblies or intermediates are shipped to the American side for final assembly, inspections, distribution, etc.

Monitoring well — a well used to measure groundwater levels or to obtain water samples for water quality analysis.

MPRSA — Marine Protection, Research, and Sanctuaries Act of 1972, 33 USC 1401 et seq. The MPRSA has been amended several times, most importantly by the Ocean Dumping Ban Act. (*See* **OBDA**)

Mutagen — an agent that causes a permanent genetic change in a cell other than that which occurs during normal genetic recombination (i.e., causes mutations).

National Contingency Plan (NCP) is the "blueprint" for remedial actions taken under Superfund. (*See* 40 CFR 300)

National Priorities List (NPL) means the list, compiled by the EPA pursuant to CERCLA Section 105, of uncontrolled hazardous substance releases in the U.S. that are identified and prioritized for long-term remedial evaluation and response. (The list is frequently updated and now identifies more than 1200 sites.)

NEPA — National Environmental Policy Act of 1969, 42 USC 4321 et seq.

NESHAPS — National Emission Standards for Hazardous Air Pollutants, mandated by the Clean Air Act and promulgated by the EPA. By early 1991, the EPA had issued standards for seven NESHAPS — benzine, arsenic (two forms), asbestos, vinyl chloride, mercury, and beryllium.

Notify — RCRA Section 3010(a) requires that any person who manages a hazardous waste (i.e., generators, transporters, owners, or operators of treatment, storage, or disposal facilities) must notify the EPA of that activity on EPA Form 8700-12.

NPDES permit system — the National Pollutant Discharge Elimination System, established by Section 402 of the Clean Water Act, requires that any person responsible for the discharge of a pollutant or pollutants into any waters of the U.S. from any point source must apply for and obtain a permit.

Nuclear Waste — Wastes that are highly radioactive, including high-level waste (HLW) from national defense activities, spent nuclear fuel (SNF) from commercial reactors, and transuranic waste (TRU) from weapons production facilities.

ODBA — Ocean Dumping Ban Act of 1988, 33 USC 1414(b),(c).

Onsite means the same or geographically contiguous property which may be divided by public or private right-of-way, provided the entrance and exit between the properties is at a crossroads intersection and access is by crossing as opposed to going along the right-of-way. Noncontiguous properties owned by the same person, but connected by a right-of-way which he controls and to which the public does not have access, is also considered onsite property.

Open burning means the combustion of any material without the following characteristics:

1. Control of combustion air to maintain adequate temperature for efficient combustion
2. Containment of the combustion reaction in an enclosed device to provide sufficient residence time and mixing for complete combustion
3. Control of emission of the gaseous combustion products

(*See also* **incineration** and **thermal treatment**)

Operator means the person responsible for the overall operation of a facility.

Organic — being, containing, or relating to compounds which contain carbon in combination with one or more elements, whether derived from living organisms or not.

OSHA — The acronym identifies both a statute and an agency. The Occupational Safety and Health Act of 1970, 29 USC 651, authorized the U.S. Occupational Health and Safety Administration to be established in the U.S. Department of Labor.

Owner means the person who owns a facility or part of a facility.

Oxidation — a chemical reaction in which there is an increase in valence resulting from a loss of electrons.

Partial closure means the closure of a hazardous waste management unit in accordance with the applicable closure requirements of 40 CFR 264 and 265 at a facility that contains other active hazardous waste management units.

PCA — tetrachloroethane; $C_2H_2Cl_4$.

PCE — perchloroethylene; also tetrachloroethylene; C_2Cl_4.

Percolate — the water moving by gravity or hydrostatic pressure through the interstices of unsaturated rock or soil.

Person means an individual, trust, firm, joint stock company, federal agency, corporation (including a government corporation), partnership, association, state, municipality, commission, political subdivision of a state, or any interstate body.

Personnel or **facility personnel** means all persons who work at or oversee the operations of a hazardous waste facility and whose actions or failure to act may result in noncompliance with the requirement of 40 CFR 264 or 265.

Phase I Environmental Site Assessment — a structured **ESA** typically including a records review, interviews, and a site reconnaissance. The American Society for Testing Materials (ASTM) publishes the *Standard Practice for Environmental Site Assessments: Phase I Environmental Site Assessment Process,* designation E 1527-93, which has become a widely used format for a Phase I ESA.

Phase II Environmental Site Assessment — a more detailed **ESA** which may include air, soil, surface and/or groundwater sampling on and near the property, as needed to characterize the site. The Federal National Mortgage Association (FNMA) publishes a guide for the conduct of a Phase II ESA.

Piezometric surface — the surface defined by the levels to which groundwater will rise in tightly cased wells that tap an artesian aquifer.

Pile means any noncontainerized accumulation of solid, nonflowing hazardous waste that is issued for treatment or storage.

Point source means any discernible, confined, and discrete conveyance, including, but not limited to, any pipe, ditch, channel, tunnel, conduit, well, discrete fissure, container, rolling stock, concentrated animal feeding operation, or vessel or other floating craft, from which pollutants may be discharged. This term does not include the return flows from irrigated agriculture.

Potentially responsible party (PRP) — any individual or company, including owners, operators, transporters, or generators, potentially responsible for, or contributing to, the contamination problems at a Superfund site.

PPA — Pollution Prevention Act of 1990, 42 USC 13101 et seq.

Publicly owned treatment works (POTW) — any device or system used in the treatment (including recycling and reclamation) of municipal sewage or industrial wastes of a liquid nature which is owned by a state or municipality. This definition includes sewers, pipes, or other conveyances only if they convey wastewater to a POTW providing treatment.

Pretreatment — treatment given domestic sewage which contains industrial waste components that would, if not removed or treated, interfere with (or pass through untreated) the treatment processes in a sewage treatment plant.

Pyrolysis — the chemical decomposition or change brought about by heating in the absence of oxygen.

Radiation means any or all of the following: alpha, beta, gamma, or X-rays; neutrons; and high-energy electrons, protons, or other atomic particles, but neither sound or radio waves, nor visible, infrared, or ultraviolet light.

Radiological waste — generally, waste material which has a radioactive component. *See* **nuclear waste**, **high-level waste** (**HLW**), **spent nuclear fuel** (**SNF**), **transuranic waste** (**TRU**), **low-level waste** (**LLW**), **uranium mining**, and **mill tailings**.

Radwaste — short or trade term for radiological waste.

RCRA — the acronym refers both to a law and a program. The Resource Conservation and Recovery Act, as amended — 42 U.S.C. Sec. 6901 et seq., and the program and regulations which implement the act. The act originated as the Solid Waste Disposal Act of 1965, 42 USC 3251 et seq.

RCRA/Superfund Hotline — a telephonic information system, manned by an EPA contractor, which can be accessed by the public. The hotline provides a wide range of information pertaining to the RCA and Superfund programs and can provide some EPA publications upon request. The number is 1-800-424-9346.

Recharge — the addition of water to the groundwater system by natural or artificial processes.

Reduction — a chemical reaction in which there is a decrease in valence as a result of gaining electrons.

Regional administrator — the administrator of an EPA (or other federal government agency) geographical region.

Rem (roentgen-equivalent-man) — the amount of radiation that will produce an energy dissipation in the human body that is equivalent to one roentgen of radiation of X-rays.

Remedial design (RD) means the technical analysis and procedures which follow the selection of remedy for a site and result in a detailed set of plans and specifications for implementation of the remedial action.

Remedial investigation (RI) is a process undertaken by the lead agency to determine the nature and extent of the problem presented by (a) release. The RI emphasizes data collection and site characterization and is generally performed concurrently and in an interactive fashion with the feasibility study. The RI includes sampling and monitoring, as necessary, and the gathering of sufficient information to determine the necessity for remedial action and to support the evaluation of remedial alternatives.

Reportable quantity (RQ) — the quantity of a hazardous substance (listed in 40 CFR 302, Table 302.4) or extremely hazardous substance (listed in 40 CFR 355, Appendix A or B) that requires reporting under CERCLA. If a substance is released in a quantity that exceeds its RQ, the release must be reported to the National Response Center, as well as to the State Emergency Response Commission (SERC) and to the community emergency coordinator for areas likely to be affected by the release. The practitioner should carefully study CERCLA sections 101 through 104, regarding the RQs and their application.

Representative sample means a sample of a universe or whole (e.g., waste pile, lagoon, groundwater) which can be expected to exhibit the average properties of the universe or whole.

Responsible party or **parties** — persons having caused, permitted, or contributed to the contamination of a site that is caught up in the Superfund process are referred to as "potentially responsible parties" (PRPs). As the Superfund process continues to the stage that responsibility(ies) has (have) been established, the term becomes "responsible parties" (RPs).

Roentgen (r) — the amount of gamma or X-radiation that will produce, in 1 cm^3 of dry air at 0°C and 760 mm pressure, one electrostatic unit (esu) of electricity. The roentgen is a unit of the total quantity of ionization produced by gamma or X-rays. Dosage rates are expressed in terms of roentgens per unit time.

Runoff means any rainwater, leachate, or other liquid that drains over land from any part of a facility.

Runon means any rainwater, leachate, or other liquid that drains over land onto any part of a facility.

SARA Title III — Title III of the Superfund Amendments and Reauthorization Act of 1986 embodies the Emergency Planning and Community Right-to-Know Act.

Saturated zone or **zone of saturation** means that part of the earth's crust in which all voids are filled with water.

SDWA — Safe Drinking Water Act of 1974, 42 UCS 300f et seq.

Sewage — domestic and industrial wastes and wastewaters discharged into sewers.

Sewerage — the system of sewage collection, treatment, and disposal.

Site inspection (SI) means an onsite investigation to determine whether there is a release or potential release and the nature of the associated threats. The purpose is to augment the data collected in the preliminary assessment and to generate, if necessary, sampling and other field data to determine if further action or investigation is appropriate.

Sludge means any solid, semisolid, or liquid waste generated from a municipal, commercial, or industrial wastewater treatment plant; water supply treatment plant; or air pollution control facility exclusive of the treated effluent from a wastewater treatment plant.

Small quantity generator — a generator who generates more than 100 kg, but less than 1000 kg of hazardous waste and no more than 1 kg of acutely hazardous waste in a calendar month.

SNF or **spent nuclear fuel** means fuel that has been withdrawn from a nuclear reactor following irradiation. Within the regulatory framework, SNF is a subset of HLW.

Solid waste — The Solid Waste Disposal Act [42 USC 6903(27)] defines solid waste as "... any garbage, refuse, sludge from waste water treatment plant, water supply treatment plant, or air pollution control facility and other discarded material, including solid, liquid, semisolid, or contained gaseous material resulting from industrial, commercial , mining, and agricultural operations, and from community activities, but does not include solid or dissolved material in domestic sewage, or solid or dissolved materials in irrigation return flows or industrial discharges which are point sources subject to permits under section 1342 of title 33, or source, special nuclear, or byproduct material as defined by the Atomic Energy Act of 1954, as amended." The RCRA regulations define solid waste as "... any discarded material that is not excluded by §261.4(a) or that is not excluded by variance under § 260.30 and 260.31." (*See* **Discarded** and 40 CFR 261.2).

State means any of the several states, the District of Columbia, the Commonwealth of Puerto Rico, the Virgin Islands, Guam, American Samoa, and the Commonwealth of the Northern Mariana Islands.

State Emergency Response Commission (SERC) — SERCs are appointed by the governor of each state, per the Emergency Planning and Community Right-to-Know Act (EPCRA). The SERCs designate local emergency planning districts, appoint Local Emergency Planning Committees **(LEPC)**, coordinate and supervise the activities of the LEPCs, review the local emergency response plans, and notify EPA of all facilities that are subject to the emergency planning requirements.

Storage means the holding of hazardous waste for a temporary period, at the end of which the hazardous waste is treated, disposed of, or stored elsewhere.

Sump means any pit or reservoir that meets the definition of *tank* and those troughs/ trenches connected to it that serve to collect hazardous waste for transport to hazardous waste storage, treatment, or disposal facilities.

Superfund — a "nickname" given the program which implements the Comprehensive Environmental Response, Compensation, and Liability Act. (*See* also **CERCLA**)

Surface impoundment or **impoundment** means a facility or part of a facility which is a natural topographic depression, manmade excavation, or diked area formed primarily of earthen materials (although it may be lined with manmade materials); which is designed to hold an accumulation of liquid wastes or wastes containing free liquids; and which is not an injection well.

SW 846 — (EPA/SW-846) *Test Methods for Evaluating Solid Waste: Physical/ Chemical Methods; Third Edition; Volumes IA, IB, IC, and II.* The document is the EPA guidance document for test procedures which "... may be used to evaluate properties of solid waste which determine whether waste is hazardous within the definition of Section 3001, RCRA." The document is available from the Government Printing Office – order number: 955-001-00000-1. The NTIS number is PB88-239 223. It also can be obtained commercially on CD. The document is updated periodically, and a recent update is designated *Final Update Package I,* (EPA/SW-846.3-1). The update can be obtained from GPO – order number: 955-001-00000-1.

SWDA — Solid Waste Disposal Act of 1965, 42 USC 3251. (*See* also **RCRA**)

Tank means a stationary device designed to contain an accumulation of hazardous waste which is constructed primarily of non-earthen materials (e.g., wood, concrete, steel, plastic) which provide support.

Tank system means a hazardous waste storage or treatment tank and its associated ancillary equipment and containment system.

TCA — trichloroethane; $C_2H_3Cl_3$.

TCE — trichloroethylene; C_2HCl_3.

TCLP — The Toxicity Characteristic Leaching Procedure, a laboratory procedure designed to produce an extract simulating the leachate that may be produced in a land disposal situation. The extract is then analyzed to determine if it includes any of the toxic contaminants listed in Chapter 2, Table 2.1. If the concentrations of any to the Table 2.1 constituents exceed the levels listed in the table, the waste is classified as hazardous. (*See* 40 CFR 261.24)

Teratogen — a physical or chemical agent which is capable of causing nonhereditary congenital malformations (birth defects) in offspring.

Thermal treatment means the treatment of hazardous waste in a device which uses elevated temperatures as the primary means to change the chemical, physical, or biological character or composition of the hazardous waste. Examples of thermal treatment processes are incineration, molten salt, pyrolysis, calcination, wet air oxidation, and microwave discharge. (*See also* **incinerator** and **open burning**)

Threshold — the lowest dose of a chemical at which a specified measurable effect is observed, and below which it is not observed.

Totally enclosed treatment facility means a facility for the treatment of hazardous waste which is directly connected to an industrial production process and which is constructed and operated in a manner which prevents the release of any hazardous waste or any constituent thereof into the environment during treatment.

Toxicity — The ability of a material to produce injury or disease upon exposure, ingestion, inhalation, or assimilation by a living organism.

Toxics Release Inventory National Report (TRI) — the compilation of chemical releases to air, water, and land from selected manufacturing facilities, as authorized and required by the Emergency Planning and Community Right-to-Know Act (EPRCRA). The TRI is published in odd-numbered years by the Environmental Protection Agency.

Transfer facility means any transportation-related facility including loading docks, parking areas, storage areas, and other similar areas where shipments of hazardous waste are held during the normal course of transportation.

Transportation means the movement of hazardous waste by air, rail, highway, or water.

Transporter — a transporter, subject to 40 CFR 263, is any person engaged in the offsite transportation of manifested hazardous waste by air, rail, highway, or water.

Transport vehicle means a motor vehicle or rail car used for the transportation of cargo by any mode. Each cargo-carrying body (trailer, railroad freight car, etc.) is a separate transport vehicle.

Transuranic waste (TRU) means waste material containing radionuclides with an atomic number greater than 92 which are excluded from shallow burial by the federal government. Transuranic elements are those having atomic numbers greater than 92. TRU waste is defined in the U.S. as radwaste that is not classified as HLW, but contains an activity of more than 100 nCi/g from alpha-emitting transuranic isotopes having half-lives greater than 20 years (typically clothing, equipment, tools, and scrap contaminated with plutonium from laboratory and facility operations).

Treatment means any method, technique, or process, including neutralization, designed to change the physical, chemical, or biological character or composition of any hazardous waste so as to neutralize such waste, or so as to recover energy or material resources from the waste, or so as to render such waste nonhazardous or less hazardous; safer to transport, store, or dispose of; amenable for recovery; or amenable for storage or reduced in volume.

TSCA — Toxic Control Substances Act of 1976, 15 USC 2601 et seq.

Underground injection means the subsurface emplacement of fluids through a bored, drilled, or driven well or through a dug well, where the depth of the dug well is greater than the largest surface dimension. (*See also* **injection well**)

Underground storage tank (UST) — any one or combination of tanks (including underground pipes connected thereto) that is used to contain an accumulation of regulated substances, and the volume of which (including the volume of the underground pipes connected thereto) is 10% or more beneath the surface of the ground.

Underground tank means a device meeting the definition of *tank*, with its entire surface area is totally below the surface of and covered by the ground.

United States means the 50 states, the District of Columbia, the Commonwealth of Puerto Rico, the U.S. Virgin Islands, Guam, American Samoa, and the Commonwealth of the Northern Mariana Islands.

Unsaturated zone or **zone of aeration** means the zone between the land surface and the water table.

Upgrade means the addition or retrofit of some systems such as cathodic protection, lining, or spill and overfill controls to improve the ability of an underground storage tank system to prevent the release of a product.

Uppermost aquifer means the geologic formation nearest the natural ground surface that is an aquifer, as well as lower aquifers that are hydraulically interconnected with this aquifer within the facility's property boundary.

Uranium mill tailings — the sandy residues from the extraction and refining of uranium ore. The tailings contain low concentrations of thorium and radium, and radioactive radon gas from the decay of the radium. The emissions of radon are the major health hazard associated with uranium mining and mill tailings.

Uranium mine tailings — waste rock and granular material resulting from uranium ore mining operations. The characteristics are similar to those of uranium mill tailings.

Volatile organic compound (VOC) — materials such as gasoline, paint solvents, and other organic compounds, which evaporate and enter the air in a vapor state, as well as fragments of molecules resulting from incomplete oxidation of fuels and wastes. In general, higher vapor pressures relate to higher volatility.

Wastewater treatment unit — device which:

1. is part of a wastewater treatment facility that is subject to regulation under either Section 402 or 307(b) of the Clean Water Act.
2. receives and treats or stores an influent wastewater that is a hazardous waste as defined in 40 CFR 261.3, or that generates and accumulates a wastewater treatment sludge that is a hazardous waste.
3. treats or stores a wastewater treatment sludge which is a hazardous waste, and meets the definition of tank or tank system in 40 CFR 260.10.

Well means any shaft or pit dug or bored into the earth, generally of a cylindrical form and often walled with bricks or tubing to prevent the earth from caving in. (Some early literature and regulatory issue used a definition attributed to A. E. Meinzer — "a well is a hole in the ground having depth greater than its diameter.")

Yellow boy — the metallic precipitate formed when acidic, metal-bearing mine drainage, leachate from ore piles, or process wastes are introduced to alkaline receiving waters.

INDEX

B

C

E

I

J

K

L

M

N

O

P

S

U

V

W